D1171291

BREADCRUMBS to CHEESECAKE

A Struggling Inner-City Neighborhood Sanitarium's Journey to Become Louisiana's Largest Medical Center

James K. Elrod

R&R
Publishers

Shreveport

Breadcrumbs to Cheesecake

ISBN 978-0-692-01976-4

Library of Congress Control Number: 2013905781

Cataloging-in-Publication Data is available from the Library of Congress

Published by R&R Publishers, Shreveport, Louisiana

Printed in the United States of America

First Edition

Dedication

Breadcrumbs to Cheesecake is dedicated to the memory of my parents, Dorothy and J. T. Elrod, who encouraged me to utilize faith in finding my pathway to the fulfillment of my dreams of personal and professional happiness. My parents' exercise of daily living had much to do with the instilling of thoughts, values and tips on leadership included in the chapter "Codes of Conduct For Leaders." When I fail to live up to my embraced codes of conduct, I remember their admonition: never stop trying. An unwavering faith, a strong sense of humility and an unwillingness to give up when the going got tough were hallmarks of my parents' lives.

Table of Contents

Significance of the Title

Some may question how "breadcrumbs" and "cheesecake" relate to hospital administration. The title was inspired by a charming lady who approached me following the dedication of the first of Willis-Knighton's eight indigent medical and dental clinics. She told me that she was aware of our hospital's earlier financial difficulties and agreed that it had been blessed beyond measure because of our caring and giving spirit. "You know what you said about not being able to out-give the Lord as evidenced by Willis-Knighton's success?" she asked. **"In the Jewish community we have a similar saying: 'Cast your bread upon the water and it will come back, cheesecake.'"**

I thanked this lady for sharing this adage of faith with me, determined that in the future, every time I talked about the bestowing of God's blessings upon our health system's ministry of healing, I would repeat her story. Through this book her story is now part of Willis-Knighton's permanent history.

Foreword

Author Jim Elrod's book details his personal history in rescuing and growing in stunning fashion what is now Willis-Knighton Health System in northwest Louisiana. To say the book defies typical classification is an underestimation: it is a history, a biography, a memoir, a study in healthcare and business management, and a written window into how a faith-based conglomerate functions and the difference that makes.

The reader here experiences a satisfying sort of textbook, lesson upon lesson about the natural reward of faith and its parallel personal values, and of free enterprise and the satisfaction and power of its work-ethic core. The reader cannot deflect or miss that this is a book of its author's real-life lessons in what still and always gives America a nearly indescribable strength.

For those of us who grew up in Willis-Knighton's locale alongside what is now a healthcare showplace, this read is nostalgic yet new, familiar yet surprising. The book details the many ways Willis-Knighton—without self-promotion, with little recognition, and with no fanfare—has provided a financial foundation for the social and cultural mainstays of its home area. In the process, the reader learns, Willis-Knighton in many ways became the community's anchor.

Jim Elrod details how he, at 27, moved to Shreveport, Louisiana in 1965 to administer a nearly defunct hospital, then spent the following seven years in a daily struggle to fight off bankruptcy. Jim Elrod and his Board of Directors not only paid back every dollar the institution owed, but used the rebirth to become a healthcare system with ten-figure assets and no need or desire for debt. That Jim Elrod and his Board never solicited or accepted federal or state grant money in the process is just one more stunning fact of their journey.

That this healthcare system's story is synonymous with that of the man who dedicated his life to saving and nurturing it is the heart of the book. Passionately, though, Elrod uses vignettes throughout the book to show how he—straight from his heart—shares credit for this survival-turned-stunning-success history with special employees and physicians, many of whom he clearly and deeply honors.

In this era of dysfunctional healthcare processes and systems, government bailouts of private sector giants around the world, and broad disavowal of the inherent value of free enterprise, along comes this book: a primer of what works and works well in life, how commitment and diligence are inviolably honored in life, and how none of those promises are separable from personal faith.

This is Jim Elrod and Willis-Knighton's story of what was taught to the offspring of Depression-era parents and grand-parents in America, and the difference those values and traditions can still make where they are chosen and practiced.

Elliott B. Stonecipher, 2013

About the Author

James K. Elrod grew up in Port Neches, Texas, and attended Baylor University, earning a bachelor's degree in business administration and a commission in the United States Air Force through ROTC. Upon fulfilling his military commitment he attended Washington University School of Medicine, where he earned a master's degree in hospital administration. Following an administrative residency at Baptist Medical Center in Jackson, Mississippi, and three quarters of law school at Mississippi College, Jim moved to Shreveport, Louisiana, where at age 27, he was named administrator of Willis-Knighton Memorial Hospital. He was awarded an honorary doctorate of science and humane letters by Northwestern State University of Louisiana in 2007. In 2012 Jim was named the Distinguished Alumnus of Washington University School of Medicine's Health Administration studies. He is a fellow in the American College of Healthcare Executives.

Joining Willis-Knighton (WK) was the beginning of a distinguished career that allowed him to transform a struggling 80-bed hospital into a major health system. As chief executive officer, he has guided the expansion of the original hospital and development of three satellite hospitals, three rural hospital affiliates, a regional network employing 350 physicians, a hospital-owned HMO, an innovation center featuring a virtual hospital, medical museum and community assembly center and the state's largest retirement community, The Oaks of Louisiana.

Elrod has been actively involved in the community, serving on boards of organizations to support economic, educational, cultural and humanitarian initiatives. Numerous organizations have honored his community commitment, leading the regional newspaper to name him one of the most influential people in north Louisiana in the past century. Several organizations, including the Human Rights Commission, have recognized him for his activities related to the advancement of human equality. He is the founding president of Shreveport's Inner-City Entrepreneurial Institute, which promotes entrepreneurial and leadership education among inner-city, low income and at-risk children. The institute's summer program, James K. Elrod Biz Camp, has been lauded by Harvard University as "a mini-MBA course for youth".

Jim's vision and entrepreneurial achievements have earned him several business leader awards from the following organizations: Chamber of Commerce, Junior Achievement, *Shreveport Times*, United Way, the City of Shreveport, Grambling University, Southern University and Louisiana State University in Shreveport.

Elrod has served on the governing boards of the American Hospital Association, VHA (Voluntary Hospitals of America), Louisiana Hospital Association and its affiliated insurance trusts and as chairman of AHA's Region 7 Policy Board. He is an advisor to the Baylor University program in Health Administration and the James K. Elrod School of Health Administration at LSU in Shreveport.

He is the longest-tenured hospital administrator in the United States, a rated pilot with multi-engine instrument flight privileges and a graduate of the FBI Citizens' Academy.

James K. Elrod (left), president and CEO of Willis-Knighton Health System, receives a plaque from LSUS Chancellor Vince Marsala at the Fifth Annual Philanthropy Luncheon hosted by the LSUS Institute for Human Services and Public Policy. Elrod was honored by the Institute for his lifetime commitment to philanthropy.

UNIVERSITY NEUROSURGERY

LOUISIANA STATE UNIVERSITY HEALTH SCIENCES CENTER
DEPARTMENT OF NEUROSURGERY

ANIL NANDA, MD, FACS
Professor
Department Chairman

BRIAN K. WILLIS, MD, FACS
Professor

DONALD R. SMITH, MD
Clinical Professor

BHARAT GUTHIKONDA, MD
Assistant Professor

ANTHONY SIN, MD
Assistant Professor

HUGO CUELLAR, MD
Assistant Professor

CHRISTINA NOTARIANNI, MD
Assistant Professor

GUOHONG LI, MD, PhD
Assistant Professor of Research

GLORIA CALDITO, PhD
Associate Professor of Biometry
Biostatistician

1501 Kings Highway
Post Office Box 33932
Shreveport, Louisiana 71130-3932
(318) 813-1555 Fax (318) 675-4615
http://www.universityneurosurgery.com

Medical Arts Bldg.
2551 Greenwood Rd., Suite 320
Shreveport, Louisiana 71103
(318) 635-6363 Fax (318) 631-5392

Medical Office Bldg.
2300 Hospital Dr., Suite 350
Bossier City, Louisiana 71111
(318) 742-8666 Fax (318) 742-8488

Willis Knighton Pierremont
8001 Youree Dr. Suite 580
Shreveport, Louisiana 71115
(318) 675-6137 Fax (318) 675-4615

Willis Knighton South
2520 Bert Kouns, Suite 105
Shreveport, Louisiana 71118
(318) 675-6137 Fax (318) 675-4615

April 4, 2012

Mr. James Elrod
619 Lake Forbing Drive
Shreveport, LA 71106

Dear Mr. Elrod,

Congratulations on getting the Distinguished Alumnus Award from Washington University. This is a richly deserved recognition for somebody that has made an enormous difference in our city, state, and region.

I always tell people you had a Bill Gates like transformational effect in Louisiana by turning a 1.5 million dollar hospital into a 2.5 billion dollar chain. Not many people can accomplish that in several lifetimes.

Above all you have been kind, generous, and understanding towards physicians especially the academic physicians at LSU to create a milieu that can foster excellence. I know that the neurosurgery department would not be able to accomplish any of this without your constant guidance, generosity and mentorship. We are all deeply indebted and are profoundly grateful for what you have done for this medical school and community. Congratulations again and may the richness of God's grace continue to be lavished on you and your family.

Sincerely,

Anil Nanda, MD, FACS
Professor and Chairman
Department of Neurosurgery
ananda@lsuhsc.edu
www.universityneurosurgery.com

Rev. 5/10 1425

Preface

In 2010 I became aware that much of the history of the health system was dying along with the people who created it. As I pondered the contributions of the many persons who have come and gone, I felt it was important to record the history of this institution to honor their contributions and inspire those who will be involved in its future.

Breadcrumbs to Cheesecake is my testimony that it is possible for a person to love his or her work, never looking upon it as a chore or drudgery. Hospital administration is one of the most exciting, challenging and rewarding of professions; yet, few people know much about it. This book also serves as a tribute to the multitudes of faithful physicians, nurses and other dedicated workers who spent their lives in service to Willis-Knighton. I wish it were possible for me to thank each of them personally.

I must acknowledge that I have been fortunate to work for the best hospital board of trustees in the country. Throughout my tenure, our trustees have accepted their fiduciary duties to safeguard the assets of our health system while exhibiting an excitement of participation and extraordinary understanding of and commitment to its mission. They have refrained from becoming involved in its daily operations and from personal and financial conflicts of interest.

Continually managing to separate their personal and professional friendships from their fiduciary duties and obligations as trustees, they have always objectively administered the affairs of the health system. They understand their responsibility to define system policies that support the health system's mission to deliver the highest possible quality of healthcare. Their financial prudence, joined by common sense, business acumen and a heartfelt compassion for those less fortunate of our community, has ensured the continued honoring of our commitment to tithe our financial rewards to enhance our community's health and well-being. Only one has resigned from the board during his tenure, and that was due to his relocation to another state.

Our Chairman of the Board, Ray P. Oden Jr., must be singled out for his many contributions to our health system during his service since 1965, much of which has been in the role of chairman. His character, integrity and spirit of human kindness

Ray P. Oden, Jr.

have well served our system and community. Our chairman's business experience and exceptional leadership skills have prepared him well to guide a board composed of community, business and physician dignitaries. Chairman Oden possesses an enormous understanding of the role a corporate board plays in the development of policies of the institution and is quick to utilize his no-nonsense approach to leadership to discourage board members from getting into political issues and procedural activities of daily operation, a responsibility of management, to implement the board's policies.

I would not only be remiss in my recognition of support in the writing of this book but possibly in trouble at home if I did not give credit to my wife, Margaret, who has continued over many years to patiently listen to excited reiterations of my middle-of-the-night ideas and inspirations. She has been my best friend, helpmate and muse through her encouragement and exploration of thoughts for this book, which she understands to be of great importance to me.

No one fathoms my love and devotion to Willis-Knighton's ministry of healing more than Margaret. She accepts the fact that the health system has been my metaphorical mistress for nearly five decades. Even in the wee hours of the morning when I awaken her to help me retrieve a file or correct some problem with my computer, she just yawns and beams a half-awake smile.

Yet she declines to lecture me about the hour of my writing or my ineptness with computers or to rebuke me as I seek her help.

On the contrary, she never misses an opportunity to dissuade me from having any thoughts of retirement, and she is always quick to encourage me to continue working as

The author and his wife (muse), Margaret Gerlach Elrod.

long as I enjoy my job. She says, "Honey, I married you for life, but not for lunch every day." She knows that I may not be the happiest of campers in retirement!

She is a brilliant scholar and former high school teacher, and she applied her tough grading system and red pencil to the editing of a few chapters in this book; she cut me no slack. On one occasion after I corrected her red marks on a chapter, a fourth rewrite, she magnanimously penned this comment on the paper: "*Très bien—bon travaille d' écrire.*" My only question to her was, "Was that an insult or a compliment?" How could she expect me, conversant in only two languages, English and Texan, to understand her?

Another person who played an inspirational role in my personal and professional life was Dr. Albert Bicknell. He, a most gifted, respected surgeon and visionary, was a member of the selection committee of WK's Board of Trustees at the time I interviewed for my job in 1965. One of the reasons I chose to take the helm of our hospital was Albert's voiced love and devotion for WK and his excitement about its future.

During my early days at the hospital, I must admit that I, a twenty-seven-year-old administrator with book learning but little experience, had emotional down times

Dr. Albert Bicknell

during WK's vast financial challenges. Privately I harbored questions as to the future of our beloved hospital. Albert would always come to my rescue, voicing his confidence in me, which served to lift my spirits and faith in our future. He never swayed in his belief that our small neighborhood hospital would someday be one of the finest hospitals in our region. Thanks to his vision, untiring efforts and encouragement of others, his dream was fulfilled.

One of my greatest honors was to present the eulogy at Albert's funeral and also that of his brother, Dr. Harold Bicknell, the city's respected orthopedic surgeon. These two remarkable surgeons, neighborhood kids who grew up a few blocks from WK, left enormous footprints on a much larger world as their skilled surgical hands touched thousands of patients, and their compassionate and caring demeanor wrought friendships with all they knew. Both served long terms on the board of trustees of our health system. Their deaths have left voids in the hearts of the WK family.

Acknowledgment must go to Robert D. Huie, my Executive Vice President/Chief Financial Officer, who has served our institution for forty years. This brilliant senior officer's financial prowess, heartfelt love and devotion to Willis-Knighton, coupled with his humility of service, without regard to status or title, have been of immense value to the health system. His unselfish service and work ethic have made him a role model for our institution. No one has ever been of greater value in service to Willis-Knighton.[1]

In his interview with me at age 21, upon his graduation from college, I could sense

---

1 My executive vice president's (a holder of two MBAs) first job assignment was to work with a crew demolishing houses for added parking. One day his wife came to have lunch with him, only to be told that he was being treated in the emergency room for a job-related injury. She was quite relieved when told he had stepped on a nail at the job site. Almost forty years later, good-natured jokes about this episode of his executive job history continue to be told around the health system.

Robert Huie

special qualities in Robert, not often found in young people. Robert has since proven himself to possess a gentleness of heart and loving spirit blended with a sharp mind and quick wit. His strong work ethic is an example to all of us. Both our fathers worked for their respective petroleum companies, in the same job capacity, from an early age until their retirements. With loyalty and longevity of service rooted in our DNAs, we continue to serve our health system. I jokingly tell others that he was so young at employment that, while I didn't pay for his first pair of shoes, I did teach him to tie them.

My wife often compares Robert and me with the Disney brothers. She refers to me as Walt Disney, the dreamer and visionary, while Robert is Roy, the financial genius with a generous dose of practicality, who helped keep the company out of financial straits while it became one of the country's most successful businesses. While I don't necessarily see myself as Walt, she is accurate in referring to us as brothers, because I have come to love Robert as the brother I never had. We have grown to be closer than most brothers, so much so that he and I almost seem to read each other's minds.

Dr. Dudley Talbot

Dr. J. Dudley Talbot, one of a few living physicians from WK's medical staff of 1965, has been one of my staunchest supporters and a surrogate father since my own father's passing some thirty years ago. This near centenarian has the most positive view of life: his glass is never half full, or half empty, but always overflowing. His early encouragement of me played a major role in my decision to spend my entire career at our mutually beloved Willis-Knighton. The Talbot Medical Museum of WK preserves the history and heritage of our health system.

A most special thanks is due to my surrogate son, Jerry Williams, who has devoted his adult life to this health system and has been one of my dearest friends and staunchest supporters. I recruited Jerry at age 18 (some thirty years ago) and was quickly impressed by his unrivaled work ethic, positive attitude, honesty and integrity. Jerry is truly a member of the Elrod family.

Finally, my heartfelt appreciation goes to Dr. Pierre V. Blanchard and Dr. Dan Moller for ensuring that our family's health was up to the task of putting in so many sleepless nights to work on this book; Marilyn Joiner and many other friends who encouraged me to write this book; Sara Burroughs, former chairman, Department of Language and Communication, Northwestern State University of Louisiana, for her editing prowess; Glenda Turner, my administrative assistant, for coordinating the efforts of our team, copying volumes of documents while enduring my mercurial temperament over the past thirty years; Lamar P. Pugh, WK's attentive and detail-oriented attorney for proof reading several chapters of the manuscript to keep me on sound legal ground; Ryan Smith, for his research and proofreading efforts; Riley Waddell, for proofreading and helping to design all of the charts and graphs; Eric Cochran, our resident computer whiz, for religiously ensuring the updating and synchronization of my home laptop and office desktop word processor files; Karen Peters, a gifted graphic artist, for designing the book cover and optimizing all images; Sharla Inman, for her support and coordination efforts while compiling this work; Darrell Rebouche, for capturing many of the images contained within; Dr. John Fortenberry, chairman of the James K. Elrod School of Health Administration, Louisiana State University in Shreveport and author of a number of textbooks, for his encouragement of me, a novice author and book publisher; Marion Morrison, medical staff assistant, for recording minutes of all meetings, including those of the board of trustees; Willis-Knighton employees and physicians, whose dedicated efforts provided me with so many accomplishments to include in *Breadcrumbs to Cheesecake;* and thousands of members of the WK family, loyal physicians and employees, whose lives of service and deeds of human compassion have earned their beloved Willis-Knighton its deserved reputation by supporting its mission to "provide the highest quality patient care at the lowest cost in the most caring and compassionate settings."

James K. Elrod, 2013

CHAPTER 1

What on Earth is Hospital Administration?

Whatever you do, or dream you can do, begin it.
Boldness has genius, power and magic in it.

Johann Wolfgang von Goethe (1749-1832)

This book could not have been written were it not for two wonderful people who encouraged me to consider the profession of hospital administration while I was an undergraduate at Baylor University in Texas: Boone Powell Sr., president and CEO of Baylor University Medical Center in Dallas, and his son, Boone Powell Jr., later to follow in his father's footsteps at Baylor, a classmate and dear friend. Both of these exceptional gentlemen took a special interest in me, encouraging me to consider their little-known profession. At that time I put off making any long-range career decisions because I was under contract with the Reserve Officers Training Corps to enter the Air Force as a commissioned officer upon graduation. My commission as a 2nd lieutenant and a flying career in the Air Force were foremost in my mind, as I had dreamed of serving my country in military aviation.

While on active duty for over three years, based primarily in Japan, I often received letters and phone calls from the younger Boone while he was attending the University of California at Berkeley and later when he was a hospital administrative resident at Baptist Memorial Hospital in Memphis.

These contacts, prompted by our deep friendship, piqued my curiosity and interest in hospital administration. Boone was always excited about the challenges and service opportunities of his profession, so much so that I began to make visits on my off-duty time to our large referral hospital on Tachikawa Air Base to learn more about the profession.

St. Louis, Not Washington!

After study and much prayer, I came to accept what I choose to refer to as a personal calling to this career. The Powells suggested several graduate programs and volunteered to recommend me to the programs of my choice.[2]

I chose Washington University School of Medicine in St. Louis and sent my application form in late spring of 1961, hoping to enter in fall 1962, a few days after finishing my tour of duty with the Air Force. The school responded that my grades at Baylor were acceptable but there was an additional requirement: personal interviews with faculty members, to be completed a year before starting classes. This was a major hurdle, as I was squadron commander of a unit on six-hour alert status for deployment in support of troops in Southeast Asia. I was not eligible for leave and wrote the school that I could not go to St. Louis for the interviews.

The response was firm: classes are limited to twelve students, the interviews could not be waived, and I could apply for admission the following year. I was disheartened; my military tour could not be extended for only one year.

Out of the blue, a letter came a month later offering a rare exception to the medical school's policies. Without guaranteeing my acceptance, it said that, if I came any time before classes began in fall 1962 and passed the interview process, the faculty might consider adding a thirteenth student to the class. Thankfully, at that time I was unaware that there were more than two hundred applicants for the twelve student slots that year.

---

2 The Powells recommended three master's programs for hospital administration, one being Washington University. Intrigued by the beauty of the Pacific Northwest, I decided to apply to Washington University, which I confused with the University of Washington. I received a kind letter informing me that I must have the wrong university in mind since they had no such program, referring me instead to the Washington University School of Medicine in St. Louis. I was a little embarrassed, and the incident made me wonder how I would perform in my new civilian career when I couldn't even find the right school to begin with!

Graduation portrait, Baylor University, 1959, age 22.

November 1959 portrait of 2nd Lieutenant James K. Elrod, United States Air Force, age 23.

To further complicate my decision-making process, the Air Force invited me to represent my command at a young officer retention program. Shortly after, I was offered a regular officer's commission to replace my reserve officer commission. A regular commission was, and continues to be, one of the most coveted distinctions bestowed on the officer corps of the Air Force. However, acceptance carried with it a commitment to extend my service obligation for a number of years. This was a dilemma: if I declined the commission, any chance of further active duty with the Air Force was jeopardized.

After much thought and prayer, I decided to put out the biblical fleece, not to test God as Gideon did, but rather to trust that He would provide me with some sign that my decision was within his will for my life. This decision required me to graciously, yet reluctantly, decline the proffered regular commission, which I admit, in spite of my faith, gave me pause, for I had enjoyed my service to my country and took great pride in serving as an officer in the United States Air Force.

I will be eternally grateful to the powers that be at Washington University School of Medicine for their understanding of my plight and their willingness to grant me a late interview, with an outside chance to earn an added slot in the class of 1964. In my heart I will always believe this act of providence permitted me to enter a profession that today I refer to as my "labor of love." And I will always be indebted to Boone Powell Sr., my mentor and role-model, and Boone Powell Jr., my dear friend and leader in our field, who never gave up on their encouragement of me to find my promised land of service to mankind. And no small measure of gratitude goes to the efforts of my guardian angel.

Lucky Number 13

The flight from my base near Tokyo was delayed three days by mechanical problems. I had less than five days to be separated from active duty at Travis Air Force Base, California; retrieve my automobile on the wharf of the Army Terminal, Oakland, California; drive to Shreveport in my 1956 Buick (which overheated a number of times on the trip) to see my daughter of three weeks for the first time (my wife was required to return from Japan six weeks prior to delivery); and board a train in Marshall, Texas, for an overnight trip to St. Louis. I was two hours late for all of my interviews due to train delays and daylight saving time changes, and I had a dreadful headache due to lack of sleep for almost five days.

Looking back at those events, it was probably a good thing, or divine intervention, that I did not arrive at any of my interviews on time because the shortened sessions meant less time for me to display my limited knowledge of hospital operations and lack of experience in hospitals, which until that time consisted merely of my appendectomy at age ten.

After my interviews I returned to Shreveport by train with assurances that I would hear of their decision within forty-eight hours. The next day a telegram notified me of my acceptance to the program with the class of 1964. The faculty had added a student slot for me, expanding the class to thirteen. Most people consider thirteen to be unlucky, but it was the lucky number that launched my career. And as fate would have it, my first date with my wife was on the thirteenth day of the month.

The telegram said that my class' orientation would be held the following Tuesday, which gave me only three days in which to move to St. Louis. Those were busy yet exciting days, filled with more than one prayer of thanksgiving for what my family and I considered a miracle of divine intervention. My guardian angel must have been as exhausted. He had certainly been working overtime on my behalf!

At Washington University, I was introduced to the exciting profession of hospital administration. Due to my lack of experience in healthcare, this hands-on program in a hospital-based setting proved to be a good choice for me. Frank R. Bradley, M.D., founder of the program, along with Harry Panhorst, director of Barnes Hospital, and assistant Don Horsh conducted the program. Our classroom was in Barnes, one of the Midwest's largest and most respected medical centers. Its multiple specialty hospitals, along with the Jewish Hospital of St. Louis, with which it merged in 1996, presented unique on-site opportunities for learning.

My class of thirteen eager students was required to observe the operations of most departments at the medical center. During lunch breaks we could observe surgical procedures, autopsies or the operations of any specialty area of patient treatment.

One of the most memorable experiences of my student life was attending a special meeting of the trustees of the hospital, medical school and the university. I vividly recall meeting the medical school and university board chairmen, Edgar Monsanto Queeny of Monsanto Chemical and James McDonnell of McDonnell Douglas Aircraft, two power executives, and observing their remarkable talents of leadership and loyalty to Washington University.

Residency in the Magnolia State

My guardian angel continued to support me in the Magnolia State of Mississippi, through my association with some of the most patient and knowledgeable teachers of my career. Not one of the department heads at my hospital of residency was ever reluctant to take time to share their expertise and knowledge of operations with me, a wet-behind-the-ears resident from Texas, who, if the truth be known, was probably in their way quite often. If they were perturbed at any time, they never showed it. I remember those dedicated health professionals with heartfelt appreciation and the fondest of memories. Those angels helped stretch the dimensions of my mind as they shared with me new ideas that were later invaluable on my first and only job as a hospital administrator in Shreveport.

My one-year residency at Baptist Medical Center in Jackson, Mississippi, comprised two broad functional assignments. The first, which I had requested at the time of my residency interviews, was to rotate through all departments in the medical center to familiarize myself with the basics of daily hospital operations. The second consisted of assignments of projects, interspersed with my departmental rotations. These projects were of four types for which I had some preparation in graduate school.

One project allowed me to use my graduate school "work design and industrial engineering" experience to address departmental problems related to work flow issues or over-staffing of personnel. For example, the first project was the development of a more

Washington University School of Medicine Masters of Hospital Administration, Class of 1964 and faculty. Elrod is seated on the far left, front row.

efficient admitting process for inpatients and outpatients. The second was the design and implementation of a totally new work flow blueprint for all functions in the business office's operations. A third project was the design of a work flow concept to integrate the hospital's data processing functions with those of the business office and other departments with the goals of efficiency, more accurate data and elimination of over-staffing.

The second type of assignment entailed scheduling my rotations to departments, when possible, to coincide with the supervisor's vacations or days off; thus the job was covered and I got "boots-on-the-ground" experience. I was fortunate to provide three weeks of coverage for the purchasing agent during his period of surgery and recovery. In retrospect, this was probably one of my most valuable experiences, as it provided me with a working knowledge of this most important and second-most costly function in hospitals. When I came to Willis-Knighton, an organized purchasing department with controlled functions for order, receipt, coding, up-to-date inventories and purchase approvals was non-existent.

My third project assignment was to act in liaison with architects, contractors and hospital management on the medical center's new Gilfoy School of Nursing campus, a state-of-the-art educational facility. It was my job to coordinate the interactions of all parties on the project to eliminate surprises and costly change orders. This project provided me practical knowledge of the inner workings of the design phase, the building and construction phase and the coordination and responsibilities of parties on such projects (this was lucky for me because I inherited a building project at Willis-Knighton).

The fourth project gave me experience in the negotiation of contracts for the hospital-based radiologists and pathologists. The contracts were unanimously approved by the medical center's governing board. A valuable resource to me was the recollection of lectures by hospital-based physicians at Barnes and Jewish hospitals in St. Louis, which were part of my curriculum at Washington University School of Medicine. It was also helpful that I had spent time in both of these departments and had gotten to know the radiologists and pathologists.

This period of compensation negotiations of hospital-based specialists was highly volatile. Salaries were growing, sometimes doubling, due to the shortage of qualified specialists in training and private practice. The emerging sophistication of radiology and laboratory equipment had sharpened the demand for physician specialists trained to use it. Income guarantees being offered around the country to qualified specialists were escalating beyond the wildest expectations of most hospital administrative staffs, considerably beyond the guarantees contemplated by our staff at Baptist.

Looking West

The story of how I have come to be the longest tenured hospital administrator in the country has its genesis in my parents' belief that sometimes God answers your prayer by not giving you what you prayed for. This conviction was based on their strong faith in God's infinite wisdom and assurances that He always knows what is best for you. These truths were certainly borne out not only in my initial call to my chosen career field but also later in the quest for my first position of hospital leadership.

If you know much about the way Texans think, you are undoubtedly aware that they view their great state as the Promised Land in the sense of opportunities and quality of life. And Texans are quick to tell you that their thinking along this line is totally objective with no hint of prejudice on their part.

I had traveled extensively: four Air Force deployments, the last one in Japan, and two years of graduate school and residency in states other than Texas. So you might say I was beginning to come around to the Texans' way of thinking: I narrowed my employment search to Texas and the border city of Shreveport, Louisiana. Shreveport was appealing to me because it was the hometown of my wife and near a large military installation, Barksdale Air Force Base, with a reserve unit posting an opening for my military specialty.

During visits to Shreveport during my residency, I scheduled appointments with three of the city's hospital administrators. All informed me that there were no administrative openings in the area, so I began to look elsewhere. Upon completing my residency at Baptist Medical Center, I was offered an opportunity to stay on the administrative staff, which I gratefully accepted. I remained in this new administrative role for nine months.

In early 1965, I was invited to interview for positions with two hospitals in Louisiana, one in New Orleans and the other in Bossier City, across the river from Shreveport. The Bossier City General Hospital, a city-owned hospital, was under construction with its opening scheduled approximately eighteen months later. I declined the job offer from New Orleans in the hope that I would be chosen for the opening at Bossier City, thinking that my graduate degree in hospital administration, military service and construction management experience gained during my residency might help me. I thought my chances of getting the job were good because, if selected, I would have been only the second administrator in Louisiana with a graduate degree and residency in hospital administration.

Three gentlemen on the selection committee, J. Murray Durham, chairman, Dr. Jake Miciotto and retired army Colonel Neil Yarbrough, stood out as very dedicated to the proposed hospital, wanting to be fair and impartial in fulfilling their responsibility to select the person most qualified to be their administrator.

During the interview, it was fairly evident that the majority of the committee, city councilmen and the mayor, had already made a decision. This fact was verified a short time later by Colonel Yarbrough. Dr. Miciotto and Colonel Yarbrough remained good friends to me. Dr. Miciotto presently serves on the WK Board of Trustees and I had many chats with Colonel Yarbrough prior to his death. These gentlemen were unsung heroes of Bossier Medical Center, for they labored to make it the best hospital it could be in spite of the political influences that kept it in turmoil a great deal of the time. I continue to view these wonderful gentlemen as the glue that held the hospital together as long as it survived.

To say that I was extremely disappointed when notified that I was not selected for the job at the Bossier City General Hospital would be an understatement. My sense of loss was accentuated by the fact that there were no other openings in the area, a location my family and I greatly desired. We believed that any hope of getting a job in our city of choice was gone.

When I informed my parents of my disappointment, their encouragement was to restate their belief: "Son, sometimes God answers your prayers by not giving you what you prayed for." This reminder was followed by the reiteration of their conviction that God had something else in mind for me, coupled with a challenge: "Get up, dust yourself off and move on because God has another plan for your life."

Nothing could have been truer than my parents' prediction. A few years later, I would come to realize that divine providence had kept me from securing the position at Bossier City General Hospital. From its opening, the city-owned hospital was hopelessly embroiled in politics. Its operations were constantly undermined by its politically influenced hiring and the periodic confiscation of its income, which was under the daily control of the mayor and city councilmen. Over the many years of Bossier City General's existence, a negative climate of political influence became so pervasive that the hospital's medical staff chose to publicly rebuke city officials, through newspapers and television, for their heavy-handed tactics of operation and cronyism. After years of strained relations between the hospital's staff physicians and the city's officials and after the move of a majority of its physicians to our WK Bossier Health Center in 1996, Bossier Medical Center, formerly the Bossier City General Hospital, ceased operation in 2001.

Less than a month after learning that I was not selected for the Bossier City General Hospital position, I received a call from Edwin Moore, Chairman of the Board of the Willis-Knighton Memorial Hospital in Shreveport, to inform me of an opening at his institution caused by the terminal illness of their administrator. Since I had no knowledge of the hospital and no previous contact with its administrative staff, I asked Moore how he had gotten my name. He told me the following story.

While in a Shreveport barber shop, he had overheard a conversation between my father-in-law and a friend, who was inquiring where my wife and I were living and what I was doing since my separation from the military. My father-in-law informed his friend that I had accepted a position in Jackson, Mississippi, upon the completion of a residency that was required for my master's degree in hospital administration. After apologizing for interrupting their conversation, Moore asked my father-in-law for my name and telephone number.

During our telephone conversation, Moore informed me that he would be in Mexico on a bear hunt for about two weeks, but would contact me upon his return. After two of the seemingly longest and most agonizing weeks of my life, he called with a date for my interview. In the meantime, while coaching a Little League team, I had talked with the father of one of my baseball players, Dick Malone, administrator of Hinds General Hospital in Jackson and later, of Baptist Hospital in Jacksonville, Florida.

He told me that he had grown up in a small town about forty miles from Shreveport. Willis-Knighton, he said, was a neighborhood hospital, the smallest one in the city and the only hospital outside the downtown area with physicians and nurses of excellent reputation. The hospital had been historically a physician-owned facility that had struggled financially over the years with few technological improvements. In spite of this, Malone encouraged me to go for an interview with the challenge, "Jim, take a hospital that is on its back and get it on its feet. You will enhance your reputation and opportunities for other jobs, while at the same time you can make a difference at Willis-Knighton by improving its chances for survival."

My interview at Willis-Knighton was conducted by a committee of five board members with three physicians taking the lead. I was so impressed and captivated with the character of those members and the love of the physicians for their hospital that I decided to join them in an effort to improve its services to the community.[3]

I must confess that my original intent was to stay at Willis-Knighton for only a few years before applying for a position with a larger hospital with more opportunities. Never did I envision that Willis-Knighton would become the challenging love of my professional life and that I would find my promised land in the piney woods and red clay hills of North Louisiana.[4]

Some friends enjoy ribbing me about being a Texan who wanted to get to his promised land, but like Moses was not permitted to enter. They say, "Well, Jim, at least you got to within fifteen miles of Texas."

Nothing could have been more true or profound than the deep faith of my parents that "Sometimes, God answers your prayers by not giving you what you prayed for." I remain steadfast in trusting in God's infinite wisdom as I continue to sense the presence of my guardian angel in my life and career. And in addition, I was fortunate enough to secure a captain's slot in the 917th Troop Carrier Group (Air Force Reserve) at Barksdale Air Force Base in Shreveport-Bossier City.

A Bold Decision

No hospital administrator has ever received greater support from a predecessor than I have. Mrs. Louise G. Fry, a registered nurse and anesthetist, was a most gracious,

3 Years later the board chairman admitted to me that he had miscalculated my age on my application, thinking that I was thirty-seven years old at the time of my interview. He told me that had he realized that I was actually only twenty-seven, I probably would not have had an interview; much less would the board have taken a chance on hiring a kid for the job.

4 Another special person (angel) in my life who has played a role in encouraging me to remain at WK for so many years is Ruth Knighton Atkins. She is the daughter and granddaughter of Drs. Knighton Jr. and Sr. No one has ever loved our hospital more fervently than Ruth and her husband, Bill. Upon my arrival, Ruth took me and my family under her loving wing, making every effort to make us feel at home in Shreveport. She continues to this day to include us in her special times with family and friends. Ruth has a zest for life that is contagious to everyone around her.

dedicated and professional administrator of the hospital, faithfully serving in this role for almost forty years. She was a true role model for health professionals. My chance to serve Willis-Knighton Health System is a result of Mrs. Fry's vision and determination to ensure that her successor had a masters and residency in hospital administration. Her willingness to relinquish the reins of the hospital to me, to entrust a twenty-seven-year-old inexperienced administrator with her beloved Willis-Knighton, was not only gracious, but was a bold decision on her part.

Her actions paved the way for my service of almost five decades, years that have been the most personally satisfying, exciting and rewarding of my life.

Even through her death some four months after my appointment, this wise and gracious lady promoted my acceptance by physicians and employees through having me serve as a pallbearer at her funeral. Mrs. Fry told me that she believed I could move her beloved Willis-Knighton Hospital toward a prosperous future and that she wanted everyone to support me as fully as she had done. And thanks to her, they came to embrace me early in my service at the hospital, and this unparalleled support has never faltered.

She was aware that since my arrival I had chosen, out of respect for her, not to occupy her office due to her illness. She said to me, "Mr. Elrod, you did not have to do that, but the fact that you did will serve you well in the future." And it did!

CHAPTER 2

An Upstart Hospital at the End of the Trolley Line: The Early History (1924-1965)

[W]hen we build, let us think that we build forever. Let it not be for present delight, nor for present use alone; let it be such work as our descendants will thank us for, and let us think, as we lay stone on stone, that a time is to come when those stones will be held sacred because our hands have touched them, and that men will say as they look upon the labor and wrought substance of them, "See! This our fathers did for us"

John Ruskin (1819-1900)

A Thanksgiving Gift to the Ark-La-Tex

In the midst of the roaring twenties, less than five years before the Great Depression struck with its devastating economic effects, Tri-State Sanitarium was under construction in west Shreveport. The great fanfare and publicity that preceded the opening of the new medical facility was probably the most attention the hospital would enjoy from the local press for many decades to come. Ads taken out in the *Shreveport Times* in advance by its founding physician-owners, Drs. L. H. Pirkle and Thomas E. Williams, touted this new-

We are thankful for the privilege of opening the doors of

A New and Modern Sanitarium In Shreveport

Latest Scientific Equipment

ON THANKSGIVING MORNING, when the doors of Shreveport's new and beautiful suburban hospital—The Tri-State Sanitarium—are opened, the public will have the opportunity to view one of the most modernly equipped institutions of its kind ever seen in this section of the South. Here are some of the modern wonders of the new Sanitarium, briefly tabulated for your information: Two large Major Operating Rooms furnished with the newest improved equipment—Balfour operating tables, Barton No-Shadow lights; every instrument in modern usage. One Specialist—or "dark"—room, completely fitted; an Obstetrical Department, furnished with every scientific fixture—second to none. Simmons' all-steel furniture, for perfect sanitation and comfort; the Bryant improved model signal system, arranged for both light and bell signals. The building is so arranged that the nurse at the sta tion may see throughout the corridor. The latest Victor X-Ray Equipment is installed, and there are facilities for the practice of Radiographic and Therapeutic work—superficial and deep therapy. We are also equipped to do electro-therapeutic work. The X-Ray is in charge of experts—Munsell L. Adair, M. D., and Amos J. Toups, Technician.

The building itself is one of impressive appearance, built along the best architectural lines, splendidly lighted, heated and arranged for sanitation and comfort. Outside rooms, cheerfully furnished; everything bright, clean, new and according to the latest scientific specifications. All the modern sciences of medicine and surgery will be practiced, and patients given a hearty welcome and the best of attention by physicians of splendid repute in the profession. You are invited to call and inspect this high-class institution, which we are proud to present to North Louisiana, East Texas and South Arkansas as a Thanksgiving offering.

***The* TRI-STATE SANITARIUM**

Located on the Greenwood Road

November 27, 1924 Shreveport Times *announcement of the grand opening of Tri-State Sanitarium, predecessor of Willis-Knighton Memorial Hospital. Built to serve the emerging suburbs, the facility was billed as a "Thanksgiving Gift to the Ark-La-Tex."*

est of the five hospitals in the city as "A New and Modern Sanitarium" with the "Latest Scientific Equipment." The ad concluded with an open invitation extended to the public: "You are invited to call and inspect this high-class institution, which we are proud to present to North Louisiana, East Texas and South Arkansas as a Thanksgiving offering."

On Thanksgiving Day of 1924, November 27, after a construction period of only 38 weeks (according to public records the permit for construction was issued on March 6, 1924) and at a cost of $86,000, the eighty-five-bed hospital was ready for the admission and treatment of patients. Across the nation, the inaugural Macy's Thanksgiving Day Parade was held in New York City. Across town, two other major construction projects were under way: the Slattery Building, then the tallest privately-owned building in Louisiana, was dedicated in August 1924, and C. E. Byrd High School, which remains one of the most respected educational institutions in the state, opened in early 1925.

According to reporters with the *Shreveport Times* writing in the following day's paper, the well-publicized grand opening was attended by so many eager visitors who flocked to get a glance of the new facility that the staff was forced to open the doors earlier than anticipated to allow the early crowd inside to escape the chilly weather.

Visitors were greeted by twenty nurses on loan from other hospitals and welcomed by "a cheerful gas-log fireplace in the dining room where refreshments were served from 6 until 9 o'clock and where a continuous musical program was rendered." The reception reportedly lasted far longer into the night than the scheduled 9 o'clock hour.

"Another Monument to Man's Humanity to Man"

Faced in deep red brick and trimmed in ornamental quoins, cast white keystones, pillars and balustrades, the three-story building exhibited simple colonial revival and federal influences popular at the time and was designed by local architect J. O. Mitchell and his associates. The Mitchell group also designed a number of commercial and civic buildings throughout the city in the 1920s.

Tri-State was situated on the corner of Greenwood Road and Virginia Avenue in a largely residential district with a park-like feel on the west edge of the bustling town center. An adjacent secondary building, a retrofitted wood frame two and one-half story classically-influenced private residence with a large two-story front porch was utilized to include the administrative office, kitchen, dining room and nurses' quarters. It was connected to the main hospital wards by an enclosed passageway.

Shreveport Magazine (May 1924) declared that Tri-State Sanitarium was erected to keep pace with Shreveport's remarkable growth. The article noted why Shreveport was in a state of such great industrial activity at that time: "First, she is located in the center of one of the greatest oil and gas fields in the world. Second, slipping along by her side, the great Red River which furnishes one of the main arteries of transportation, and ensures the lowest possible freight rates. Third, she is surrounded by one of the greatest cotton belts in the south...the proximity of [Texas and Arkansas] to Shreveport makes her the natural trade center of a large area of them and makes [their] citizens feel as much at home in Shreveport as they do in any city within the confines of their own state." Shreveport was at this time an emerging city of the new south, a place to pursue prosperity.

A *Shreveport Times* article on November 30, 1924, said of Tri-State Sanitarium, "Another monument to man's humanity to man has been added to Shreveport's list. There are now five general sanitariums here in a city of 65,000 population. It would be hard to find a city of similar size able to make that boast elsewhere."

The article added, "Shreveport is acquiring a reputation throughout the southwest as a city where the best medical treatment can be obtained–as a city where may be found every facility known to man for the healing of the sick...Shreveport's industries serve a wide territory. People for more than a hundred miles around buy in Shreveport, come here for their amusements and ship their products from here. Its factories [and] wholesale houses distribute to a million people. And when sickness falls upon the people of this territory, they instinctively turn to the same place for aid." More particular to the immediate area, the new hospital was well situated on the westernmost edge of the city trolley service and one block from the last street car stop at the Louisiana State Fair Grounds.

Tri-State, the first hospital erected outside of Shreveport's downtown area, was by

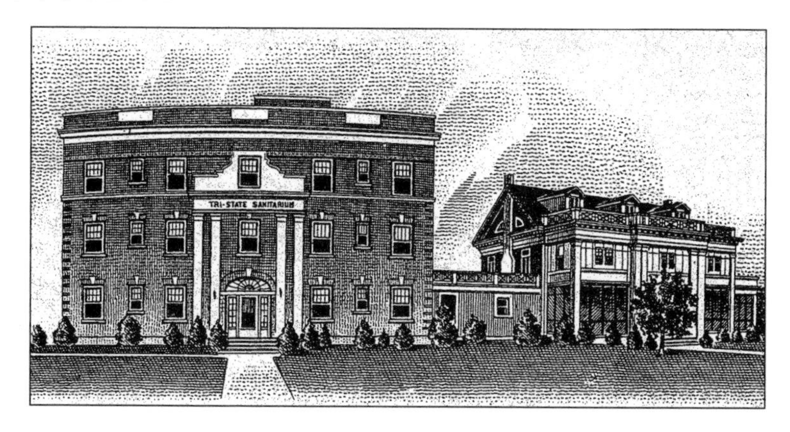

The Tri-State Sanitarium campus, 1924. The former residential structure to the right was retrofitted to include the hospital's administrative office, dining hall, kitchen and nurses' quarters. The building was removed in 1928 to facilitate the addition of hospital beds.

and large designed as a suburban neighborhood hospital for residents who lived and employees who worked in the western portion of the growing city. The *Shreveport Magazine* article noted that the Fair Grounds car line is "one of the best car lines from the point of service anywhere in the south" and "this modern institution...is being built to fill a long felt need in this part of the city."

Drs. Williams' and Pirkle's *Shreveport Times* advertisement described in detail the Tri-State Sanitarium building as "one of the most modernly equipped institutions of its kind ever seen in this section of the South." Some of these "modern wonders" were two operating rooms "furnished with the newest improved equipment" and an obstetrical department, "furnished with every scientific fixture," second to none. The advertisement noted the building as "one of impressive appearance, built along the best architectural lines, splendidly lighted, heated and arranged for sanitation and comfort [with]...rooms, cheerfully furnished; everything bright, clean, new and according to the latest scientific specifications. All the modern sciences of medicine and surgery will be practiced, and patients given a hearty welcome and the best of attention by physicians of splendid repute in the profession."

Patients of the sanitarium represented all strata of society, from prosperous oilmen and merchants to blue-collar workers including both rural and city folks. Large numbers of railroad and oilfield workers and their families received care at the sanitarium. Patients traveled from southwest Arkansas, east Texas and northern Louisiana for care, hence the chosen name, Tri-State Sanitarium.

A Place on the Approved List

The early operations of Tri-State seem to have lived up to its promise in the medical community. As announced by the *Shreveport Times* on April 1, 1928, the sanitarium was approved by the nation's highest accrediting organization. "The American College of Surgeons officially announces that Tri-State Sanitarium has been awarded a place on the approved list for 1926, thus signifying that they have adopted the basic requirements which ensure the best care of the patient."

Less than a year after opening, expansion efforts were under way. In May of 1925, members of the Willis-Knighton Clinic had formed Willis, Knighton, Garrett & Willis, Inc. with a capitalization of $50,000. They originally built a clinic on Margaret Place across town, but by 1928 had outgrown that building. The majority of this group relocated to the Tri-State Sanitarium in 1928, along with Dr. W. S. Kerlin, who had joined their practice upon graduation from Tulane Medical School. Dr. Broox Garrett Sr. remained at the Margaret Place clinic and would later become a driving force in the operation of the T. E. Schumpert Sanitarium.

The Willis-Knighton Clinic was located in a new building erected specifically to house the clinic physicians and their practices. The addition was located immediately west of the main hospital building and was connected to the latter by an enclosed passage. The clinic was a one-story building constructed with muted colonial influences in an apparent nod to the original hospital.

The clinic at the Tri-State Sanitarium was completed at a cost of more than $20,000 and dedicated on February 21, 1928. "The building is modern in construction, and is well equipped for public service," the *Shreveport Times* reported. A notice appearing in the same paper two days prior read: "J. M Teat, realtor, reports that he has leased to Drs. J. C. Willis and J. E. Knighton and their associates, Dr. J. C. Willis Jr. and Dr.

The expanded campus of Tri-State Hospital, 1929. An open air terrace is featured on the one-story building to the far left, the original Willis-Knighton Clinic. The larger structure to the right is the bed, office, kitchen and dining addition to the main hospital (visible at center).

W. S. Kerlin, the Willis-Knighton Clinic for the period of 15 years at a total rental of $225,000. The clinic will open Monday night. It adjoins the Tri-State Sanitarium on Greenwood Road."

The most highly regarded feature of the structure was a rooftop open air terrace for use by hospital staff and recuperating patients in search of fresh air. This feature remained popular with the public as long as the building stood.

Also under construction in 1928 was a large addition to the main hospital building where the converted wood frame residential building once stood. This new hospital wing was a large three-story addition that increased the hospital capacity to 118 beds and virtually re-directed the main entrance to front Virginia Avenue.

Although the architectural styling chosen closely resembled the original facility, the rear of the new addition abutted rather awkwardly with the façade of the original building with seemingly little thought to visually tying the two structures together. Also, the brick chosen for the addition was of a much lighter shade than the original structure, making the transition obvious.

In 1929, the vice president of Baylor University, Justin F. Kimball (originally of Dubach, Louisiana) formed a cooperative unit comprising teachers from the Dallas area who paid $6 each year to the Baylor University Hospital and were assured of receiving hospital care when they were in need. As the August 1961 issue of *Shreveport Magazine* relates, the following year Dr. Kimball sent to Shreveport a representative who interviewed persons relative to setting up a similar plan in the tri-state area. This was the beginning of the Blue Cross concept.

The first organized unit of the plan in the United States, aside from the pilot program at Baylor, was formed in Shreveport at Tri-State Sanitarium and at North Louisiana Sanitarium (later Doctors' Hospital). About two years later T. E. Schumpert and Highland hospitals joined the health plan, making it the first in America open to the public. Mrs. Louise G. Fry, the administrator of Tri-State, and her assistant R. E. Blue were among the first advisors of this new model. Fry, a graduate of the T. E. Schumpert School of Nursing, was named superintendent (administrator) of the Tri-State Hospital in 1929 and served faithfully until her death in 1965.

A New Beginning

Before work was completed on the new addition, Tri-State Sanitarium changed ownership and medical supervision from Drs. Pirkle and Williams. On April 20, 1929, the original eighty-five-bed facility plus additions and ancillary operations was sold to a new group of physician owners. Perhaps to keep up with modern trends and to signal to the public a differentiation of ownership, the new owners changed the name to Tri-State Hospital, Inc.

The major stockholders of the purchaser group, owning over 80 percent of the outstanding stock, were Drs. J. C. Willis Sr., J. E. Knighton, J. C. Willis Jr., W. S. Kerlin, Douglas Kerlin and Thomas E. Strain.[5] Most of the stockholders of the new

5 One of the most visionary doctors that I have had the privilege of knowing, Dr. Strain had completed his internship at Tri-State Sanitarium in 1926, upon graduation from Baylor School of Medicine. He lived with his family in a small house at the rear of the property. Two of Dr. Strain's sons, Thomas Jr. and James, later joined their father in one of Shreveport's most distinguished pediatric practices at the west Shreveport hospital for the duration of their long and illustrious careers. Though Dr. Strain was one of the oldest on medical staff when I arrived, his advanced age was no factor in his visionary leadership.

hospital were born in Claiborne Parish, and several of them had practiced together before moving to the new clinic at the Tri-State Sanitarium. Claiborne Parish was then and remains now among the most rural of Louisiana districts, but has been the home of many professionals of both local and national fame, such as Karl Malone (former NBA star), Geoffrey Beene (fashion designer), Bobby Rush (blues musician) and Dr. James Andrews (renowned orthopaedic surgeon). The new Tri-State physicians relocated from a clinic operation near T. E. Schumpert Memorial Sanitarium to the campus of Tri-State after outgrowing their office space on Margaret Place.

A public notice appearing in the *Shreveport Times* on February 19, 1928, recorded: "Drs. L. H. Pirkle and T. E. Williams have purchased lots 28 and 29, Gladstone subdivision, from Dr. J. C. Willis Jr. for $5,250. J. W. Teat, realtor, handled the transaction." With Drs. Willis, Knighton and their associates now running Tri-State, Drs. Pirkle and Williams relocated their offices to the midtown area, evidently with the intent to operate smaller private practices.

However, after the transfer of ownership, the founding physicians of the Tri-State Sanitarium soon dissolved their practice relationship. Dr. Williams remained at the hospital as a visiting physician for a time before relocating his private practice across town to the North Louisiana Sanitarium, while Dr. Pirkle is believed to have stopped practicing medicine for a while and entered into the field of real estate. Shreveport was booming, and many new subdivisions were being laid out across town.

Later, Dr. Pirkle, a graduate of Tulane Medical School, maintained an office in downtown Shreveport and served on the Caddo Parish school board for twelve years and as its president for four years prior to his death. In his *Shreveport Times* obituary dated November 6, 1948, Dr. Pirkle was noted as a giving person, and he bequeathed a portion of his estate to Centenary College and Louisiana Polytechnic Institute (now Louisiana Tech University).

Willis and Knighton

Dr. Willis Sr.[6] (class of 1889) and Dr. Knighton Sr. (class of 1899) graduated from the Nashville School of Medicine (of Vanderbilt University) and had practiced together since 1900 in Homer, Louisiana. In 1904, Dr. Willis moved his practice to Shreveport. In 1909, after post-graduate work in Baltimore, Chicago and New Orleans, Dr. Knighton joined Dr. Willis in Shreveport, and they practiced at T. E. Schumpert Sanitarium, where Dr. Willis became chief of staff upon the death of his colleague, Dr. T. E. Schumpert.

Dr. Willis had been mobilized in 1916 to service in a military hospital in Brownsville, Texas, during the border raids of Mexico's Pancho Villa. Dr. Knighton was chief of medical services at the Shreveport Charity Hospital (later renamed Confederate Memorial Hospital, later to be known as LSU Health Shreveport) for eight years and staff chairman of the Pines Sanitarium (a tuberculosis hospital located west of Shreveport) for two years while maintaining a private practice.

Until Dr. Knighton joined Dr. Willis in practice, Dr. Willis had shared an office and practice with Dr. John Hendrick Sr., founder of the highly-respected Highland Clinic and Hospital (1917), both of which continue in operation. Both Dr. Willis and Dr. Hendrick received training in surgery at the Mayo Clinic in Rochester, Minnesota; Dr. Willis took additional training at Johns Hopkins in Baltimore. The friendship of these two prominent surgeons and their mutual respect caused a special bond to exist between the Highland Hospital and the Tri-State Hospital, which has continued throughout the years.

According to his obituary, "Dr. Knighton was a lover of nature and studied the flora and fauna of Louisiana from a scientific stand-point, contributing articles to nature publications." Also of interest was that Drs. Willis and Knighton were the proud fathers of sons who followed in their footsteps in medicine, choosing upon completion of training

6 Of interest to my wife's family, Dr. J. C. Willis Sr. was born in the town of Arizona, Louisiana, the birthplace of my wife's maternal grandmother, Mrs. Mattie Pennington Barnette Harp. My wife's uncle, W. Clinton Harp, was named for the distinguished Dr. James Clinton Willis Sr., the physician who delivered him. The town of Arizona, once the center of a populated and thriving cotton-producing area on the rail line, was abandoned after the turn of the twentieth century, and there is little evidence of its existence today.

Dr. Joseph E. Knighton (left) oil on canvas, 1930s. From the collection of the Talbot Medical Museum. Dr. James E. Knighton (center) oil on canvas, 1960s. On display at WKMC. Dr. James C. Willis Sr. (right) Oil on canvas, 1930s. From the collection of the Talbot Medical Museum. Portrait of Dr. James C. Willis Jr. unavailable.

to enter practice with them. An article years later in the local newspaper stated that "two families started a hospital." Though Drs. Willis and Knighton certainly did not establish their medical home, their leadership moved it to the next level of achievement.

While working with the Pines Sanitarium as a staff physician, Dr. Knighton participated in numerous free health clinics in support of the early detection of tuberculosis thorough chest examinations. Patients diagnosed with tuberculosis were admitted to the sanitarium for treatment.

The Tri-State School of Nursing

Here's to the giver of powder and pills,
Whose object in life is to cure people's ills—
She strengthens the weary—comforts the sad,
Cheers up the depressed and makes them all glad;
She puts "ease" in disease—works, early and late—
She's the Registered Nurse of the Pelican State.

Toast given at the 1925 Louisiana State Convention,

National Health Congress

The Tri-State School of Nursing was opened with the founding of the hospital in 1924. The nurses were boarded in the upper floor of a former residential structure next door to the sanitarium. The *Shreveport Times* editorial covering the opening reception of the sanitarium recorded that this former home of E. Wayles Browne "will afford nurses' quarters on the second floor and a dining room and kitchen on the first floor. The nursing staff was headed by Florence Watson.

The school opened with twelve students and attained an average census of about twenty students by the late 1920s. The first class of five nurses graduated in May 1927, and an elaborate outdoor ceremony was held on the Sanitarium grounds with live music and festive pageantry. According to the *Shreveport Times*, the entire program was broadcast live by local radio station KSBA. Afterward, a class reception and dance was held in the nurses' dormitory hall.

The nursing school was a significant achievement of the founding physicians and their successors. They had dutifully noted that Shreveport's place as a growing medical center for the greater region would require a fresh supply of nurses. In time the school's favorable reputation for educating and training nurses became widely known by both physicians and patients of the Ark-La-Tex.

Gehlen Hall, ca. 1940. This repurposed former private residence housed classes of Tri-State Nursing students for 25 years until it was finally razed following the close of the school in 1949.

The students of the Tri-State nursing school played a major role in the hospital's operations from the start, and the toil and work ethic exhibited by the student nurses became the stuff of local legend.[7] The student nurses received room and board in lieu of pay. Their education consisted largely of on-the-job training with Tri-State physicians under the supervision of Mrs. Florence Watson, Mrs. James Willis and later Mrs. Louise Fry.

One nurse fondly recalled her on-the-job anesthesia training experience prior to a formal course for nurse anesthetists. She noted that her instructors took the students to a local veterinarian's office to practice "dropping ether" on dogs and cats undergoing procedures.

Once admitted, student nurses faced tuition of $202.50, for which they were given a generous time to pay. Students were required to bring with them various items, such as one pillow, white hose, three hair nets, white slips, clothing suitable for hiking or picnicking, one party dress, one nice silk dress, a laundry bag and writing materials.

Student nurses shared a living space with several other students at a time, and, as the

7 One of the graduates of the Tri-State School of Nursing was Miss Virginia Cassidy, mother of the former President of the United States, William (Bill) Clinton of Arkansas.

hospital initially had no housekeeping staff, were required to maintain patient rooms and common areas of the hospital in a sanitary condition. Scrubbing hospital walls and baseboards was a common routine.[8]

The Tri-State School of Nursing class of 1945. The photograph was taken on the grounds of Gehlen Hall.

Nurses cleaned windows and bathrooms and mopped the floors. In the afternoons the student nurses were often required to shell peas on the back porch of their dormitory and prepare other vegetables for the dietary department and patients' meals.

The social aspect of the life of the students was always centered on the hospital campus. Dances, banquets, pinning ceremonies and outdoor activities all took place within the confines of Tri-State. To the students, the most hallowed ground was the bench under a huge live oak near the main hospital entrance, which was the site of many wedding proposals and giving of engagement rings.[9] Nursing students were not allowed to marry as long as they were enrolled, and could stay out late (11 p.m.) only on Saturday nights. On Sundays the nurses rolled bandages, patched gloves, sharpened knives and shined needles.

The recollections of 1934 Tri-State graduate Mrs. Ozelle Benefield Jones provided much of this information on the lives of the student nurse's duties, but their diligent toil is also highlighted by some of the documents left behind in our files from past genera-

8 On my first day as administrator, while practicing my "management by walking around" philosophy, I observed a registered nurse on her hands and knees scrubbing baseboards in the hallway. She politely stood up, introducing herself as Pauline Uli. I asked her if she shouldn't have a housekeeper perform this task. She informed me that there was no housekeeping staff, and further, that all Tri-State Nursing School graduates were trained to accept such duties. Astonished, I established a housekeeping department for the hospital soon thereafter.

9 I have typically enjoyed the support of the nursing staff with one major exception. In 1965 I had a tree removed because of the obtrusive nightly roosting of starlings. The birds' noise and bathroom habits created a bad situation. The oak was felled before I understood its significance to the Tri-State graduates. The tree was formerly known as the "spooning tree," a place where students were often engaged and romanced. What helped my situation most with these sentimental nurses was that the last class of the nursing school had graduated in 1949 and few contemplated future engagements.

tions. Found among a 1940s stash of papers related to the nursing school was a one-page reminder to the students of the duties of their profession in the Victorian era:

Nurse's Duties in 1887

In addition to caring for your fifty patients, each nurse will follow these regulations:

1. Daily sweep and mop the floors of your ward, dust the patient's furniture and window sills.

2. Maintain an even temperature in your ward by bringing in a scuttle of coal for the day's business.

3. Light is important to observe the patient's condition. Therefore, each day fill kerosene lamps, clean chimneys, and trim wicks. Wash the windows once a week.

4. The nurse's notes are important in aiding a physician's work. Make your pens carefully; you may whittle nibs to your individual taste.

5. Each nurse on day duty will report every day at 7 A.M. and leave at 8 P.M., except on the Sabbath, on which day you will be off from 12 noon to 2 P.M.

6. Graduate nurses in good standing with the director of nurses will be given an evening off each week for courting purposes or two evenings a week if you go regularly to church.

7. Each nurse should lay aside from each payday a goodly sum of her earnings for her benefits during her declining years so that she will not become a burden. For example, if you earn $30 a month, you should set aside $15.

8. Any nurse who smokes, uses liquor in any form, gets hair done at a beauty shop, or frequents dance halls will give the director of nurses good reason to suspect her worth, intentions and integrity.

9. The nurse who performs her labors and serves her patients and doctors faithfully and without fault for a period of five years will be given an increase by the hospital administration of five cents a day, providing that there are no hospital debts that are outstanding.

The paper, it seems, served as a gentle reminder to the nurses enduring the war years in a hospital encumbered by staffing and supply shortages that such difficulties, when placed in a historical perspective, were quite bearable. Or, perhaps the students themselves distributed the note for a laugh and reflection of how little had changed in the field of nursing in the many decades since Grover Cleveland was President of the United States.

Student nurses on duty in the laboratory and tending to a patient in the emergency department.

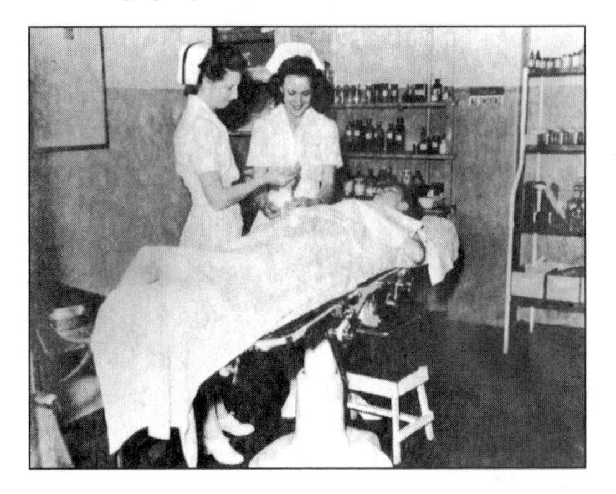

Facilities Unsurpassed in the South

Tri-State Hospital had expanded its services and physical plant rapidly in the late 1920s and was gaining a deserved reputation for quality medical care and a friendly, caring staff. However, the new decade was bringing new challenges and with nearly a quarter of the nation's total work force unemployed by the mid-1930s, many patients could not pay for medical services.

At times payment from patients was accepted in the form of produce and livestock, which helped keep the dietary department well supplied if not the books of the hospital balanced. A list of bad debts for the year 1932 reached seven pages.

Tri-State Hospital's ability to expand its scope of services or acquire new technology was quite limited. Enrollment in the nursing school plummeted as families recalled their daughters from school to work and help care for their needs at home. Mrs. Jones' class of 1934 began with thirty-three students; only seven would graduate.

Mrs. Louise Gehlen Fry, administrator of Tri-State Hospital (later Willis-Knighton Memorial Hospital) 1928-1965.

The situation was dire, and some of the students who would be eligible for graduation could not afford the train fare to New Orleans to take the state board exams. When one of the business office employees heard of this situation, she informed her husband, a local Kansas City Southern train conductor, Troy Thomas, who made the route from Shreveport to New Orleans and back frequently.

He told the girls they could stow away in one of the passenger cars and ride to take the exams free of charge. Later, out of guilt he admitted to his supervisors the presence of the unauthorized passengers. He expected a backlash or reprimand, but none was given. Instead the Tri-State student nurses were allowed for the next several years free passage on the KCS trains to New Orleans to take their state exams.

The family feel of Tri-State carried the hospital through this trying time. Through the efforts of a small cadre of physicians and nurses the hospital doors and nursing school were kept open for service to the community, though our records show that during some years it was operating at a loss. These talented individuals continued to provide a quality of medical care that was touted across the region. Evidence of their accomplishments appeared in two articles in the *Shreveport Times*.

On October 21, 1932, an editorial announced that "Five Hospitals in Shreveport Offer Facilities Unsurpassed in the South" and noted that the city had "the distinction of having four private hospitals having the most modern equipment that can be found...

residents of the Tri-State area feel that Shreveport has the best to offer and that they are in safe hands here. Every hospital enjoys patronage from residents throughout this section." The recognized hospitals were Charity Hospital, Highland Sanitarium, North Louisiana Sanitarium, T. E. Schumpert Memorial and Tri-State. Further, a December 28, 1932 article touted the fact that Tri-State Hospital was one of only twenty-three hospitals in Louisiana with the coveted approval of the American College of Surgeons, the nation's only hospital accrediting agency.

The war years were of little comfort to the hospital and nursing school as they emerged from the depths of the Great Depression. The February 15, 1945, issue of the Tri-State nursing school newsletter, *Echoes of Gehlen Hall*, warned of ominous government plans to draft graduate nurses into the armed forces at the rank of private. Fortunately, none of the girls were drafted before war's end.

Post-War Optimism and Bleak Realities

In May 1946, ninety-six nurses graduated from the various nursing schools around Shreveport. The largest class, Tri-State's twenty-seven, was photographed for an article in *Shreveport Magazine*. Nonetheless, the nursing school was formally closed after the class of 1949, and generations of future students went into the nursing program of Northwestern State College in Natchitoches (today Northwestern State University of Louisiana).

The diploma nursing programs at North Louisiana Hospital, Highland Hospital, T. E. Schumpert Memorial Hospital and Shreveport Charity Hospital were also merged with Northwestern's program at that time. Today, the Northwestern State University nursing school is the fourth largest nursing school in the United States.

Tri-State Hospital was experiencing a long period of decline; the Depression and War years had damaged the finances of the hospital to such a degree that scaling back hospital services was necessary to avoid closing the doors. Excess capital was virtually non-existent, and other than the erection of a temporary $3,000 storage building in 1946, there had been no additions or improvements to the hospital's physical plant since 1929.

On November 14, 1949, liquidation of the struggling Tri-State Hospital's assets began. The directors were searching for an answer to their stagnant market share. The hospital was renamed Shreveport Hospital and Research Center, Inc. upon the purchase of all owner's stock and reopened as a not-for-profit institution. Such status would allow the hospital to accept tax deductible contributions from the public.

In January 1952 the hospital name was again changed, this time to Willis-Knighton Memorial Hospital, Inc., following the death of Dr. Joseph E. Knighton Sr. However, name-changing and restructuring did little to improve the hospital's outlook, and a review of the board minutes from the late 1940s through the early 1960s presents the stark image of a proud institution in imminent danger of closing. Between 1949 and 1963 less than $350,000 was spent on improvements to the physical plant, all of which was borrowed.

In contrast, the greater community of post-war Shreveport was a place where optimism and a sanguine belief in the direction of the country prevailed. Residential construction and commercial industry were booming in the city; building permits were issued at a feverish rate, and the city limits were stretched in all directions. In the last half of the 1940s, there was great faith in Shreveport's future, particularly when it came to the region's budding medical industry. In February 1949 *Shreveport Magazine* published a comprehensive piece on the remarkable healthcare infrastructure already in place across town and presented detailed plans for realistic imminent growth.

As the community was gearing up to move into the 1950s, the article said, "this city has everything it needs to become important medically–more than 35 percent of its doctors are specialists (the average town can be served by a 15 percent ratio)–adequate hospital facilities–a wide service area–and an interested cooperative community." There were five private hospitals and one charity facility, which offered a total bed capacity of about 1,500. Each of the facilities was noted as "fully-equipped, modern" and contained the "latest for diagnosis and treatment of all kinds of diseases."

Throughout the *Shreveport Magazine* article emphasis was placed on the possibility of opening a new medical school due to the shortage of doctors in the country.

"Shreveport has enough clinics and hospitals to expand postgraduate and initiate undergraduate study." Each hospital was approved for intern training and already had a cooperative nursing school. The article also noted that "the city's further participation in medical education at the present time is evidenced in the graduate program of training at Shreveport Charity Hospital, where, in addition to 25 approved internships, there are 22 residents in training in eight approved specialties."

Less than a year later, on November 3, 1957, T. E. Schumpert Memorial Sanitarium dedicated its new nine-story building, which was outfitted fully with the latest in hospital technology and surgical amenities. With its imposing façade, the very architecture of the new Schumpert seemed to draw the eye skyward toward the heavens–as if the building itself was beckoning the observer to consider the healing powers and mercy of the Lord.

Soon, the new hospital dramatically altered the Shreveport healthcare marketplace. As the market dominance of the new Schumpert grew to almost embarrassing proportions (to the humble nuns), so too did Schumpert's influence on the direction of Shreveport's healthcare market–a position that would not change for decades to come.

CHAPTER 3

Blessed Beyond Measure: The Willis-Knighton Health System Since 1965

So neither the one who plants nor the one who waters is anything, but only God who gives the growth.

1 Corinthians 3:7

Willis-Knighton Health System is the largest medical center in Louisiana and a number of surrounding states. It is the medical home to thousands of paying and indigent patients (and their families) and the patient care workshop of over a thousand physicians and other health professionals. The system employs 350 providers who work within an exclusive physician network. Our staff strives to provide the highest quality of care on a broad continuum of medical services, from "Shots for Tots," our pre-school immunization program, to organ transplantation. Included in our mission is a requirement to provide this care at the lowest price in the most caring and compassionate of settings.

In the last few years, Willis-Knighton Health System has received the following recognitions: 1) featured on ABC's "*Good Morning America*" as the nation's hospital with the lowest death rate from heart failure in 2009, 2) included in *U.S. News and World Report* for three years as one of the nation's fifty best hospitals in several disease categories, 3) rated by Thompson's 100 as one of America's top one hundred hospitals in 2000 and 2005, 4) recognized by Health Grades for over a decade as one of the top hospitals in the country [top 5 percent], 5) rated in 2009 as the seventh health system in the nation in a comparative study of composite scores of core measurements (i.e., patient satisfaction and safety, quality of care, morbidity, mortality, readmission rates, infection rates and other quality of care standards), 6) featured in a 2009 issue of *Nursing Professionals* magazine as one of the best one hundred hospitals in America for nurses' working conditions and 7) honored with the Consumers' Choice Award for the last ten years as the best health system in the region. Also, WK continues to be recognized as the region's most philanthropic business enterprise, surpassing even the admirable efforts of the local United Way.

For many years, Willis-Knighton Health System has operated the region's foremost Centers of Excellence: organ transplant, fertility, heart, cancer, eye, laparoscopic surgery, robotic surgery (one robot on each campus), obstetrics, hepatobiliary, rehabilitation, spine treatment and behavioral medicine programs. WK operates the region's most active occupational medicine program and urgent care clinics with full-time physician coverage. In addition, WK's wound care program offers treatment in the only twelve-patient hyperbaric chamber in Louisiana.

Due to the efforts of Diane Coffman, Joyce Hooper and chief radiologist Cliff Coffman, M.D., for over forty years, the system's imaging and therapy capabilities are unsurpassed in the state: a total of eight CAT scanners (including 64 and 128 slice units) and eight MRI units (1.5 to 3.0 tesla) are available on all four campuses. Ten heart catheterization labs, two electro-physiology labs and one cardiac hybrid lab are operational on three campuses. The latest generation PET scanner, two linear accelerators and a tomo-therapy unit are housed in the WK Cancer Center, to be augmented by the installation of the region's first proton beam therapy unit (with pencil beam guidance) in 2014.

Willis-Knighton is the largest private benefactor of health education programs for Louisiana colleges and universities. As the major partner of LSU Health Shreveport School of Medicine, it is the clinical home to medical and surgical residency programs, the WK/LSU Organ Transplant Program, the WK/LSU Fertility and Reproductive

Center and a number of hospital-based clinics providing care for patients of urology, gastroenterology, orthopaedic, maxillofacial surgery and pediatric subspecialties. Approximately $8 to $9 million a year of financial support is provided the medical school to support these programs. A $1 million research chair at the medical school was funded through a grant to the Bio-Medical Research Institute.

A graduate education program at LSU-Shreveport is supported through a $1 million chair in health administration in the James K. Elrod School of Health Administration, and a number of professorships in nursing education are funded at the nursing programs of Grambling University, Northwestern State University and Southern University-Shreveport.[10] WK supports a number of medically related technical training programs at Bossier Parish Community College, Southern University of Shreveport and Louisiana Tech University. Our health system is the major contributor to the Alliance for Education's effort to improve elementary and high school performance and testing scores.

Willis-Knighton Health System is the largest provider of senior adult active lifestyle communities in Louisiana. A gated 312-acre campus offers 120 independent living cottages, 124 high-rise and 48 assisted living apartments and a 160-bed skilled nursing facility, nestled among lakes, bayous and pecan groves. A 130-bed skilled nursing facility with rehabilitative services and an extended care facility with twenty-four beds are located on the campus of our flagship hospital. Two long-term acute care units (LTACs) are located on the flagship campus and at WK Pierremont.

Growth of Phenomenal Proportions

Willis-Knighton has not always been a large, financially strong hospital with the commanding market share that it enjoys today, nor has it always played such a prominent role in the state of Louisiana and nationally. The transformation from a small neighborhood sanitarium to a nationally ranked and recognized health system is a story worth telling.

10 Professorships are named in honor or memory of devoted WK nurses.

Between 1965, the year of my arrival as administrator, and 2012, our health system experienced phenomenal upswings in bed size, patient volume and financial health; bed capacity grew from **80** beds to **1,192** (901 acute and 291 skilled nursing beds); hospital inpatient admissions, from **5,967** to **51,343**; emergency visits from **15,322** to **206,920** (*Modern Healthcare*, February 27, 2012, reported that in 2010, WK's emergency departments ranked as the thirteenth busiest in the United States); births from **9 percent** to over **85 percent** of our market; annual gross charges, from **$1.4 million** to **$2.4 billion**; annual net income, from **$89,575** to **$84.1 million**; and annual EBITDA, **$121,204** to **$135.2 million.**

Profit is Not a Dirty Word: No Margin, No Mission

We do not apologize for making a profit in our tax-exempt charitable organization; profit is mandatory if WK is to continue providing the highest quality of care while serving as the region's largest safety net hospital. However, this achievement must be the result of operating a financially sound, efficient and cost-effective operation with less than market rate charges for services.

Early in my career, a wise Irish Catholic nun summed up an administrator's fiscal responsibility to me by commenting: "Jim, never forget–no margin, no mission." My interpretation of her advice was that good works require a modicum of profitability.

Pay as You Go

WK cannot raise capital for new buildings, technology or new services by issuing stock; as a not-for-profit hospital, WK's stockholders are the patrons it serves. All investments must be financed from operations or through borrowing. Our preference is to pay as we go. Every penny of our profit must be returned to the community in the form of capital reinvestment to ensure the continued mission of providing health and well-being services to our community.

In fiscal year 2012, our $84.1 million in earnings, over $50 million in depreciation,

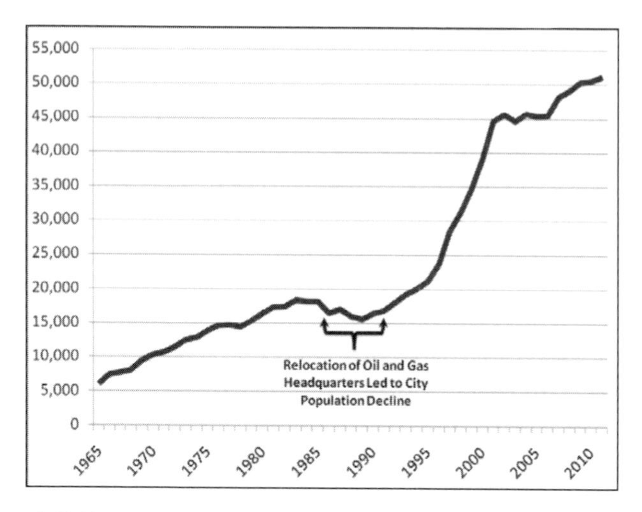

Graph 1: WKHS admissions, 1965-2012. Remarkably, much of this growth has occurred while the community population has remained relatively stable. Note: the dip in admissions 1985-1990 is attributable to a major oil and gas downturn that caused a dramatic exodus of those employees and families.

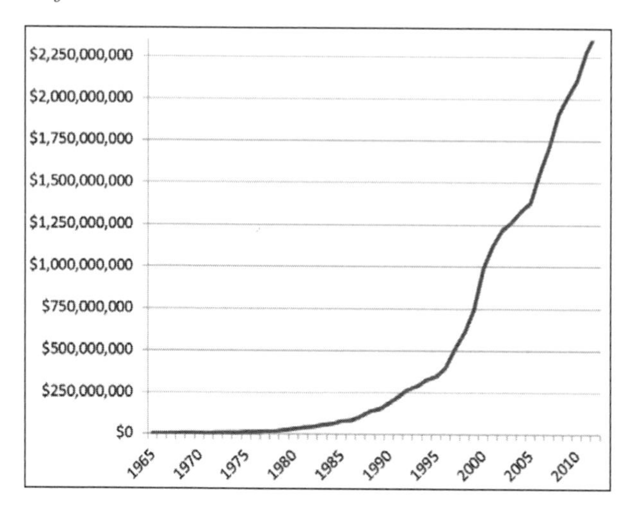

Graph 2: WKHS total revenue, 1965-2012. The health system's revenue has climbed steadily since 1975, after WK emerged from insolvency.

were utilized to finance the following enhancements to our health system: 1) annual capital expenditures required to ensure the availability of the latest generation of technology [$34 million]; 2) buildings and improvements to accommodate new services [$50 million] and 3) annual payment on long-term debt, bond cash reserves and other expenditures [$36.6 million]. A reminder: in this year WK's "tithes" of cash to support other worthy not-for-profit community organizations (outside our walls) amounted to $13.5 million which is a deduction from total gross income. Were it not for our cash tithes our earnings would have been $97.6 million ($84.1m + $13.5m).

Examples include supporting: 1) indigent medical care provided outside our hospitals, 2) humanitarian charities that address issues of poverty, intellectual and developmental disabilities and senior citizens, 3) institutions providing educational programs from pre-school through medical school, 4) cultural activities that support a higher quality of life, 5) organizations that promote youth activities in the community, 6) civic organizations and groups that promote safety and economic development and 7) a commitment of support to our regional military organizations.

The health system's financial success has been achieved even though our patient service charges are lower than our major competitor's. A study of our hospital charges was prepared by Cleverley and Associates, a national authority on hospital rate comparisons. This 2011 study reflected that our average charge per discharge on a case and wage adjusted basis is 12 percent lower for inpatients, and our average charge per APC (ambulatory payment classification) on a relative weight and wage index adjusted basis is 30 percent lower than our competitor. Most important, all earnings are reinvested to the benefit of our regional community (East Texas, Northwest Louisiana and Southern Arkansas). In essence, our success supports the hospital's mission to "continuously improve the health and well-being of the people we serve."

The financial health of the hospital has improved from a position of dismal financial results and no credit rating to today's ratings by Moody's and Standard and Poor's of an A classification. This rating was awarded even though WK had spent over $600 million since 1995 on: 1) building projects, 2) the operation of a hospital-owned HMO (health maintenance organization), 3) significant start-up costs and continued support of a network of approximately 350 employed physicians and 4) the continuing development of a 312-acre vibrant senior adult community.

Since 1965, the campuses of WK facilities have increased from three acres and a building of 57,778 square feet to the present size of more than 600 acres with approximately 3.5 million square feet under roof. Despite land acquisitions and building costs, the system's financial position is one of cash assets exceeding all long-term liabilities.

Of particular note is the fact that WK's phenomenal growth has occurred even though the Shreveport metropolitan area has experienced a population growth rate less than that of most sections of the country. Furthermore, our employee relations have led to an employee turnover rate in 2009 of less than one-half of the healthcare industry's national average (12.3 percent vs. 28.0 percent) as recorded by the U.S. Bureau of Labor Statistics.

Eight hospitals in Shreveport and Bossier City closed their doors during the thirty years that WK was growing (Bossier Medical Center, Doctors' Hospital, P & S Hospital, Riverside Hospital, Fairfield Hospital, Barksdale AFB Hospital, Charter Forest Hospital and Pines Sanitarium). Other than WK's four hospitals, only Schumpert (St. Mary and Highland campuses), Veterans Administration and LSU Health Shreveport Medical Center remain.

The Setting for a Miracle

Anyone can hold the helm when the sea is calm.

Publilius Syrus (1st century B. C.)

No business exists in a vacuum, and Tri-State Sanitarium (later Willis-Knighton Health System) was no exception. For almost forty years no expansions were made to the hospital's original structure, other than a bed addition in 1928. A review of events that stymied growth of Tri-State from its opening in 1924 until 1965 reveals its plight was exacerbated by conditions national in scope.

The Great Depression, World War II, the Korean Conflict and economic recessions presented financial challenges and issues of manpower that daunted the enthusiasm of hospital leaders. They were discouraged from undertaking plans or commitments that might expose them to additional financial risks. Our nation's military conflicts forced the conscription and recall of reservists, including a number of hospital physicians and nurses, for military service, restricting the growth of the hospital's staffing.

From its opening to the early 1970s, Willis-Knighton's leaders were always in a "catch 22" position. Increased patient volumes and revenue were essential for the hospital to generate capital required to fund new physical plants, technology and clinical services to compete with its major rival, T. E. Schumpert Memorial, one of the largest and best-equipped hospitals in the state.

Increased admissions, required to grow the hospital's revenue, are directly linked to the number of physicians practicing in a hospital. The hospital's aging medical staff had experienced little growth because of the lack of available physician office space on the hospital's campus. Some aging physicians were no longer treating hospitalized patients.[11]

Therefore, the recruiting of new physicians required a substantial financial investment, either by the hospital or by its physician groups. Willingness was necessary on the part of either the physician groups or the hospital to subsidize the practices of newly recruited associates. No physician group stepped forward to accept such financial obligations, which were essential if new physicians were to be added to the hospital's medical staff. The hospital's poor financial position precluded any such monetary commitment.

Willis-Knighton's history is the story of a small neighborhood hospital that in its first forty-one years of operation (1924-1965) seemed to have been passed up by time as it diligently labored, never managing to achieve much financial stability or success.

11 One day a beloved but aging staff physician went to pay a courtesy visit to a dying patient whom he had treated for years. Unbeknownst to him, the patient had already been pronounced dead by her attending physician, and her family had been informed. A few minutes later, the elderly physician, unaware of the death, spoke to the family, entered the patient's room and put a stethoscope to her chest. Then he returned to the family and said, "Well, she's pretty much the same." The family responded, "You mean she's not dead?" The attending physician overheard the conversation and took the older doctor aside to tell him of the death. The elderly physician then suddenly realized that his hearing was worse than he knew; he closed his office that day, never to practice again.

Yet it succeeded in providing an unsurpassed quality of patient care in a compassionate setting, more often than not without the benefit of technologically advanced equipment of the day.

This quality of patient care was made possible through the unrelenting efforts of a small medical staff of highly skilled physicians and surgeons, a cadre of capable and dedicated nurses, most of whom were graduates of the hospital's Tri-State Nursing School, and other equally capable caregivers and non-clinical personnel whose love, loyalty and dedication to the institution were legendary. A major source of continuing pride at Willis-Knighton is the fact that the hospital has never failed to be fully accredited by The Joint Commission since the inception of this voluntary program in the early 1930s, or by TJC's predecessor, the American College of Surgeons.

Sadly, the small hospital's opportunities for growth and prosperity were thwarted by a number of unavoidable events. One economic obstacle that hurt Willis-Knighton throughout the 1950s was the cost associated with its conversion to a non-taxable, not-for-profit status in 1949, which required spending unrelated to patient services. (The money was required for the purchase of the previous owners' stock in the hospital.)

Much to the credit of the hospital trustees, they recognized that continuing down the same path of ownership was not the best way for the institution to compete with the newly announced, ultra-modern and technologically superior hospital being built across town.

In 1959, believing that a reputable sponsoring organization with financial strength might be the answer to their dilemma, they sought out several groups of prospective organizations to acquire the hospital. Offers to donate the hospital were officially made to four religious denominations, the Baptists, Methodists, Presbyterians and Episcopalians, but were rejected by all of them. (Of interest to the author is the fact that the chairman of the delegation from one of the denominations, Boone Powell Sr., was one of my sponsors in the profession and the father of one of my closest friends at Baylor University.)

A Paradigm Shift

An event in 1957 was to have a detrimental impact on Willis-Knighton for years to come: the opening of the new T. E. Schumpert Memorial Hospital on Margaret Place, a short distance from the downtown area in Shreveport. Reverberating changes were wrought upon the hospital scene: the market share of the city's other hospitals began to decrease, and the public's perceptions of Schumpert caused it to dominate the market. Seemingly overnight, Schumpert became a behemoth of hospitals, not only in Shreveport/Bossier City but also in the state. Schumpert became the largest private hospital in the state of Louisiana.

The opening of this grand facility had an immediate negative impact on not only the images, but also the numbers of patient admissions and finances of the city's other hospitals, an impact greater than that of the Great Depression or our nation's wars.[12] Until that time, the various hospitals of Shreveport enjoyed a relative degree of parity in the number of patient beds, annual admissions, amenities and vintage of facilities.

The permit for the nine-story hospital's construction was the largest issued since 1949, according to a *Shreveport Times* article. In August 1953 the *Shreveport Magazine* said, "Largest amount of money ever raised in a public fund campaign in Shreveport, $1,165,298, insures start of construction of a new private-pay hospital for the city." Ground was broken in August 1953. Another *Shreveport Times* article said, "Funds to finance it were furnished through the Hill-Burton Act, from public subscription, and by the Sisters of Charity of the Incarnate Word, who have operated Schumpert for 46 years."

In 1957 the new hospital, which added more than two hundred beds, opened to great fanfare and media attention. The newspaper praised its modern structure and high-tech design. "Nearly 700 visitors from cities as distant as Denver, Colo., previewed the luxurious $6,500,000 T. E. Schumpert Memorial Sanitarium," recorded the *Shreveport Times* on October 31, 1957.

12 Shortly after arriving in Shreveport, I was invited to lunch by the administrator of Highland Hospital. Upon my arrival he said, "Jim, let me show you where Shreveport's hospitals, other than Schumpert, make most of their profit." Then he walked me out to their pay parking lot to collect quarters from the coin machine.

Already the subject of multiple additions and positioned in a declining neighborhood, the aging Willis-Knighton Memorial Hospital was no architectural darling of the community by 1960.

When the new T. E. Schumpert Memorial Sanitarium opened in 1957, a new standard for healthcare facilities was abruptly brought to Shreveport. Clearly, the gauntlet was thrown; the building was impressive enough to merit its own line of postcards (above).

To the general public, a new standard for hospital design, amenities and equipment was established by the modern T. E. Schumpert Memorial Hospital. The hospital's new image had a positive effect on what was to become its successful physician recruitment initiative. The lure of this new physical plant was the centerpiece of a marketing plan that produced a skyrocketing dominance of the marketplace for over a quarter of a century.

The new hospital facility and the recruitment of so many quality physicians catapulted Schumpert into the ranks of the finest hospitals in the South. Within a short time after the opening of its new hospital, Schumpert's inpatient census was equal to the combined censuses of all the other private, non-governmental hospitals in Shreveport.

While Schumpert was becoming the publicly perceived dominant hospital in the region, the city's other hospitals did little to challenge it. This lack of reaction was partly due to the fact that, with the exception of Willis-Knighton, all of the other hospitals were physician-owned and thereby ineligible for federal grants or tax-deductible contributions. Schumpert's patient volume continued to grow at the expense of its competitors, unchallenged until Willis-Knighton's first satellite facility, South Park Hospital (now WK South and Women's Center), opened to the public in 1983. This twenty-six-year lead of market dominance was a daunting challenge for the city's other hospitals.

The opening of South Park, the first satellite hospital in the state, did have some impact on Schumpert's market share in southwest Shreveport. But in nautical terms, our health system's two hospitals were merely two small ships doing battle with an aircraft carrier. We did not wrest away Schumpert's market dominance. However, it was a moral victory because Willis-Knighton had done what no other hospital in the city had even attempted in over twenty-five years, and that was to take an action that challenged Schumpert's dominant position. This event was the beginning of a long struggle for the hearts and minds of patients of the Ark-La-Tex, but it did little at that time to impact the large, high-quality hospital's growth and prosperity.

Why Call It a Miracle?

Willis-Knighton's phenomenal growth might be considered a divine miracle when one ponders the challenging financial and sociological issues that I faced as the newly appointed administrator in 1965. A factor seemingly insurmountable: T. E. Schumpert Memorial Hospital was the 800-pound gorilla in the Shreveport marketplace of private healthcare. Other factors were quite challenging: 1) Willis-Knighton did not participate in the Medicare program and 2) unlike most states, Louisiana had a Medicaid program that reimbursed its community hospitals less than half the cost of providing care to indigent patients.

Financial Challenges

The hospital was in a dismal financial state in 1965, virtually a position of insolvency and undeclared bankruptcy. Final costs of the in-progress construction project had been underestimated; there was no provision for the additional cost of change orders, purchase of equipment and furnishings, interim interest on the construction note or money to operate the new addition. A declaration of bankruptcy was not a viable option because of its potential impact on the hospital's (long-term) image and reputation–thwarting our ability to recruit new physicians, employees and patients. Further, the hospital's ability to borrow funding for future projects would be adversely impacted. The reality was that Willis-Knighton had a stack of unpaid bills.

1. No provision had been made for the capital that would be required to upgrade the older building to the standards of the new addition. This renovation was essential because the new addition could not accommodate all of the inpatient admissions and ancillary services. Parts of the older building had to remain in service following the renovation (some continue in use even today).

2. The accounts payable owed to vendors had become so delinquent that some were beginning to demand cash payments upon delivery of goods. Issues of security and accountability of cash drawers for immediate payments were mounting. This situation was exacerbated by a manager's heretofore unknown routine of hiding invoices from the auditors and administrator because, as this kind gentleman said, "I

didn't want to upset anyone about our bad financial situation." A two-week search uncovered over one-half million dollars' worth of unpaid invoices that had been secreted in desk drawers, file cabinets, closets and under stairwells of the hospital. Aging of the accounts payable overdue bills ranged from a few months to over a year. I asked one of our largest vendors, our laundry processor, Ben Levy of New Way Laundry, whose delinquent account was months in arrears, why he had continued to service the hospital without payments on a current basis. He replied, "Jim, I figured the hospital was as good a charity as I could find to give money. Your predecessors were good people and I wanted to see WK continue to serve this community."

3. The hospital's financial position was severely restricted; its plight became worse as unexpected bills for services were received or discovered. This situation was partly due to the lack of a purchase order system with controlled authorization of approvals. No central control mechanism for tracking purchases or proof of receipt of goods was in place.

4. The hospital's chart of accounts did not provide management with the level of breakdown of detail necessary for close scrutiny of departmental financial matters. This incompleteness negated any ability to enforce exact cost accountability; thus departments could not produce accurate budgeting and forecasting projections. Budgetary expense control opportunities were limited.

5. Revenues from inpatient and outpatient charges for services generated by the X-ray and laboratory departments of the hospital were owned by an outside party, the Willis-Knighton Clinic, and were not available to the hospital. Since these clinical services are two of the most profitable product lines in a hospital, the reclamation of ownership and recapture of this revenue became one of the new administrator's first priorities. This loss of revenue was a bone of contention with non-clinic physicians, who objected to the clinic's ownership of any hospital services.

6. There was not a system in place to ensure the complete capture and subsequent billing for all patient charges for services that were rendered. Some of the department supervisors and head nurses were delegated the authority to adjust, discount or write off altogether patient charges for services received based on certain circumstances. (Or maybe they just misunderstood their authority!)

7. No system to ensure monthly patient billing and collection of accounts receivable was in place. There was no aged trial balance of accounts receivable (a report that lists accounts in chronological order of delinquency) to permit more productive collection efforts.

8. The processing of data for financial, human resources and purchasing was done by hand (no computerization).

9. There were large "off book" revenues that should have been accounted for on the hospital accounting system to ensure proper internal controls. Some examples: revenues from vending machines, X-ray silver extraction, purchasing rebates and interest earned on bank deposits of such "off books" assets. (A savings passbook with a balance of over $70,000 and $23,000 in cash were found in the desk of the former administrator. I was informed that this fund had been used for years to pay travel and education expenses of the staff).

10. No financial statement had been presented to management and the governing body for a number of months due to the illness of the outside accountant.

11. No employees had received salary increases or adjustments for over four years. This below market wage scale for our hospital employees made the recruitment of staff most difficult. Further, no retirement plan was provided.

12. Because many of the hospital's lower-paid employees did not have bank checking accounts, it was the hospital's routine to pay their salaries in cash. This required the payroll clerk to accumulate enough currency in bills and coins to place in employee pay envelopes, a time-consuming and laborious task. The physical and fiscal internal controls and audits of these funds were also exceedingly difficult.

13. The hospital was experiencing a high number of "no shows" on the weekends in some departments (partly caused by the cash payments). This predicament prompted the implementation of the health system's present "sick pay" policy of compensating employees for unused sick days. After a number of my department heads and I were forced to prepare a breakfast meal on a couple of weekends, we quickly came up with the idea to create this attendance incentive. Necessity is the mother of invention.

14. No new physicians had been recruited to the hospital for some time. This situation restricted growth of patient admissions and corresponding revenue.

15. The only off-street parking available to the hospital was a physician-owned pay lot across the street and the clinic's lot for patients, hospital employees and visitors, rented on a monthly basis from the clinic. Patients and their families were lost to the hospital because of the shortage of free parking around the hospital (other hospitals in the city had adequate free parking).

16. There was no system for the daily monitoring of personnel working to ensure control over total hours worked by departments. No monthly calculation of FTEs (full time employee equivalents per occupied bed) and corresponding expenses were available for purposes of monthly comparisons. Actual costs of manpower became known only after payroll check preparations, too late to make adjustments during pay periods. There were always surprises at the end of the month.

17. Prior to my arrival, all take-home prescriptions were filled by an outside retail pharmacy because the hospital did not have a registered pharmacist on staff. Patients had to wait long periods before discharge for their prescriptions to be filled. This routine tied up much-needed hospital beds unnecessarily while providing the hospital with no monetary gain.

18. Laboratory procedures, other than routine blood and urine testing and a few others, were forwarded to an outside reference laboratory for the more sophisticated studies, at significant expense, because either WK lacked the equipment necessary or our lab personnel were not adequately trained. This outsourcing procedure was at a high cost of lost revenue to the hospital.

19. There was a distinct lack of communication between departments, exacerbating the financial plight of the hospital. There were no routine managerial meetings to discuss measures and new cost-cutting ideas, or to streamline operations and enhance patient services.

20. The hospital's financial plight presented a dilemma of a personal and sensitive nature to me, its new administrator, within a few months of my arrival. The chairman of the board of trustees informed me that the board had voted a salary increase for me, which I appreciated but respectfully declined due to the hospital's anemic financial position. While I could have used the extra money, I felt strongly that it would not be in the best interests of my relationships, acceptance and future support from employees since the vast majority of them had not had an increase for over four years. On more than one occasion, my assistant and I voluntarily held a few of our pay checks due to insufficient funds in the payroll account.

As I wrote the above section of the book, I quietly laughed to myself as I recalled a statement of Benjamin Graham, dean of American Security Analysts: "Financial success is never having to balance your checkbook." By this definition or virtually any other, our little hospital was far from being financially successful in 1965; we were forced to balance our checkbook almost hourly, as I recall. Willis-Knighton's major competitor enjoyed a financial advantage, as many of the community philanthropic organizations funded its buildings, equipment and services to the exclusion of other hospitals. At times it was thought by many that some charitable fund-raising organizations were unofficial fund-raisers for Schumpert. However, in fairness, maybe this perception existed to some degree because all of the non-governmental hospitals in Shreveport except Willis-Knighton were privately owned for-profit hospitals and therefore ineligible for tax-exempt contributions.

Further clouding this issue for Willis-Knighton was the fact that, even though it was a not-for-profit hospital, it had been operated for over a quarter-century as a physician-owned, for-profit hospital. This common public misperception regarding the tax-exempt status of Willis-Knighton lingered for a number of years even though our marketing programs were directed at educating the public about our not-for-profit status.

Physical Plant and Equipment Challenges

The physical plant of Willis-Knighton upon my arrival in April of 1965 was sorely inadequate in terms of functionality, design and equipment. And in the 1924 and 1928 buildings, there were numerous plant deficiencies:

1. A few areas of the old building were not air-conditioned. The parts that were air-conditioned were less than adequate in cooling and heating because of the age of the units (circa 1940), deteriorating insulation materials and the way the installation was retrofitted (with inadequate air returns).

2. The corridors and patient rooms were coated with World War II surplus paint purchased from the local Air Force base.

3. All patient rooms were furnished with manual beds and furniture purchased at the time of the hospital's opening. Some had been repainted with the surplus green paint.

4. Furniture in the waiting rooms and the entrance lobby of the hospital dated from the opening of the hospital.

5. One wing of the hospital consisted of a number of undersized single-patient rooms that had been converted from clinic treatment rooms.

6. There were two patient wards furnished with seven beds each (no bedside table for some beds) that required the shifting of a number of beds each time a patient was moved.

7. The lighting in corridors in parts of the building consisted of incandescent light bulbs hanging from the ceiling, some without fixtures.

8. The lights and surgical tables in the operating suites were purchased in 1924.

9. Much of the equipment in the laboratory was outdated and difficult to calibrate.

10. All food prep equipment, stoves, ovens and the dishwasher were outdated. The kitchen's antiquated refrigerated cooler's wood walls were insulated with sawdust, which presented health and sanitation issues, such as roach infestation.

11. The materials management storeroom was housed in a separate Quonset hut, purchased as war surplus, with no air-conditioning, ceiling fans or insulation in the walls or ceilings. The maintenance building was also a war surplus structure.

12. The labor and delivery room was a single-patient room next door to the operating suite, retrofitted to accommodate the delivery of babies.

Despite all of these physical plant shortcomings, there was one amenity unique to Willis-Knighton. A partially covered sun terrace graced the rooftop of one wing of the building. The terrace provided the healing effects of sun, shade and fresh air to patients and their families. To this day I am reminded by former patients and family members of this favorite of hospital retreats, which was removed in the mid-1970s to permit construction of the hospital's massive west addition that fronts on Hearne Avenue and Greenwood Road.

It must be reiterated that, even though an addition to the hospital was under construction at the time of my arrival, this project was not large enough to permit vacating all of the original building. The project consisted of two new patient units totaling 60 beds. Close scrutiny of the double rooms revealed that they were too small to permit the placement of two beds, two bedside cabinets, two lounge and two side chairs. Any thought of adding sleeper sofas was out of the question. Only four of the sixty new beds had in-room bathing facilities, while patients in other rooms were required to use com-

With the exception of a few coats of military surplus gray and green drab paint, the interior of the hospital building changed very little in WK's first forty years (above). Original floor tile was uncovered during a recent renovation (inset). Some original hand-crank operated patient beds of mid-1920s vintage were still in use in 1965 (below).

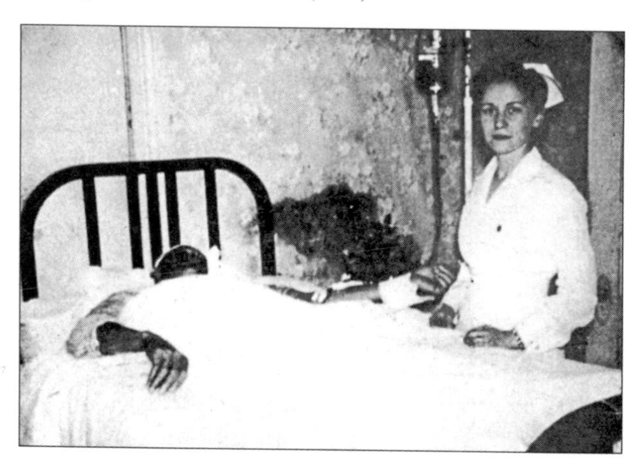

munal showers. There were many complaints about the two-bed rooms and the lack of in-room private bathing; patients said they would prefer to be admitted to a single room with a shared full bath in the 1920s era sections.

We decided to make the new double rooms into singles, which required us to take a number of the previously vacated older patient rooms out of mothballs and furnish them with new patient room furniture. Although this reduced our bed count, it also reduced patient complaints.

The addition also provided a lobby, emergency department, cafeteria, kitchen, renovated X-ray, labor and delivery, and nursery. Since our average census had grown to over ninety-five patients a day by the time it opened, we had to continue operating a number of departments and three nursing units in the old building. Costs of refurbishing the old building, elimination of unsightly out-buildings and additional parking were not included in the planning phases or in the hospital's budget. Another unbudgeted expense was required to upgrade the surgical equipment, sterilizers and air-conditioning units of the original operating rooms, which had to remain in service.

No provision had been made for exterior treatments that would aesthetically tie the old and new buildings together with a coordinated façade or painting scheme. The original building's facade was dark red brick; the new building was beige brick. It was hard to make the three-floor abutted façade connection between the two attractive because their confluence point, a few feet from our new main entrance, was highly visible.

One overriding issue that would continue to hamper any future growth of our campus was that we had no vacant land. In seeking counsel from board members as to what land to acquire, I received the following advice from Alan Penniman, owner of more than 100 grocery and convenience stores: "Jim, my advice is that you buy every piece of land that adjoins the hospital's." This advice led to the expansion of our flagship campus one lot at a time, from 3 to 165 acres.

Sociological and Demographic Challenges

From a purely sociological perspective, Willis-Knighton Memorial Hospital in the late 1960s was beginning to experience the negative perceptions commonly faced by the nation's inner-city hospitals. What had once been the quiet Queensborough neighborhood of well-maintained, single-family dwellings was changing. For decades it had been the home of many retired blue-collar workers and of many notable people in the entertainment world.

According to local historian Eric Brock, Queensborough was a prominent place in the city during the life of the famous "Louisiana Hayride" radio show. Elvis Presley, Truman Capote, Slim Whitman, Webb Pierce, "Gentleman Jim" Reeves, Red Sovine and Johnny Cash at various times lived in the area around the hospital. Hank Williams Jr. and Van Cliburn were born at Willis-Knighton. But as the older residents' heirs chose to live in suburbia, or those older residents were physically and financially unable to maintain their properties, slumlords began to move into the area, converting single-family dwellings into multiple apartments and failing to maintain them.

This once tranquil neighborhood at the city's last trolley stop suddenly changed from a quiet residential area to a bustling commercial and business district. Three churches were within a block of our front entrance, one with a parochial kindergarten, elementary school and parsonage adjacent to our only parking lot (rented and inadequate). The three-acre hospital campus was also surrounded by an array of businesses: two liquor stores, a 24-hour stop-and-shop grocery, a large furniture store, two pharmacies, a chain grocery store, a donut shop, a bank and an auto repair garage. These businesses were quite successful, thanks to hospital employees and visitors. Further detracting from the neighborhood was an old, dilapidated vegetable stand at the intersection of the new interstate and Greenwood Road, less than two blocks from the main entrance.[13]

Ten family-occupied houses were across the rear alley from the hospital. An enor-

13 A known "house of ill-repute" was within one block of the main entrance of the hospital for many years. When WK was finally in the financial position to buy out the owners of the building in an ongoing effort to clean up the neighborhood, the move had some unintended consequences. Beforehand, there were always one or two police cruisers parked in the vicinity of the building. This highly visible "protection," which added a much-needed sense of security to the area, suddenly disappeared after the removal of the prior tenants.

mous amount of money would be required to displace the businesses and residences, and their purchases would take years. Most of the homeowners and businesses were quite satisfied with their properties and didn't want to sell and relocate. Any growth of our campus boosted their values and forced the hospital to pay higher prices. Security enhancements at the hospital also enhanced their values.

This dilemma eventually led to the formation of a property acquisition group, including two realtors, with an undisclosed relationship with the hospital. We leaked the word that Willis-Knighton couldn't afford to buy more property, a tactic that countered the rumor that we had deep pockets and were willing to pay above market values for the land we needed. Because this tactic was somewhat successful, but slower than hoped for, another strategy came up for consideration.

Abandon Our Queensborough Campus?

A number of physicians and business leaders in Shreveport encouraged our trustees and management to abandon the existing hospital campus and relocate our entire operation to a new campus in either west or southwest Shreveport. This relocation strategy was so strongly supported by some physicians that they took me on tours of a number of potential sites, large enough to accommodate a new and totally modern hospital, one that might rival T. E. Schumpert Hospital in aesthetics of design, bed capacity, technology and image.

This strategy gained momentum as the hospital's offers to purchase land for campus expansion were rejected by adjacent landowners. It was a widely held belief that any expansion of the campus would take years to accomplish because the property owners were demanding exorbitant prices or unwilling to sell. Land in west and southwest Shreveport was much less expensive than land near our campus properties; a ten-acre parcel of land could be purchased for the price of a one-eighth acre lot near our campus, and no demolition was necessary. An important consideration was an ability to take immediate occupancy of the new land compared to an unknown time frame for a lot on our campus, as some landowners threatened to remain in their houses as long as they lived.

After much prayer, deliberation and soul-searching, this relocation concept was dismissed for the following reasons:

1. Physical plant investments of 1965 through 1970 were of such magnitude that abandonment of the campus would require a duplication of capital outlay for new campus buildings.

2. Access to capital to develop a new hospital campus was questionable, considering our grim financial state.

3. The location of our campus, which had been in operation since 1924, was a well-known landmark to residents of the Ark-La-Tex.

4. The recent opening of the I-20 interstate highway made it easy for patients to access our campus.

5. Our high visibility from major thoroughfares contributed to a perception of greater safety.

6. Our campus visibility from the elevated interstate highway for over three-quarters of a mile was a great marketing asset and in the future would help to showcase the growth of our campus.

7. However, the most important and determining factor was that a retreat from our present campus would mean leaving our section of town without a hospital to serve their health needs, or at best requiring those patients to travel greater distances to access care. Of consideration was the growing number of indigents moving into the neighborhood who needed medical care and jobs. The relocation of our hospital and the corresponding negative impact on nearby businesses would leave many of our employees and those of the impacted businesses without employment within walking distances of their homes. Another consideration: most of the remote areas under consideration for relocation had no city bus service. Weighing heavy on us was our heartfelt commitment to our neighborhood of over forty years. We could not bring ourselves to abandon it.

In view of the hospital's finances and despite the disadvantages inherent in remaining on our inner-city campus, we decided to remain in Queensborough. However, I remained convinced that if Willis-Knighton were to survive in this inner-city location, satellite hospitals strategically placed in growing suburban neighborhoods would become a necessity in our plans. This strategy would permit us to remain true to our neighborhood while allowing for future expansion into other under-served areas. This initiative began in 1983 with the opening of South Park Hospital (later, WK South).

Media Bias Challenges

In 1965 the WK hospital staff and physicians and those of other city hospitals shared the perception that Schumpert had a lock on newspaper and television articles on healthcare and had enjoyed this media favoritism for many years. This bias was evidently not based on anything we had done, or on any hard feelings on the part of the media toward us or the other hospitals. Perhaps, the media perceived Schumpert, a religiously affiliated hospital, as the only one with a Judeo-Christian ministry of healing, a spiritual component to their mission. And I cannot help believing that the media had in their minds crowned Schumpert as the present and future gold standard for hospitals; as far as physical plants go, it was the gold standard. The fact that one of the television stations was across the street from Schumpert did not help to dispel the charges of favoritism, as the station reporters featured Schumpert employees and physicians on many of their telecasts.

Having no other options, this media favoritism forced our hospital to adopt new forms of paid advertising. Advertisements are certainly more expensive and generally less effective than free, heart-tugging, human interest stories covered by the media. One of the first heretofore untried methods for our hospital marketing was the placement of billboards on main thoroughfares throughout the region. In our marketing efforts, valuable and practical health information continues to be coupled with specific marketing for WK.

Challenges of the State of Louisiana

The Louisiana income tax is a hindrance to hospital administrators in this state as they engage in physician recruiting competition with hospitals outside of the state, especially those only fifteen miles away in Texas, a state with no income tax.

Reimbursement for health services provided to Medicaid patients in Louisiana by non-state hospitals is presently at a rate of less than half of the actual costs of providing such care. These low reimbursements are a result of the shortfall of moneys left after the state's use of the combined federal and state Medicaid funds to subsidize its archaic charity hospital system. Community hospitals receive smaller payments for the same health services than state charity hospitals, and yet they provide care for approximately 70 percent of the state's Medicaid patients. Since 1965, Medicaid-eligible inpatients treated in Willis-Knighton hospitals have consistently averaged approximately 15 percent of our total patient admissions. This inequitable and inadequate Medicaid reimbursement continues to exacerbate the challenges for all Louisiana community hospitals.

Does David Have a Chance Against Goliath?

In the mid-1960s, our slumbering little hospital was awakened by the ushering in of a new era of potential growth, provided it took advantage of a narrow window of opportunity created by three major events: the implementation of Medicare for seniors, the opening of the Interstate 20 highway with two access ramps two blocks from the hospital campus and the arrival of only the second administrator in the hospital's history. At twenty-seven years old I had little experience and a lot of untested book learning, but I was endowed with a willingness to work hard and blessed with a strong faith that this assignment was my calling to the service of my fellow man.

In spite of these potentially advantageous events, many in our community doubted the ability of WK to survive, much less thrive, in competition with Schumpert. Its associate administrator expressed that doubt in a telephone conversation with me.

On my first day of duty at Willis-Knighton, Good Friday of 1965, Schumpert's associate administrator called to welcome me to town, which I appreciated. He asked me how many inpatients I had that day, to which I answered "37." He then told me that his hospital census that day was 433, and that he was surprised that I, as a course graduate and only the second one in the state, had accepted the position I held. He told me it was rumored that Willis-Knighton was on the cusp of financial failure and that it had been offered to several religious denominations for the taking, but that all of them had rejected it. He wished me the best in my new endeavor. I thanked him and hung up.

I have always chosen to view his call as a cordial and sincere welcome to the community and never as an intent to take the wind out of my sails. Over the years we became not only professional colleagues but also good friends. After his retirement, he and I often had lunch together, never failing to reminisce about our old days of competition.

However, I must admit that his well-intentioned call on my first day of work invoked in me a competitive fire in the belly and a determination to give his large, high-quality and market-dominating hospital a run for its money in terms of growth and quality of services to Shreveport/Bossier City. While our hospital, at the time, did not possess the campus or technology of Schumpert, I was determined to surpass it by offering more personalized care in a compassionate setting.

The Problem

It's tough to make predictions, especially about the future.

Yogi Berra (b. 1925)

The question foremost in the minds of our hospital's staff and trustees was, "Does Willis-Knighton have the financial strength to compete with Schumpert's attractive, first-class, high-tech facility, its quality patient care and its money?"

No one at Willis-Knighton had to question our ability to compete in the quality of patient care, but we were quite concerned with the advantages Schumpert possessed as a result of its exceptional building and financial strength. Another advantage that Schumpert had over WK was that its neighborhood was both perceived as safer and closer to the majority of the city's population and downtown workers.

A great deal of money would be required for Willis-Knighton to 1) upgrade its physical plant by replacing outdated structures; 2) expand the campus to provide more physician offices and patient parking; 3) buy expensive new technology; 4) increase salaries to offset the four years without raises and make recruiting easier; 5) commit its medical staff to engage in marketing their services, recruiting physicians and bolstering admissions; and 6) create a public perception that the WK neighborhood was safe and that the hospital was an urbane and professional healthcare setting.[14] This last essential proved to be difficult, as news articles continued to suggest that the hospital neighborhood was a blighted, crumbling and crime-ridden inner-city ghetto.

Prior to the opening of our new addition, I heard a scream from a patient room and rushed to investigate. The patient was sitting up in bed pointing at a corner of the room while hysterically exclaiming, "Please get that animal out of my room!" A search revealed nothing. I was told that the patient was probably hallucinating as a result of post-operative pain medications.

I returned to my office, only to hear the scream repeated. This time, upon entering the patient's room we discovered an opossum in the corner climbing down a floor-to-ceiling pipe. The animal had entered through a crawl space under the original 1924 structure. This event brought about the permanent closing of patient rooms in that section of the building.

Creatures of fur and feather seemed drawn to the old Tri-State building. In 1966 some window ledges of the older section were suddenly occupied by dozens of pigeons with all of their inherent health and hygiene issues. Four of the window ledges were outside our original 1924 vintage surgical operating rooms, producing a less than optimum backdrop for surgical teams. Much to our dismay, the birds' attraction to our window ledges continued even after a series of pest control treatments, with increasing numbers moving in. For weeks the unsanitary infestation continued. One morning I discovered the cause of this problem: one dietary employee was feeding the pigeons with left-over food from the cafeteria. Miss Minnie was unaware of the consequences of her actions. The feeding stopped, but the population of birds was slow to deplete because no one wanted to take the most obvious action for a speedier elimination.

14 One of the least sophisticated visitors that ever entered our doors was an escaped champion hog from the Louisiana State Fair livestock show. A short time before my arrival, a very large hog escaped from the show, ran the four blocks to our hospital and entered by way of the loading dock. Needless to say, this visitor created a great deal of excitement among the staff as they tried to catch it. Luckily for the hog, pork was not on the menu that day.

T. E. Schumpert Memorial Hospital was a formidable competitor, and while WK could not compete with its physical plant, we could certainly compete in the arena of patient care because of our loyal cadre of quality physicians, nurses and other employees. As I came to fully understand that the exceptional level of both care and compassion that our professional staff provided was of greater importance to patients and families than attractive physical plants, I began to encourage our staff to adopt the commercially successful mantra of a national auto rental company: "We're number 2, we try harder." Borrowed from Avis, this axiom became a guiding principle for the WK family.[15]

Accepting that perceptions are generally viewed as reality, I developed a plan of correction, within the scope of the hospital's financial ability, to overcome some of the less than favorable perceptions of WK. The plan was written after I held one-on-one meetings with all physicians on the medical staff to solicit their input on areas of concern. All were also asked to share their visions of the hospital's future with me. Most commented that this was the first time they had been given the opportunity to express their concerns and provide input to management. The holding of those sessions in their offices at a time of their choosing gave them a greater sense of buy-in.

Administrators should always maintain open communications with the hospital's medical staff members, and physicians should be encouraged to fully participate in the management of the medical staff operations. Who better to police physicians than physicians themselves?

In the days prior to full-time emergency room physician coverage, sometimes the physicians were a bit overworked and not always fully engaged in their medical staff activities. When I attended my first committee meeting at WK, a list of physicians delinquent in the completion of their patient charts was presented to the medical records committee with an accompanying motion to curtail admitting privileges of physicians with incomplete charts. One overworked and exhausted surgeon, asleep in the meeting, was nudged awake and asked to second the motion, which he promptly did. A couple of

15 Our reputation of placing patients first was at times taken to the extreme. In one incident an addressograph machine was found unattended, emitting sparks, smoke and beginning to catch fire. The clerk admitted to her supervisor that she had seen the sparks and smoke but that she had been instructed not to keep patients waiting for admissions, but to get them to their rooms as quickly as possible. Upon telling me of the incident, her female supervisor saw the quizzical look on my face and consoled me by saying, "Mr. Elrod, the only thing I can say is that sometimes she acts like a dumb bunny – but she means well."

weeks later at the monthly staff meeting, the surgeon who seconded the motion learned that his name was on the list of physicians with suspended privileges. This laughable event softened the impact of the suspended privileges of a number of physicians.

Speaking of medical staff meetings, I'd like to note that, because I did not choose to occupy my predecessor's office during her terminal illness, I utilized a dining table and a 1924 metal chest-of-drawers situated in a small dining and medical staff committee meeting room that was utilized for all medical staff meetings. Frequently, I would be forced to hastily stow my working papers and building documents in the chest. I must admit that there was not much privacy afforded me during those early months of my career.

A Tale of Two Hospitals

My first few years as administrator of Willis-Knighton Memorial Hospital are best summed up in Charles Dickens' opening of A Tale of Two Cities: “It was the best of times, it was the worst of times.” One minute I was confronted with the severity of the hospital's financial state, and the next minute I was almost euphoric about the future as I came to know the wonderful physicians and staff. My growing love for Willis-Knighton battled my practical view of financial and other realities, which told me that the hospital faced almost insurmountable obstacles. One moment I would ponder whether this small hospital could survive the financial storms facing it; then I would feel profound excitement about its potential for future successes. The stages of my reflections, frame of mind and inner struggles were constantly changing.

I concluded that it was in my best interest and that of the hospital to stop riding a roller coaster of emotions. This new thinking positioned me to enjoy the positive aspects of my job while accepting its negative realities as merely challenges of opportunity. These challenges could be reckoned with and overcome if I concentrated on deliberate corrective actions that offered promises of success. I chose this approach.

Further, it became quite evident that our struggling hospital needed a quick and decisive plan to reverse our fortunes. This plan had to address strategies to correct our financial plight, improve our existing facilities (thereby enhancing our public image) and develop game-changing strategies to pave the way for growth.

I became determined to be the skilled mariner who could navigate this rough sea of challenges and problems and guide my ship to a safe harbor of prosperity. Admittedly, I consoled myself with the thought that if my maritime skills proved less than adequate, I could surely don a life jacket and make my way back to my home state of Texas, knowing in my heart that I had given my best efforts to this hospital and its family, which I was coming to love more with each passing day.

During this period a founding physician of the hospital, Dr. W. S. Kerlin, whose health problems were forcing his retirement came to my office with tears in his eyes. He said, "Jim, I am so sorry that I can't continue helping you turn our hospital around. But rest assured, I will pray for you and Willis-Knighton every day." I am often reminded how his prayers and those of legions of others have had a profound impact on the success of our beloved hospital and its ministry of healing. Only after his death did I become aware that he had bequeathed a large part of his estate to his beloved hospital.

On many occasions over the past forty-eight years I have reminisced about the challenges that our small hospital and its dedicated workers faced in those early times of undeclared bankruptcy, and I find myself smiling as I recall Walt Disney's saying: "It's kind of fun to do the impossible."

CHAPTER 4

Polishing Our Tarnished Halo

The future never just happens, it is always created.

Anonymous

Developing a Game Plan

At the beginning of my tenure it was abundantly clear that our proud institution was on borrowed time. All the signs—our physical plant, technology and finances; a patient base that was not growing; a medical staff that was aging—meant that our window of opportunity for success was closing at an alarming rate. WK needed a game plan, and quickly.

Luckily, I was too young and naïve to fully appreciate the gravity of the situation. Fresh from college and a great residency, I had plenty of theoretical solutions in mind to test. After consulting physicians, the board of trustees and many employees, I decided our game plan would initially focus on strategic short-term management solutions to our many problems. Our poor financial condition forced us to take baby steps toward progress, rather than undertaking massive initiatives. In hindsight, these limitations set the table for augmenting our superb care with modest hospitality and inexpensive aesthetic changes to our campus.

To develop a winning game plan we decided that, whatever our strategy, we must focus not only on winning in today's market, but also on planting the seeds for our future. Management decisions should never sacrifice the future for short-sighted gain. It was imperative that the hospital hire individuals that would understand our strategy. After all, running a hospital is not a one man job. I will always remember my first hire, Mack Harris, an African American gentleman with a caring heart and a smile that radiated genuine concern for our patients. Having a hospitality background, Mack was the perfect person to help improve our image.

While the tasks seemed insurmountable at times, we were committed to meeting the daunting challenges that WK faced as we clung to the belief that a hospital doesn't have to be big to be good.[16] We continued to derive inspiration from the truth in an old Chinese proverb: "The man who removes a mountain begins by carrying away small stones."

Strategy 1: Improving Image and Aesthetics

Behave toward everyone as if receiving a great guest.

Confucius (**551-479 B.C.**)

Upon my arrival at Willis-Knighton, I determined that we had to change our public perception. The misperception of the hospital's capability of delivering the highest level of patient care was caused by the reality of its aging building and out-of-date equipment. The public saw it as a hospital far behind its major competitor's beautiful campus with an imposing, aesthetically pleasing, nine-floor building and technological superiority. If WK was to overcome this perception, our campus needed a facelift.

Our "polish our halo" plan was undertaken with the strongly held belief that first impressions are lasting. This plan covered the following "hot ticket" impression makers:

1. Appearance of campus grounds (routine care of lawns, flower beds and trees) became a priority. Streets, sidewalks and medians, although

16 An old adage of fairytale days instructs us that the wandering beseecher must kiss a lot of frogs before finding a lovely princess, but the myth contains an important empirical lesson for business leaders. My interpretation of this fable is that a leader must be willing to attempt any number of bold solutions if they expect to discover the best solution to their organization's problems. But I'll add to this fable that the kisser must also have at hand a copious supply of mouthwash!

city-owned, were routinely maintained to I-20 on Greenwood Road and Hearne Avenue.

2. We improved the general appearance, state of repair and lighting of physical structures. The 1920s-era buildings' red brick was painted to match the 1965 addition of beige brick.

3. Free parking lots near hospital entrances with safety lighting and security patrol were provided as houses were purchased and removed.

4. A security program with high visibility of personnel and a patrol vehicle was begun under Bill "Rowboat" Wroten, a renowned LSU football player in the 1930s.[17] I recruited Bill, a native of Haynesville, Louisiana from my residency hospital in Jackson. His loyalty and dedication to Willis-Knighton for over thirty years served as a model for so many who came after him. His acts of kindness to patients and their families were legendary.

5. All patient rooms and corridors in the old building were painted in the neutral tones of the 1965 addition. This transition from the green military surplus paint of the original buildings was an instant success with patients and staff.

6. We put directional signage on the campus and inside the hospital to enhance way finding.

7. Switchboard operators were moved to the lobby area of the new building to greet and direct patients and visitors, while continuing to answer the telephones. Operators were instructed to say in a courteous tone: "Thank you for calling Willis-Knighton Memorial Hospital. May I help you?"

8. Environmental control of air conditioning and heating was monitored throughout the day. The dated equipment in the older section of the building required constant attention to ensure comfort of patients, families and employees.

9. A housekeeping service was instituted, thereby relieving the nursing staff of housekeeping duties, and permitting them to spend more time attending the needs of their patients.

10. Housekeeping, maintenance and lawn service personnel were required to wear uniforms.

---

17 Bill and I encouraged our newly appointed security officers to extend every possible courtesy to our guests. Once, it was reported that a visitor's car battery had been stolen in our parking lot. Later I was told by an embarrassed security officer that he was actually responsible for the battery theft. I asked, why do you think that you are responsible? He replied, "I approached a guy, who was trying to remove a battery from a car. He told me that his battery was dead and that he was taking it to be charged. I went to my car and got a wrench to help him remove the battery." Later, the owner of this battery-less car reported the theft. Clearly, this was an act of kindness gone awry!

11. The quality of food served patients, visitors and employees was excellent, but its presentation had to improve to match its palatability. (A few years later, I discovered a terrific donut recipe and added it to the hospital cafeteria breakfast food offerings.)[18]

12. A routine to ensure cleanliness of public spaces and patient rooms, especially toilets, required hourly inspections (documented for compliance).

13. All staff members had to be properly attired in uniforms or acceptable plain clothes. These more highly visible staff members were encouraged to go out of their way to accommodate patients and visitors.

14. Bulletin boards in nursing stations and departments helped to eliminate the cluttered look of the hospital. No more unsightly papers and posters were taped or tacked to walls.

15. As the only holder of a master's in hospital administration degree in the region, I volunteered to teach the Louisiana State University-Shreveport's undergraduate curriculum of healthcare education in evening classes. I hoped to create a more positive public perception of Willis-Knighton Memorial Hospital.

16. Monthly inventories of medical, surgical and administrative supplies, drugs and food stuffs were conducted and studied. Until that time, no monthly inventories of supplies or drugs were routinely made.

17. Employees learned that the best way to create positive first and lasting impressions was to remember this: patients and families are more interested in how much you care than in how much you know.[19]

18. A patient representative (ombudsman) program was initiated to ensure that all inpatients were visited during their hospital stay. This program continues under the capable leadership of Janet Bailes, administrative assistant at WK Pierremont, a 30-year employee who began with us as a candy striper.

19. Daily inspections of the hospital and grounds ensured compliance with the new policies.

Sometimes management by walking around presented challenging situations. Even

18 It seems everyone knows that I have an affinity for our hospital's chocolate donuts. Glenda Turner, my administrative assistant for the past thirty years, likes to remind me of the following:"Remember the time you came in the office complaining of nausea and you asked me to go to the cafeteria for you? I thought you might want something bland to settle your stomach, but instead, you asked me to get you two chocolate donuts and some crispy bacon. Oddly enough, you felt better almost immediately."

19 Sometimes arrogance is the strongest impediment to acts of courtesy. Once, a moonlighting resident from the university hospital providing emergency room coverage left his convertible with its top down under an oak tree favored by a flock of campus starlings. Our security guard encouraged him to move his automobile, but he retorted, "I'll park my car wherever I d--- well please." The next morning the resident found his convertible in a messy condition. The staff of the hospital helped him scoop and clean the interior of his car, but the resident never again provided coverage for our ER.

all the classroom education, textbook theory, specialized and military training and active military service had not prepared me for some of the unusual situations that I was to encounter in my first few months as administrator of Willis-Knighton. One of the most bizarre challenges I faced involved the dietary manager and her staff.

Shortly after the opening of the hospital's award-winning kitchen, I observed that two of our long-term cooks were not at their work stations. I routinely exchanged banter with these two gentlemen. I asked the kitchen supervisor if they were ill, to which she said no, but with a strange expression on her face. She eventually told me that they were in the frozen food locker, where I found them sitting on cartons holding a Bible. As they warmed up and their teeth stopped chattering, they told me that they were being disciplined by the dietitian for an offense, but they were not sure why. Since this was not the first time that I had been concerned with her bizarre behavior, she was terminated. My good friends, the "freezer theologians," and I often laughed about this episode. Although the three of us could laugh about it later, it was obviously a serious offense.

Earlier, our clinic manager had reported to me that the dietitian was riding her bicycle through the halls of the clinic each morning to get to her office. She was also reported to have stood up during the worship service of one of the largest churches in our neighborhood to chastise the minister about his theology and to offer to debate doctrine with him.

About a month after her termination, I received a telephone call from the administrator of a hospital in East Texas who told me that he had employed our former dietitian. He said he was hesitant to ask a crazy question, but he wanted to know if she had ever disciplined dietary workers by locking them in a frozen food locker with a Bible. I chuckled at the question, whereupon we shared our weird experiences with the bright but strange lady.

Two administrative staff members played prominent roles in WK's "polish the halo" program and assisted me on a daily basis to monitor those image influencers. Sarah Dale and Jim Jones were most responsible for the hospital's rapid turnaround. Mrs. Dale, a sophisticated lady with an eye for detail, and Jones, a retired Air Force sergeant who arrived at the hospital before 4 a.m. every day to start inspections, were two of the most dedicated and hard workers in the life of WK. For a number of years, the three of us spent untold hours on plans to create a positive image of WK. Quality care had always been provided by the physicians and staff, but the buildings, grounds and equipment left a lot to be desired until this program of correction was completed. I believe this sentence best explains why Mrs. Dale, a lady who was like a mother to me, and Jones, one of my dearest friends, gave so much of themselves to WK: "The greatest use of life is to spend it for something that will outlast you" (author unknown).

Three other outstanding department heads also played a major role in the turn-around of our hospital in both perception and quality of care. David Peery, M.S., was the first clinical department head employed to manage the laboratory. Peery, a bacteriologist, did a yeoman's job in enhancing laboratory services while personally providing the hospital with previously unavailable studies. Jacob Schmidt, our first purchasing agent, played a major role in the financial turnaround of WK when he established a purchasing and inventory system and did double duty as the hospital's business office manager for a few years. Another most dedicated and astute employee was Sophie Stevens. Her dedication, positive attitude, work ethic and prowess with the old Burroughs posting machine was unmatched.

Although our cosmetic changes did not affect our core product, quality clinical care, these adaptations went a long way to change the community's perception of our hospital. I was convinced during these early years of changing our image that what WK was doing was executing a new marketing strategy.

Years later, when I picked up a copy of *Positioning,* Ries and Trout's 1981 work, I realized the physical alterations and other value-added services that we were making some fifteen years earlier were in reality the repositioning of our brand. The book quickly became a required read for all of our administrative and upper-management staff.

Strategy 2:
Remedying Our Poor Financial Health

There isn't much thrill in success unless one has been close to failure.

William Feather (**1889-1981**)

The statement that "Imitation is the sincerest form of flattery" sums up my feelings as I relate some events of the first few months of my appointment as the administrator of the Willis-Knighton Memorial Hospital in 1965. I confess that because of my lack of experience, I religiously used my copious notes from financial management classes at Washington University to develop a comprehensive plan to address the hospital's financial challenges. This class was taught by Harold Hinderer, chief financial officer of the Catholic Hospital Association and adjunct professor of the program. He was one of the most knowledgeable and practical professors of my undergraduate, graduate and law school experiences. In my heart and mind, I share any business successes I have had over the years with his teachings and thank God that I paid attention during his classes.

Willis-Knighton was in a dire financial condition, virtually handcuffed by its insolvency (undeclared bankruptcy). In fact, the poor outlook of the hospital's finances and perhaps its very future were becoming public knowledge. During a hospital visit on the eve of her surgery, one loyal WK patron from Arkansas asked her daughter to pray for Jim Elrod. Her daughter, Mollye McCalman, asked "Why, is he ill?" The patient told her daughter that she heard that he recently went to the bank to borrow a lot of money because of the hospital's failing financial condition. Later, the daughter informed me that her mother loved WK and was more concerned about the hospital's financial condition than she was about her own impending major surgery. I will always cherish this act of love.

We devised various solutions to the most damaging financial problems:

1. The single most effective financial tool we used to help WK emerge from undeclared bankruptcy was "bankers' hours." I relied on the

fact that at the time, banks were not as customer-friendly, closing every day at 3 p.m. Our payday routine was to hand out paychecks to all personnel after 3 p.m., too late to be cashed at any bank. This Friday routine gained the hospital three to four days of float to cover our over-extended cash position. Aware of the hospital's financial plight, our employees bore this inconvenience for several years.

2. Copies of an organizational chart for the hospital, modeled after military organizational structures and indicating lines of authority, were distributed to all department and section supervisors.

3. Regular meetings of department heads were held to promote team building, communications between departments and reporting and compliance with financial and personnel budgets. Some were intended to encourage the adoption of strategies for the hospital's growth.

4. Job assignments were reviewed and updated when appropriate. Nurses were no longer charged with manual housekeeping duties on their units, leaving them more time for patient care and charge monitoring duties.

5. The drug room was reorganized to ensure rapid filling of inpatient medications. We established processes for collection of charges for dispensed drugs and for handling of narcotics that met state and federal dispensing laws. A security system equipped with camera monitoring and a security key identification and control procedure ensured the protection of pharmaceuticals. A routine for conducting monthly inventories of the drug room was instituted to ensure the monthly counting of inventories and discovery of out-of-date items. Later, a registered pharmacist was employed.

6. A staffing policy with approved levels of personnel departments and required daily reporting of paid hours of work was instituted. Prior to this time, employee hours were not routinely monitored.

7. A new certified public accounting firm was engaged with clearly delineated expectations for the handling of audits and timeliness of financial reports.[20]

8. The hospital's payroll was outsourced to our new CPA firm to ensure confidentiality of salaries, thereby eliminating a significant morale issue. It seemed that individual salaries of personnel were public knowledge around the hospital. Cash payments of wages were discontinued.

20 William Jefferson Cole, CPA, and a former Air Force officer, was engaged to help turn the hospital's critical financial condition around. Jeff has served in this capacity since 1965 and has been an invaluable advisor and strong supporter of the Willis-Knighton Health System. He was gracious enough to spend time verifying many of this book's financial details. Jeff became the senior partner in one of the region's largest public accounting firms due to his business expertise and exemplary leadership.

9. Vendors were notified that purchase orders issued without an authorized signature would not be honored for payment and that all supplies were to be delivered to the warehouse for distribution, not to individual departments as was the previous routine.

10. Monthly inventories of all office and medical supplies, drugs and food items were implemented to determine the value of supplies on hand, level of inventories and discovery of expired items. The hospital was losing opportunities for the replacement of some out-dated items not identified and returned within a reasonable time frame.

11. A monthly payroll report was prepared so department heads could monitor monthly comparisons of payroll expenses.

12. Internal financial controls were implemented that eliminated the use of cash drawers for transactions.

13. A purchase order system that ensured that the same person did not order, receive, code and approve the payment of purchases was implemented. This procedure was put in place after I collected all purchase order forms and maintained them in my office for a few months to gain control of purchases. I reviewed every purchase order for a period and sometimes discovered verbal orders for products that were in abundant supply in other departments in the hospital. This system was turned over to the new purchasing agent upon his arrival.

14. We employed an experienced purchasing agent from a large local company with business affiliations with WK who knew about our laxity of handling and controlling purchases. Jake Schmidt[21] spent several months locating stockpiles of supplies that were not under control of any one designated person and moving them into an automobile repair garage the hospital purchased across the street from our main entrance. This site permitted the operation of a warehouse with storage capacity, security of inventories through limited access and standardization of products within departments. Miscellaneous department heads and nurses throughout the hospital no longer issued purchase orders.

15. A new chart of accounts was adopted to permit greater detail of accountability and control of each function.

16. We installed a pharmacy control system with special attention paid to the usage of controlled substances. Prior to my arrival, narcotics and other controlled substances were locked in desk drawers of the

21 Jake was proud that his image around the hospital was that he was very frugal. He had a special test before issuing new ballpoint pens to the nursing staff. If the pen being turned in was inoperable, Jake would heat the pen with a cigarette lighter to thin the ink for writing, telling the nurse to bring it back when it was completely dry. After they realized that he was joking with them, he would issue a new ballpoint pen. At least, I think he did.

administrator, with nurses lining up in the corridor each morning to pick up patients' doses. This bizarre ritual was quite a shock to me the first morning after I moved into my predecessor's office after her death. I complied with their request for orders the first day, but with witnesses present, we inventoried and moved the narcotics to a safe in the hospital drug room.

17. All miscellaneous cash receipts (income from vending machines, X-ray silver sales and income from bank deposits) were placed on the books of the hospital.

18. We developed a simplified monthly inventory system for all department supplies to reduce time required for actual counting and recording.

19. A system was implemented to ensure the capture of all charges for hospital services, one that could not be overridden by employees who might attempt to discount or eliminate them. No-charges, reduced billings and lost charges were virtually eliminated.

20. A computer-generated process for billing patients was implemented and strict credit and collection rules adopted. Automatic computer aging of accounts receivables became available. The time frames for referring unpaid bills to the local credit and collection agency were established and enforced.

21. The hospital did not own its laboratory and X-ray services. I was convinced these revenue sources were essential to the hospital's future success. It was a sensitive issue: the physician-owners, the leading cadre of hospital supporters, were willing to give up their ownership to help the hospital, but could not afford to donate the services because they had financial obligations tied to the income from these services. I spent time with the clinic owners soliciting their support to convey ownership of these ancillary services to the hospital and working out terms of the buy-out. At significant financial sacrifice, the clinic physicians offered a proposal for this critical transfer of ownership that was within the hospital's financial capability. Their generous offer was better than I had hoped. Never was a word uttered by any of these most magnanimous physicians about the hospital's take-over of their profitable services or the personal financial losses they sustained.

22. Another issue facing the hospital was our non-participation in the Medicare program. Therefore I, along with several medical staff members, convinced the hospital's trustees that our participation was financially necessary and that WK could meet all conditions of program participation.

23. Another strategy that we implemented was to discourage admitting personnel from ever turning patients away until a complete inven-

tory of patient rooms was taken by physically checking every room in the hospital for late checkouts or patients soon to be discharged. My 1966 quip, "Our hospital is never fully occupied until there are at least three patients in my office" continues after all these years to bring laughs to our staff while reminding us to search diligently for unoccupied beds for the acutely ill. We never want to leave a sick person on a gurney in an emergency room all night, only to discover that empty patient rooms were indeed available.

Strategy 3: More Than a Few Good Men

Military lore dictates: If it moves, salute it. If it doesn't move, sweep it up. If it's too big to sweep up, pick it up. If it's too big to pick up, paint it.

I faced a dilemma when I arrived at WK: our hospital salaries were too low to attract experienced hospital workers and we provided no retirement plan. As employees retired or became unable to work due to health issues, I was having difficulty hiring replacements. One solution, overlooked by local hospitals, was to hire military retirees. Thanks to Barksdale Air Force Base our area is one of the top ten military retiree spots in the nation.

As I contemplated employing retired military personnel, the above quote, regarding a sergeant-major's golden rule for duty in the officers' mess, kept going through my mind. To paraphrase: pay attention to small things–to do nothing is unacceptable!

Until this time, few retirees had been considered for jobs in area hospitals because of their lack of healthcare experience. Hospital leaders were seemingly unaware that while most military retirees had been initially trained in technical jobs, as they progressed in rank, their last years of service were in management positions comparable to civilian roles of responsibility. Many were forced to take jobs that did not fully utilize their leadership skills and management experience.

There was a plethora of available talent being underutilized. With a little training, these veterans could be prepared to undertake responsible non-clinical roles at WK. Their work ethic and experience in leadership were valuable assets. Adherence to mission accomplishment was imbedded in their DNA, and as battle-hardened veterans, they would not give up easily on assignments. Admittedly, at the time, I did not fully appreciate how valuable their military-taught technological proficiency would become to healthcare as computerization and technological sophistication became the wave of the future.

I was convinced that many of these patriotic and experienced retirees would bring great value to WK, and at a salary the hospital could afford. Since they had retirement incomes, they were willing to start at lower salaries. I assured them that as our finances improved (WK emerged from undeclared bankruptcy), I would increase their pay to market rates. This I did at the earliest possible date.

My first military retirees were Master Sergeants Jim Jones, Ocie Silas, Jim Cotton and Lt. Colonel Harold Loughran. Over 40 of these retirees faithfully served our health system for many years, most until their second retirements, becoming role models for dependability and work ethic. Other qualified military personnel, such as Chief Master Sergeant James Vanderberry, followed them to WK.

Charles Laster, a former Army officer and devoted WK employee for 40 years, is credited with the development of the health system's data processing operation and its ownership of a regional fiber optic communication network that connects all WK facilities in our metropolitan area. Proprietorship (rather than leasing) of this fiber optic network provides enormous savings to the health system.

The WK family takes great pride in the fact that our hospital system has provided so many deserving military retirees, who served our country with distinction, a second career wherein they could contribute to the health and well-being of so many people in the civilian world. And I, personally, will be eternally grateful for the lives and service of those hard-working veterans who came to WK's rescue and assisted in the turn-around of our struggling neighborhood hospital. These old soldiers didn't just fade away; they were a major part of the answer to our prayers in 1965.

Strategy 4: Our Good Samaritan Program

"It is the customer who determines what a business is...what the customer thinks he is buying, and what he considers 'value,' is decisive."

Peter F. Drucker (1909-2005)

Years before this author penned these words, I had come to believe that it was incumbent that WK, due to its location in a healthcare market dominated by an unquestioned market leader, had to become a highly customer-focused company with a mission that met more of its customer's needs than just patient treatment. With this thought in mind, I came up with three initiatives that I believed would offer our customers (patients) and their families services that they would perceive of great value that were not offered by any of our competitors.

In order to meet our patients' holistic needs (mind, body and spirit), three initiatives were undertaken. These activities encompassed within our Good Samaritan program are actions which paralleled the efforts of the biblical Good Samaritan as he attended to the physical and emotional needs of his neighbor.

Ombudsman (Patient Representative)

The first project was a patient advocate (ombudsman) program with a uniformed former airline flight attendant as hostess. She was the "go-between" or liaison between patients and families and hospital management. It was a first for Shreveport hospitals. Duties of the hostess included doing things not normally expected of a hospital, such as visiting each patient daily and handling any need that might arise with a patient or his family.

A *Shreveport Times* article of April 11, 1967, reported, "One patient admitted to the hospital through the emergency department kept worrying about her kittens. The hostess went out to her home, let the kittens out, fed them and made provisions for neighbors to take care of the animals until the patient was released from the hospital."

Complimentary Lodging

The second project was to offer a free service of lodging that would not only be unique to our region but would induce patients to give us the opportunity to serve them. Unoccupied patient rooms in the older section of our building, vacated as patients were relocated to our new patient additions, were repainted, furnished and converted for use as in-house, overnight lodging units for families of patients. Priority was given to family members with loved ones in the intensive care unit, families from out-of-town and those needing opportunities for respite. This was our first Good Samaritan program.

For over forty years, this program has continued with only a few changes: 1) the medical center's hotel rooms were relocated from the older section of the building to a newer unit in the hospital upon the relocation of obstetrics and pediatrics services to WK South and Women's Center and 2) our three satellite hospitals do not have permanent blocks of out-of-service patient rooms to open to patient's families for overnight use, but they utilize unoccupied beds located throughout the hospitals for this purpose. No vacant patient rooms are left unoccupied when there are families in need of overnight accommodations.

After all these years, I find it unthinkable that hospitals with vacant patient rooms, not in service at any given time, would not utilize them for patients' families, choosing rather to allow rooms to remain vacant as families sleep in less comfortable seating in waiting rooms. Such accommodations add quality of life to the inpatient experiences of patients and families, if for no other reason than a patient's mind is put to ease because he or she knows that loved ones are nearby and safe, not forced to sleep in waiting rooms or travel outside the hospital.

Our Good Samaritan service costs little, yet it means so much to a patient and their family. The only costs to the hospitals are for periodic housekeeping and the laundry of linens and towels. To quote multitudes of guests of the Good Samaritan program, WK's initiative to provide this service speaks volumes as to the caring heart of our hospital and its people. The daily logging in of the Good Samaritan room occupants is handled by our hospital's twenty-four-hour switchboard operators and monitored by on-duty nursing supervisors who determine priority of use for the accommodations.

Free Transportation

Intra-system non-emergent referrals requiring transfers of patients between our four metropolitan hospitals, three rural hospital affiliates, eight indigent medical clinics and WK's network physician offices dictated the need for a system-owned transport operation. No charge is made for transportation of patients for purposes of patient accommodations (tests, treatments, or admissions).

Recognizing the marketing potential of these vehicles traversing the roads of northwest Louisiana, all patient transport vehicles were painted with identical colors, logos and a listing of all of our urban hospitals. The transport crews consist of a permanent staff of drivers and EMS-trained technicians, supplemented by EMS-trained personnel from our city fire department. Our fleet of over one hundred vehicles, including delivery trucks, is often referred to as "WK's rolling billboards."

Strategy 5: Promoting a Family Feel

What do we live for if it is not to make life less difficult for each other?

George Eliot (1819-1880)

While attending the funeral of one of our beloved nurses, two of our retired nurses challenged me to never let the family feel of our institution die because that spirit is what has set us apart from other hospitals in our region. Although they had been retired for a number of years, they expressed their love and support for their successors at Willis-Knighton.

I remember one afternoon in 1965 I stopped to introduce myself to a nurse whom I had not yet had the pleasure of meeting. I asked whether I could do anything for her, and her request was, "I hope you can help us get a raise because none of us have had one for over four years." I asked, "Why have all of you continued working here?" The nurse, Pauline Uli, R.N., looked at me as if I were from another planet. Her indignant answer was, "Because we love Willis-Knighton and would never think of working anywhere else. We are a family."

Some "family feeling" reinforcement activities we undertake for all trustees, physicians, employees and members of their immediate families during their difficult times of great personal loss, illness and other employee bonding activities are as follows:

1. Management and employees make a concerted effort to attend all funerals.

2. Visitations are regularly attended to comfort and support the families of the deceased.

3. Floral arrangements or memorial gifts are sent to all funerals.

4. Food is provided to the family from our dietary department and usually delivered by a department supervisor or a vice president. (I can only believe that this activity is out of the norm for businesses with almost six thousand employees spread over four hospital campuses, several centers of excellence, offices throughout a four-parish area for three hundred and fifty employed physicians, three skilled nursing facilities, a 312-acre retirement community and a medical staff of approximately one thousand physicians.)

5. Requests for personal eulogies to be given at services are routinely honored. (I have personally given so many eulogies for deceased physicians and employees that I am jokingly referred to as "WK's Official Eulogizer." I guess it is better to be the person giving the eulogy than the one for whom the eulogy is given.)

6. Once a year my wife and I make charitable contributions to projects that we consider to be valuable community assets. The gifts are made in memory of people who have died within the past year. All contributions are accompanied with a request that the benefiting organizations send acknowledgements of our gifts to the spouses, parents, siblings

or children of the deceased. Remembrances of loved ones months after their deaths are not only greatly appreciated, but of great comfort to the families as they realize that their loved one has not been forgotten by his coworkers and friends.[22]

7. Contact is maintained with the deceased's family for a period of time to offer any assistance they may require. No one wants their loved ones to be forgotten.

8. During the hospitalization of trustees, physicians, employees and their immediate family members, our management team provides a fruit basket or other treat for their patient rooms and reserves a complimentary "Good Samaritan" guest room for their families.

9. The following events, which our system sponsors for our employees and physicians, promote a higher sense of morale and closeness of our staff through family involvement:

   A. The health system hosts an annual all-day family picnic and barbecue during the Louisiana State Fair. Guests eat in a large tent and play games with prizes. Parents and children have unlimited access to rides on the midway. In 2012, almost 10,000 employees and family members attended the event.

   B. An annual fall barbecue at a lakeside location is held for physicians, department heads, business and civic leaders and supporters of our health system.

   C. The annual Christmas party with approximately eight hundred invitees is held in the hospital's auditorium.[23]

   D. At the time of annual personnel benefit renewal sessions, all employees are given WK monogrammed gifts (jackets, beach towels, beverage coolers, sweaters, umbrellas, and camp/beach chairs, to name a few).

   E. Twenty-five scholarships are awarded each year to children of employees to support their attendance at a community college or university. Awards are based upon hours of community service and an essay on its value.

   F. WK employees and their spouses enjoy discounted meals in the cafeteria and membership at our wellness centers. This is done not only to benefit employee morale, but to promote a healthy workforce.

---

22 During the course of my profession and my attendance at the bedsides of hundreds of terminally ill patients and subsequent funerals, I have become more accepting of this profound truth: "Death is not always our enemy." This philosophy helps a person come to a better understanding and acceptance of death and sustains him during times of grief and deaths of loved ones. To deny this truth is to encumber your ability to support the needs of others during such times.

23 For over thirty years, the health system's Christmas party and fall barbecue have been catered by the food service department of WK Medical Center. Under the leadership of Kim Bickham, R.D., and associate Kim Foulk, R.D., the decorations and sophisticated menus have reflected well upon the reputation of WK's food service capabilities. On special occasions some of our physicians reared in South Louisiana's Cajun country prepared a Cochon de Lait (roasted pig on a spit) for our guests.

G. Several hundred tickets to the annual Independence Bowl game are provided free-of-charge to WK employees and patients of our indigent clinics (many of whom could not otherwise afford them).

We recognize that there are tragic events in the lives of our employee family that will require financial assistance for them (i.e., home destroyed by fire, tornado, flood; domestic situations requiring a move on the part of an employee; cases of prolonged illness; domestic violence requiring relocation; burials). Years ago, my CFO and I created and continue to contribute to a charitable fund to address such needs. This fund is outside of the health system's books and accepts contributions from employees. Oversight of the Willis-Knighton Employee Benevolent Fund is by a committee of employees with authority to approve gifts of assistance. We believe this effort embodies the belief that charity begins at home.

When opening a new facility or expanding our service operations it is customary for managers to don work clothes and branded (new facility) t-shirts and take a day out of their schedule to aid the clean-up and move-in process to the new facility. This practice generates a sense of sweat equity for the teams involved, introduces our management staff to new hires and perpetuates a feeling of "buy-in". Our managers are not above any chore or assignment and have garnered much respect from and support of employees through their efforts in opening these new facilities over the years. These "dust and discover" days (which include typical WK food and refreshments) have been an effective tool in developing a spirit of camaraderie, team-building and have been most effective in alleviating potential enmity between employees of the new facility and those of the old. This sense of success tends to permeate long after the day is finished. The involvement of so many managers becomes a most effective marketing tool for spreading the word about the new facility around the health system, as well as the community at large.

I believe that our family feel is so strong and pervasive that our family members often find it difficult to retire. At the conclusion of our eighty-plus-year-old assistant administrator's retirement party, where we recognized his forty-plus years of service, he turned to me saying, "I hope all of this does not mean that I can't come to work tomorrow." To which I answered, "Mr. Blue, you can come to work as long as you choose to do so. You have more than earned that right." That day we reserved a private office for him, and he came to work every day until the day of his death some years later.[24] His gentle and caring demeanor was an inspiration to everyone, and his love for WK was legendary. Reginald Blue's work ethic and sacrifices for the hospital continue to inspire all of us.

Strategy 6: Adding Clinical Services and Technology

I confess that I must work to temper my competitive nature with a hefty dose of introspection and self-discipline as I adhere to this belief: Ships are safe in harbor, but that is not what ships are built for. Time was of the essence; we had to have a few quick (and affordable) wins if we were to survive.

After addressing in 1965 the pressing issues of aesthetics and finances, which played a major role in changing public perception, our WK team embarked on a mission to add clinical services and technology heretofore unavailable in our market. These "firsts" of their kind projects had to be affordable which limited us to undertaking no more than a few at a time. Within a few years a number of highly visible and value-added clinical and technological "firsts" were offered.

In 1966, the region's first intensive care unit (six beds) was opened in a renovated area immediately adjacent to WK's new emergency rooms, under the capable direction of Opal Wimberly, R.N., a most outstanding Tri-State nursing graduate. This unit served to train nurses from a number of regional hospitals that were opening critical care programs. In conjunction with the intensive care unit, a department of respiratory therapy with the area's first registered therapist was instituted.[25] The hospital's first bacte-

24 Mr. and Mrs. Blue died within 24-hours of each other. Having no immediate family in Shreveport, I was honored to make arrangements and serve as a pallbearer for their double casket funeral service in Homer, Louisiana. This kind gentleman from Claiborne Parish was a close friend of Drs. Willis and Knighton at the time they purchased Tri-State Sanitarium. Mr. Blue served as the assistant administrator of the hospital for some forty plus years and was on the first board of Blue Cross and Blue Shield of Louisiana.

25 For over thirty years WK's respiratory therapy departments have been under the capable leadership of Mike Chandler, R.R.T. The health system's wound care center (with the state's only 12-patient hyperbaric chamber) was the fulfillment of his visionary efforts.

TODAY'S NEWS TODAY—WITH TODAY'S PICTURES THE SHREVEPORT JOURNAL, SHREVEPORT-BOSSIER CITY,

4-28-66

Willis-Knighton's 'New Look'

By MARILYN ROBERTSON
Journal Staff Writer

In a brief two-month span, a local hospital has installed and pioneered the clinical-level use of the latest in diagnostic equipment, with one aim foremost: to provide patients with the prompt, highly accurate detection of a variety of ailments.

Carving out three times the work area existing last October, Willis-Knighton Memorial Hospital on Greenwood Road recently brought its clinical laboratory a dramatic step forward with the installation of modern diagnostic equipment valued at $20,000.

AS A RESULT the hospital's "new look" now encompasses more than half the buff-brick and glass exterior and a modern wing, both added in recent months.

Continuing an expansion program which last year included additions of the new wing—housing among other innovations an intense care unit—Willis-Knighton officials have remodeled a large center section of the hospital, enlarging the chemistry laboratory.

Over the last two months, David Peery, laboratory director and biologist, and his staff members have seen the chemistry laboratory emerge, spacious, well-lighted and efficiency-oriented in an area ad-

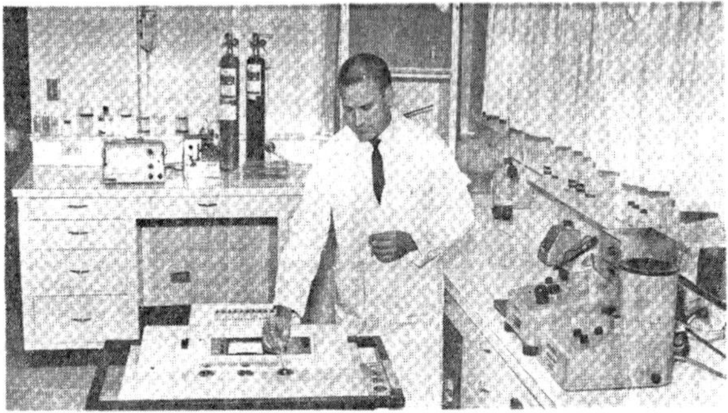

NEW EQUIPMENT—David Peery, laboratory director at Willis-Knighton Memorial Hospital, demonstrates a Volemetron, one of several pieces of new equipment totaling $20,000 recently installed at the hospital. The Volemetron, the only one presently in use here, is employed in the study of thyroid function and in conducting blood volume tests. Other new equipment, visible behind and alongside Peery, is shown in the recently-remodeled chemistry area which was opened up adjacent to the existing laboratories. (Journal Photo by Lawrence Lea)

The public was introduced to Willis-Knighton's new laboratory and director David Peery in April 1966. The article noted: "in a brief two-month span a local hospital has installed and pioneered the clinical level use of the latest in diagnostic equipment."

THE SHREVEPORT TIMES Sunday, Dec. 12, 1965 7-G

You're Cordially Invited to Attend The

OPEN HOUSE OF
WILLIS-KNIGHTON MEMORIAL HOSPITAL

TODAY
2:30 P.M.
TO
4:30 P.M.

TODAY
2:30 P.M.
TO
4:30 P.M.

2600 GREENWOOD ROAD

Shreveport Times *open house announcement for the 1966 addition, the first addition to the hospital since 1928.*

riologist was employed to supervise the operations of the laboratory. The laboratory was equipped with state-of-the-art technology that allowed batch test processing, providing the most rapid laboratory test results available. A full-time anesthesiologist was recruited to provide anesthesia services in the operating room and to supervise our nurse anesthetists.

Unique to a hospital of our size, in 1970 a renal dialysis unit was opened in our original building under the supervision of Hazel Clements, R.N. This dedicated lady was a licensed practical nurse (L.P.N.) at the time of opening. Governmental mandates later required that her position be held by a registered nurse, so she enrolled in night classes and earned her R.N. degree. Hazel worked for WK for almost 30 years.

Within the next few years, we added: 1) an ombudsman (patient representative), 2) the region's first home health service and 3) a full-time physician-staffed emergency room in 1973 (a first for this area). We were also successful in recruiting a most talented ophthalmologist, Dr. William Steen, the first to perform a number of newly developed eye surgical procedures in Shreveport. Dr. Steen's reputation made him a regional draw for patients to our hospital, which for the first time since the early years of Tri-State Hospital opened doors for patients from throughout the Ark-La-Tex.

Since the introduction of these new services and technology over forty-eight years ago, one of my overriding beliefs has been that, if a project is undertaken for the sake of competitiveness rather than patient care and the hospital's economic health, then it is probably a mistake.

When I think about being the first at doing anything, I recall the tongue-in-cheek comment made by our hospital attorney, T. K. Giddens, in the early 1970s, when we received state approval for the building of our Diagnostic and Surgical Building, the state's first physician office condominium. Giddens is a brilliant lawyer, top student of his law school class and one of the most practical and common-sense men I have ever known. When he quipped, "I hope we don't come to learn why no one else wanted to be first," it caused me to reflect on the reasons a person in health care should be motivated to be first in any accomplishment.

Summary of Successes

Our initial game-changing strategies were highly successful in changing public perceptions, heightening esteem for our hospital, improving our financial position and effectively staffing our growing services. Quantification of these successes was the growth of our patient volumes and financial successes in the securing of charges for services. The administrator's annual report to the board of trustees for fiscal year 1966, less than seventeen months after beginning the earliest of these efforts, reflected that our admissions increased by 1,814 patients (30.4 percent) and patient revenues increased 48 percent over the previous year.

As a result of our improved financial position, we were able to share our financial successes with our employees; we authorized the first raise for all employees since 1961. Since that time, cost of living increases have been consistently provided. An employer-sponsored defined benefits retirement plan that gave credit for all past service of employees was started in the early 1970s and continues to this day.

The next several years brought more growth in patient volume to WK. By 1970 we wanted to add more patient beds to our hospital and were fortunate to secure a ten-year loan with manageable monthly payments which ballooned at term. In 1971 a 62-bed addition was completed above the existing Willis-Knighton Clinic. To our dismay there was a lengthy delay in occupying this long-awaited and badly needed addition due to blocked drain lines caused by construction workers cleaning their tools in unit sinks and water closets at the end of their workday. This caused a build-up of plaster in drain lines that totally clogged the plumbing lines in the building. Weeks of jack-hammering, boring of lines and replacement of piping were required prior to occupancy!

I attribute much of the success of these and later nursing units to Evie Romine, R.N., who was to become a professional role model for so many of the future nurses recruited to WK. On more than one occasion this exemplary nurse was offered the position of director of nursing, which she repeatedly rejected to stay closer to the patients. Eventually, I persuaded her to accept the assistant director's position, which permitted her to continue many of her daily clinical duties and remain close to her nursing staff. She was a professional role model and a nurse's nurse.

With an improving financial condition and additional beds, we soon realized we were facing a critical shortage of nurses. To overcome this shortage, our recruiting plan included implementing a new "courting" strategy focusing on the student nurses of Northwestern State University, an ever-growing student body. Students were taken out to dinner, where I presented them with a challenge: you may accept a position at an established hospital and face fewer challenges in your career, or you may join the proud ranks of WK and help grow a fledgling institution into a bustling future medical center. By showing these fine students more personal attention than our rival institutions did, we were successful.[26] One of those recruits, Jennie Hill, R.N., who worked with us some 38 years, reminded me that she took the job because I told her: "You will always have a job, you will always have sawdust in your hair (from our constant building projects) and you will always have a twinkle in your eye because you are a part of something larger than yourself." These modest social events led to the long-standing academic affiliation with Northwestern State University, today the fourth largest nursing school in the country. WK remains NSU's largest private partner, sponsoring numerous professorships.

One of the indicators of how much our medical staff appreciated management's accomplishments was a Christmas gift of a silver service set given to me in 1970 with an inscription of appreciation. Dr. Harvey Carter, president of the medical staff, told me the gift was made possible through individual contributions from the medical staff members to express their appreciation. Even today, this is one of my most prized possessions.

Other physicians chose to thank me in other ways; one took me on a fishing junket to the best bass fishing lake in the region. If you know anything about northwest Louisiana, then you know that bass fishing is a major sport. I joined several physicians and

26 One of the first NSU nursing graduates who joined our ranks recalls vividly her first day of work at WK—the day she arrived by police escort. The young lady was excited about her first day and she wanted to look her best. Unfortunately, she took so long getting ready that she was running late. Speeding on her way to work, she was pulled over by a policeman. Her response was hysterical, but between sobs and running mascara, the policeman soon understood her predicament. He told her to calm down, and that he would escort her to the hospital to make it on time. When the pair pulled up to the main entrance I was standing there. My question to her was: "Ms. Wycoff, are you going to have a police escort to work every day?"

The re-oriented main entrance of WK Medical Center opened in 1978. The radial nursing tower features core nursing stations and better visibility of patient rooms.

The lobby at Willis-Knighton Medical Center opened in 1978. With the addition of the radial patient tower, numerous patient service lines and a polished new entrance, a small neighborhood hospital began its transformation into a regional medical center.

their sons on a trip to Toledo Bend Lake. One of the physicians, a surgeon, was fishing in a boat with his elder son, who was constantly casting his artificial lure into the tops of large trees that had been partially submerged by water upon the opening of the gigantic lake.

After the surgeon had to paddle his bass boat over to the trees several times to untangle and retrieve his son's lure from the limbs, he told his son that, if he persisted in casting into the tree tops, he would have to just jerk his line and possibly lose his lure. "So don't do it again," he said. The son cast again into the tree limbs, with his father hollering at him, "I told you that if you want to retrieve your lure, you're going to have to pull on your fishing line even if you lose it. I'm not going to untangle your bait." The son protested, but his father told him to just pull hard on the line. The son pulled hard on the line, retrieving the lure but causing a large rotting tree to fall across their boat. The boat nearly sank, and their open tackle box, ice chest and lunch items were thrown overboard. All we could hear the rest of the day from their boat was, "Well, I only did what you told me to do" followed by a string of colorful language from the surgeon. That day I learned that not even a Texan could out-exaggerate a Louisiana fisherman when it comes to telling others about the number or size of the bass he caught that day.

By 1973, as we emerged from a state of insolvency (became up-to-date on payments of short-term debt, including accounts payable), our growing patient census required us to add more beds. A fourth and fifth floor addition was erected over the original 1966 addition, thereby allowing us to cease using some patient beds in the original 1924 hospital building. Finally, WK's nursing units and patient rooms were on par with or more modern than those of our competitors.

The addition of the 155-bed Virginia Hall Nursing Home and the Diagnostic and Surgical Building[27] (with office space for thirty physicians, this 55,000 square-foot physician office building was the first medical condominium in Louisiana) to our campus provided much of the increased patient volume that began to tax our cramped physical plant. The first pedestrian mall to be located on a hospital campus in this region of the

27 We considered the erection of this building a significant accomplishment for Willis-Knighton. In fact, the total usable space of this structure was about 2,000 square feet larger than the original hospital facility as it existed in 1965.

state was completed, thanks to the visionary insight and supportive leadership of Shreveport Mayor Clyde Fant. WK received approval from the city to close Virginia Avenue, which bisected our campus, to provide a safer environment.

In 1976 work began on a five-floor radial patient tower with core nursing stations (one of the first in Louisiana that permitted a more functional layout of the X-ray, laboratory, surgery and emergency departments) and a much more impressive entry, lobby and admissions area. Adjacent to the lobby were separate intensive care and cardiac care units (across the corridor from the heart cath laboratory). This building completely transformed our image from a small neighborhood hospital to a medical center. Upon completion of the radial tower in 1978, the hospital was renamed the Willis-Knighton Medical Center.

Though we could not have realized it at the time, this event would trigger a new day of growth and prosperity for our small inner-city hospital. Like the mythical phoenix, WK was beginning its ascent from its ashes.

Strategy 7:
Marketing Plans to Develop Brand Loyalty

Marketing is like kissing your wife. You don't know if it's doing any good, but you better not stop doing it.

John Luster, WK board member from 1981 to 2002

Upon my arrival in 1965, I began to visit with Shreveporters from all sections of the city and soon became aware that the vast majority of them did not patronize Willis-Knighton, nor did they know much about the hospital. At that time, WK's market share was less than 9 percent of the city's inpatient admissions and had been stuck at that level for years.

Many referred to our hospital as "Tri-State" or "the east Texas hospital." (I came to learn that this latter reference related to the fact that WK was on the west side of the city, the only hospital outside of the central part of Shreveport and the closest one to Texas, situated on the historic Highway 80 to Texas.) This last misleading reference had served to put into the heads of central and southeast Shreveporters the notion that WK was "way over near Texas," off the beaten path and too far for them to travel for healthcare. Another concern was the perception that the Queensborough neighborhood was deteriorating and that the crime rate was up; people feared for their personal safety.

I also came to realize that my early marketing efforts had to address several goals: 1) ending the public's routine use of the hospital's old name, "Tri-State Hospital," rather than the name "Willis-Knighton" under which the hospital had operated for over fifteen years, revealing that the public knew little about our facility, 2) dispelling of the public perception that our hospital was not outside the city (it had always been centrally located, but was now even more convenient to most of the city's neighborhoods because of the new Interstate 20 with two on/off ramps just two blocks from the campus), 3) devising a program to create not only a perception of safety for patients, families and employees, but genuine security, 4) creating a shortened name and distinct logo for brand identity, replacing the tongue-twisting and lengthy "Willis-Knighton Memorial Hospital, Inc." moniker,[28] with one that would bolster the public's perception that the hospital was no longer physician-owned and for-profit, but now a community-owned not-for-profit institution and 5) overcoming perceptions that Schumpert's patient care was superior because of its aesthetically pleasing building and highly touted technology.

The WK level of patient care was certainly good enough to sell itself. If our marketing program was successful in enticing patients and families to seek care within the walls of our hospital, I was convinced our quality physicians and staff could dispel negative perceptions of WK through capable and compassionate actions. Because we were somewhat behind the eight ball of public perception, I began to look for unique services that might be offered to patients and families. By turning patients into guests we sought to entice them to become loyal WK patrons.

28 If you have ever lived in the South, you are aware that almost everyone and everything is given an affectionate nickname, and that holds true for our hospitals: Willis-Knighton Medical Center (North) is "Willy K" or "Big Willy"; Willis-Knighton South is "Little Willy"; WK Bossier Health Center is "Bo Willy"; WK Pierremont Health Center is "Silk Willy"; North Caddo Memorial Hospital is "Bubba Willy"; and finally the WK Clinic in Bradley, Ark., is affectionately known as "Hillbilly Willy."

What Else Can We Do?

Previously, I had used class notes from graduate school to make financial changes at WK. Now I dusted notes and texts from marketing classes at Baylor. These were the only resources available, for this subject was not addressed in my graduate hospital administration curriculum. Why not?

The controversial subject of marketing hospitals and physicians had until that time fallen into a gray zone of questionable ethical behavior and was therefore not addressed in hospital administration programs.

Within a few years, this thinking totally changed, as hundreds of chain-owned, for-profit hospitals entered the market with modern marketing strategies, forcing community hospitals and eventually physicians to follow suit. By that time, Willis-Knighton was well ahead with its cutting-edge marketing strategies such as these:

1. Because our local media were not as inclined to cover the activities of our hospital or others in the city except T. E. Schumpert Memorial Hospital, we decided to purchase advertising space in local print media. An advantage of print advertising is that you can be sure that the facts of your hospital's activities are fully and accurately presented. Disadvantages are the additional costs of paid advertising versus free articles in the media and the fact that human interest articles may better enhance the image of the hospital than does paid advertising. But as the old adage goes, "Beggars can't be choosers. Take what you can get!"

2. Willis-Knighton became the first hospital in the state to use commercial billboards along heavy-traffic routes to advertise its services and activities. Our billboards not only promoted WK but also gave medical and disease prevention information. Our first billboard, with the caption, "Diseases can become extinct, too. Be sure your children are immunized," and a cartoon of a perplexed and sad-looking dinosaur, was a widely applauded marketing effort.

3. A first in this market, ads with photos of new medical staff members were distributed in local newspapers to introduce newly recruited physicians to the community and to recognize their distinguished achievements. Information includes the curriculum vitae of the physicians and their business contact information.

4. POP (pediatric orientation program) was introduced in cooperation with the public and private schools of two parishes of northwest Lou-

Willis-Knighton's first billboard campaign was directed at eradicating children's diseases. The campaign was well received by the public due to the use of the cute dinosaur and the heart-tugging appeal to fight childhood diseases.

isiana. This program for first-graders, a first in the state of Louisiana, was designed to teach personal hygiene and lifestyle habits (nutrition and exercise) and to dispel children's fears of doctors, nurses and hospitals. This program is credited with creating a bond between WK and a younger generation of parents who are now making health decisions for their families. This success in bonding is believed to be partially responsible for the growth of WK's number of births, now exceeding 85 percent of the local market of private patients, a long way from our earlier 9 percent share.

5. One of my most challenging marketing efforts was to brand the identity of Willis-Knighton with a shorter name and emblem that would be less wordy and dispel perceptions of its former physician ownership and for-profit tax status. The outcome of this endeavor was the unveiling of the distinctive and artistically designed WK which continues to this day to appear on all health system printings, publications and websites. A few years ago, a day-long marketing study at a large shopping mall revealed that our WK was the second most recognized logo in this region, bested only by the golden arches of McDonald's.

6. Mascot animals were adopted for marketing the pediatric units of Willis-Knighton Medical Center (Willis the Knight'n Frog) and the Center for Women's Health for WK South (Willis the Bear). The pediatric unit was decorated with caricatures of the frog and his friends, ceramic frogs and a red wagon (Willis' Karriage) for transporting patients to other departments. A Willis the Bear (commemorative

plush bear) is sent home with each newborn. Approximately 4,000 bears are distributed each year.

7. Bottled water served in all of our health system facilities is customized with decorative labels inscribed with the logos, "Willie Water" and "The Oaks of Louisiana," for purposes of instilling a sense of pride in patients, residents, employees and visitors.

8. The health system sponsors radio and TV programs designed to educate the public through health tips that will help align daily habits of life with best health practices. It supports the region's National Public Radio station.

9. Vim & Vigor magazine is a syndicated publication of approximately 70 hospitals and health systems that is targeted to about 35,000 households within our market region. The beauty of Vim & Vigor is that it has the appearance of a commercial newsstand magazine and not a marketing publication. The publication promotes our health system, its network physicians and The Oaks of Louisiana (WK's retirement community). Using covers with celebrity photos and content that reinforces healthy lifestyles, the magazine delivers sixteen pages of custom content crafted by WK staff.

10. Over a number of years, WK has provided funds to erect marquees and message boards at numerous elementary, junior high and high schools throughout the area. These elevated, two-sided lighted signs are highly visible with space for messages and student recognitions and awards.

11. An early warning weather and storm Doppler radar program was co-ventured with a local television station to provide early alerts to residents of the region. This program, the WK Storm Tracker Live Doppler Radar System, has been credited with minimizing personal injury to citizens.

12. A teletypewriter (TTY) communications system, a first for the region, was installed to assist the hearing-impaired with telephone communications.

13. The Shreveport Fire Department's seven SPRINT (Single Paramedic Rapid Intervention Non-Transport) vehicles, donated by WK at a cost of $700,000, are identified on the rear door as a gift of the health system. This unique EMS service of Shreveport, one of only a few in the nation, was made possible solely by this gift.

14. A number of local fire departments (city and parish volunteer) have been provided EMS (Emergency Medical Services) vehicles with WK logos.

15. Over a number of years, patrol and crime scene lab vehicles have been provided to the Shreveport Police Department and the sheriff's offices of Caddo and Bossier parishes. These vehicles are identified as gifts from our health system. Two-way radios and body armor have also been provided to the city police.

16. Hundreds of cultural and educational community presentations have been sponsored by WK in the interest of enhancing the lives of our residents. A printed schedule of the weekly health education presentations appears in local newspapers.

17. "Investing in Our Community" ads are carried on a routine basis in printed media to ensure community awareness of the good works performed by WK through its tithe of its financial blessings. These ads are presented in hope of reminding our community of the good works of the identified agencies and their need for financial support to further their missions. They subtly encourage the general public to financially support the charitable works highlighted in each advertisement. The morale of WK physicians and employees is enhanced as they take great pride in these ads and reflect on their personal contributions to the success of the health system, and in turn the health and well-being of their neighbors.

18. A number of highly visible outpatient facilities and services introduced throughout the region by WK have been great branding identification assets. These effective marketing resources include the health system's eight indigent clinics, two pediatric Medicaid clinics four occupational medicine clinics, three urgent care clinics and seven wellness centers, all displaying the WK logo. Offices of the 350 network physicians are similarly identified as WK facilities.

19. The health system provides support for the Queensborough Neighborhood Association, providing a building for its offices and financial support for its programs.

20. A number of office buildings and other surplus space (amounting to almost 40,000 square-feet) vacated by growing WK outpatient services have been provided at no charge to not-for-profit or civic organizations. Examples of these organizations include: Alliance for Education, Caddo Parish Sheriff's Department, Inner-City Entrepreneur Institute, LifeShare Blood Center, LSU Psychiatry, Northwest Louisiana Interfaith Pharmacy, Northwest Louisiana Area Health Education Center and Volunteers for Youth Justice.

21. While not done for this purpose, the thousands of hours of annual voluntary service of WK's employees on behalf of humanitarian works are one of the strongest and most effective of our marketing efforts. The community is made aware that their welfare is foremost

in the hearts, minds and efforts of our employees. Our hospital family gives back to the community, and the community appreciates WK.

22. In an effort to enter into the sports medicine market, WK established strategic partnerships with local colleges, high schools, and professional sports organizations. Many of these teams did not have certified athletic trainers at their disposal. Thus, the decision was made to provide them with professional trainers, free of charge. Not only did this increase WK's brand visibility within the region, but it also dramatically increased the hospital's surgical and rehabilitative sports medicine volume. WK has provided sports medicine coverage to four colleges, six area high schools, and three professional sports teams (hockey, baseball and arena football). Along with being a title sponsor for the Independence bowl, WK provides medical care before, during and after the game.

Strategy 8: Here Today, Gone Tomorrow... Or Too Good To Last

No horse gets anywhere until he is harnessed. No steam or gas ever drives anything until it is confined. No Niagara is ever turned into light and power until it is tunneled. No life ever grows great until it is focused, dedicated, and disciplined.

Harry Emerson Fosdick, D.D. (1878-1969)

Shortly after my arrival, WK, along with all hospitals in the country, was faced with a challenge to resist the temptation of a government reimbursement system that I believed was destined to erode our operational focus and discipline if we did not hold ourselves to a higher standard of performance.

Upon the implementation of Medicare (a federally-funded healthcare program), reimbursements for patient care were based on a "reasonable cost" standard. Providers were reimbursed on their reported cost plus a profit margin of 2 percent. This system, however well-intentioned, provided little incentive for hospitals to cut costs and operate more efficiently. In my opinion, the only way a cost-plus arrangement would reduce the price of a product or service was for it to reward the highest performing (lowest cost and highest quality) hospitals with a bonus.

For years, many hospitals did not hesitate to inflate their costs by increasing their physical plant size, bed capacity, ancillary services, technology and personnel far beyond their actual needs. Their inducement for such behavior was Medicare's willingness to pick up the tab on depreciation, interest, and related costs for such projects. In our state, one large hospital's main priority was to achieve the largest bed count of any hospital in Louisiana. Unfortunately, many other hospital projects, like that one, were driven by large egos rather than by market needs.

I must admit, given the circumstances, there were times when I was tempted to take advantage of this attractive reimbursement opportunity. Many of my colleagues in the industry chided me for being overly frugal. They believed I should enjoy the program's benefits today and stop worrying about its future financial ramifications. One fellow administrator expressed it this way: "Jim, stop leaving money on the table."

Holding Fast

As fast as laws are devised, their evasion is contrived.

German Proverb

In the late-1960s, believing that the "gravy train" would run its course, WK's management team was determined to take a proactive approach to the changes we anticipated in the Medicare program. Our approach was three-fold and would require a great deal of discipline on the part of our physicians, clinicians, and managers. First, we shied away from the temptations associated with the "reasonable cost" reimbursement structure. Second, we realized that rising Medicare costs were directly attributable to long lengths of stay and overutilization of services. Thus, it was imperative that we address this issue within our hospitals. Third, our health system needed to develop a systematic way of measuring and controlling utilization so that our clinical staff could analyze their practice patterns. This type of data could boost our efficiency by engaging the very players most responsible for our workshop, the physicians.

On the advice of Dr. Albert Bicknell, we made a conscious decision to limit the number of beds we had in operation. This decision was not difficult given the critical nursing shortage existing at that time.

While it sounds counterintuitive, Dr. Bicknell realized that the only way a hospital could effectively begin to address long lengths of stay was to change the medical staff's behavior. By limiting the number of beds in our facility, physicians understood that in order to get their next patients admitted they would have to work with the nursing staff to discharge patients in a timely manner. We saw a remarkable decrease in our lengths of stay over the next few years.

Our management team has always believed in the mantra that "what is measured gets done." Taking this to heart, we set out to develop a systematic way of looking at the utilization of our patient services. Our hospital used a program called CFIS (Clinical Financial Information System), which integrated our clinical information with financial performance. For the first time, our staff could present our physicians meaningful utilization and cost-associated data, so that they could compare their practices to those of their peers. This information was used to create better patient care plans, later known as clinical pathways.

Willis-Knighton had advantages over other regional hospitals as a result of its ownership of unique services that permitted a more aggressive approach for movement of a patient through appropriate continuums of care. WK provided both intermediate and skilled nursing care housed in Virginia Hall (a facility adjacent to the hospital), inpatient rehabilitation, outpatient services, and home health and hospice care provided in the patient's home. The patient's need-based care plan was under the direction of his or her physician.

Another unique service of WK was its in-house patient transport service. All patient transportation was provided by the hospital's own transport service to any required out-patient facility at no charge to ensure a seamless transition from inpatient to home care.

Our instincts and persistent efforts paid off when Medicare reimbursements switched from "reasonable cost" to DRGs (Diagnosis Related Groups). DRG-based reimbursement paid hospitals a flat rate for each patient diagnosis regardless of their actual lengths of stay and the use of resources.

Darlene Hall, Trish Koopman and Lisa Maxey were instrumental in this change. These capable young women came to WK after the completion of their medical records program at Louisiana Tech University. They were zealots for detail and had a positive attitude for change that became contagious. It was through their passionate efforts that we were able to hold ourselves to a higher standard of accomplishments than our regional peers. WK has greatly benefited from their loyal service for over 30 years.

Strategy 9: Providing Work Places for Physicians

Physician-owned office buildings on its campus are life insurance policies to a hospital.

Dr. Albert Bicknell (1929-2000)

Shortly after my arrival, my dear friend Dr. Albert Bicknell commented to me, "Jim, the best way to ensure the future growth of our hospital is to somehow find a way for the hospital to finance a physician office building on the campus that would be available and affordable to potential physician recruits." After completion of our first two patient bed additions in 1973, which permitted the removal of all patients from the 1928 addition, it was evident a physician office building was required to recruit new physicians. Because the hospital was financially unable to borrow additional funds to finance the entire project, our attorney, our certified public accountant, Albert and I began to search for ways to accomplish the building of this critical facility.

The Diagnostic and Surgical building, the first medical condominium in the state of Louisiana, opened in 1974. The facility was a major catalyst for physician recruitment to the Willis-Knighton campus.

One affordable idea was to develop a medical condominium with the hospital as the promoter of the project; the physicians would purchase their offices through personal loans from a local bank, secured with the offices as collateral. A building association of physician owners and the hospital (as promoter and responsible for the routine maintenance) would be formed to handle monthly operational expenses. All parties would share on a pro-rata basis (a ratio of owned space to the entire building square footage) of expenses. But there was one problem with the idea: there were no medical condominiums in the state of Louisiana, and the secretary of state was reluctant to grant approval. After studying the state's requirements for condominiums, our attorney, T. K. Giddens, prepared the first legally qualifying documents for this medical project.

In 1974, the Diagnostic and Surgical Building was opened across the street from the hospital's main entrance. The building was totally occupied at opening by physicians representing medical and surgical specialties heretofore unavailable on our campus. Throughout his lifetime, Dr. Bicknell referred to this medical condominium as WK's most valuable insurance policy; the physicians had ownership in their offices and income tax advantages and were therefore less inclined to relocate their practices. They were with us for the long haul.

Some of the physician office buildings owned and operated by WK on the four campuses of the health system are pictured above.

The Diagnostic and Surgical Building was the first of many physician office buildings (combined with a replacement value of over $250 million in 2011) to be built by WK over the years, but it was one of the last medical condominiums to be built in the city. Our hospital system became capable of fully financing future buildings; a later IRS Code reduced the value of tax considerations of physician ownership of condominiums; and we developed an employed physician network, so no further medical condominiums were built.

As physicians have retired from active practice, their condominium offices have been purchased by the health system for appraised values: only one D & S building office remains under physician ownership. However, this concept of physician ownership proved to be the right strategy for over twenty years, enough time for our health system to secure its future. The concept was the catalyst for the many WK physician buildings pictured in this section.

Strategy 10: Geniuses in the Basement: Our In-House Bio-Med/Rad Service Engineers

There's no ceiling on effort!

Harvey C. Fruehauf (1896-1968)

In the early 1970s, as WK was beginning to emerge from bleak financial times, I was confronted with another financial challenge. Much of our medical equipment was not of the latest generation when compared to that of our major competitor. A local bank was willing to loan us money to purchase updated technology, but could not finance the annual vendor maintenance service contracts, which averaged approximately 14 percent of the purchase prices.

Our solution was to eliminate some of the out-sourced vendor maintenance contracts in favor of an in-house service. We recruited Tom Brown, a retired military medical equipment service technician to organize our first bio-medical engineering service. This bold move for a small hospital provided more timely repairs, returned equipment to service more quickly, and reduced the costs of expensive manufacturer service contracts.

Although WK's limited physical plant was already crowded, we found an unused basement area, which we retrofitted with heavy-duty fluorescent lighting and workbenches. Early efforts paid off with faster and less costly repairs of WK's equipment. However, I must admit that at that time I did not fully comprehend the many advantages this small in-house group of highly skilled, technical service engineers would continue to provide our health system. Their service was nothing less than remarkable.

Convinced that there were opportunities for similar savings in the radiology department, Dianne Coffman, chief technician, and her successor, Joyce Hooper, encouraged me to consider an in-house service engineering program to maintain all radiology and nuclear medicine equipment.

In 1980 we were fortunate to employ Wesley Smith, an extraordinarily talented field engineer from a national medical systems company, to join our hospital team. Before his employment, Wesley had been servicing most of our X-ray equipment. Since his arrival, all imaging modalities including X-ray units, CAT (computerized axial tomography) scanners, ultrasound, nuclear medicine, MRI (magnetic resonance imaging) units and the PAC (picture archiving communications) system have been serviced by this department.

This cadre of technical engineers later assumed responsibility for servicing most other equipment within the health system's owned and managed hospitals, centers of excellence, imaging centers and the offices of medical staff physicians. Additionally, their services were offered to all affiliated hospitals of the health system. Since the installation of X-ray units is handled by our system's technical engineers, our employed network physician offices that require imaging equipment can be placed in operation in record time. We do not have to work with the time constraints imposed by equipment vendors.

In 2012 there were twenty highly-trained engineers responsible for servicing all facets of modern medical technology within the health system. A number of unique contractual relationships exist between our health system and our regular vendors such as GE, Siemens and Philips: 1) shared contracts for discounts on parts, 2) local stocking of high-usage parts to expedite repairs, 3) factory and follow-up training for our engineers prior to purchase of new equipment, 4) binding agreements ensuring the honoring of warranties on all purchased equipment that is installed by WK's service engineers and 5) assurances from the vendors that in the event of shipping delays, all parts may be readily available for pick-up at their regional distribution centers by the flight crews of our aviation services department, including holidays and weekends, for transport to Shreveport/Bossier.

The following numbers illustrate the growth and value of this unique service:

1. In 1989 medical equipment assets at WKMC and WK South totaled $29 million (book value after depreciation), which included 3,453 devices.
2. In 2012 medical equipment assets at our four hospitals, centers of excellence, wellness centers, physician network offices and The Oaks of Louisiana totaled $225 million (book value after depreciation), which included 20,076 devices.

In 2012 WK's Bio-Rad engineers met all service demands associated with the maintenance of all the technological equipment of the health system at a cost of $8.5 million (including salaries, costs of parts and shared parts) while avoiding an estimated annual $26.8 million expense for maintenance service contracts if performed by outside equipment vendors, resulting in a savings of $18.3 million for the fiscal year.

Never would I have envisioned in 1970 that this invaluable service, the first in this region, would remain the only full-service Bio-Rad technical support program of its kind in this region, for most hospitals continue to outsource this service at considerably higher costs. WK owes much to the technical geniuses in our basement.

CHAPTER 5

Transforming a Neighborhood Hospital Into a Regional Medical Center

Willis-Knighton Medical Center, 165-acres with eight centers of excellence.

Strategy 11: WK Medical Center (Our Hub)

Willis-Knighton Medical Center (365 beds) is the flagship hospital (hub) of the WK fleet of satellite hospitals (our spokes), thanks to the strategies outlined in detail in the following pages. These strategies have succeeded in growing this small inner-city sanitarium into the largest medical center in Louisiana, while permitting it to remain in

The post-1978 main entrance of Willis-Knighton Medical Center (above) faces the intersections of U.S. Hwy. 80 (locally Greenwood Road) and U.S. Hwy. 79 (locally Hearne Avenue). The hospital's east façade (seen below) is at the intersection of Greenwood Road and Albert Bicknell Drive. The original campus has grown from the limited space between these two intersections to encompass several city blocks.

the neighborhood that it has faithfully served since 1924. Growing a bed capacity from 80 to 1,192 did not just happen, but was the result of the dedicated efforts of a team of physicians, nurses and other employees who diligently overcame financial hardships and physical plant limitations.

Strategy 12: Raze the Ivory Tower

The tragedy of life is in what dies inside a man while he lives—the death of genuine feeling, the death of inspired response, the death of awareness that makes it possible to feel the pain or the glory of other men yourself.

Norman Cousins (1915-1990)

The corporate offices of the Willis-Knighton Health System are located on the flagship campus, along with the system's board room, administration, auditorium, education center, business office, data processing, human resources, materials management, fleet services, physician network services and marketing and the laundry processing plant, which also supports our four owned and two managed hospitals and The Oaks of Louisiana.

A conscious decision was made years ago, that no matter how large or prosperous the health system became, corporate offices would remain, not merely on one of our campuses, but housed within the hospital. This daily contact with physicians, patients and families helps to keep our mission foremost in our minds, so we do not forget that we are in the patient care business and not merely in a financial enterprise. Patients and their care are our business and our reason for being! A daily nurturing of the empathy we share with the sick and injured of our community is paramount to delivery of the highest quality of care in the most caring and compassionate of settings. Our corporate leaders have a chance to mold and support the *esprit de corps* of the organization by mingling and working alongside our patients and employees, who are greatly responsible for the success of our health system. We are determined not to forget who we are and where we came from.

Strategy 13:
Centers of Excellence

He who stops being better, stops being good.

Oliver Cromwell (1599-1658)

In the late 1980s, a strategy for expanding specialty patient services was adopted at WK: the development of centers of excellence, product lines of high profile, specialized patient services. WK's strategic focus became the creation of services that enhanced not only the quality of care but also the hospital's profitability through increased volume and economies of scale, producing lower costs per units of service. These outcomes were the result of a concentration of expensive, innovative technology and physician specialist and sub-specialist expertise at one site. Another benefit derived from this tactic was the positive impact (halo effect) these centers had on our hospitals' public image.

Our first two centers of excellence were WK South's Center for Women's Health, which specialized in obstetrics, neo-natal and pediatric care and the Steen-Hall Eye Institute on the main campus, both opening in 1989. These centers and others that followed did much to enhance the quality of patient care in the region while promoting WK's image and reputation.

Most of these centers were eventually located on the campus of Willis-Knighton Medical Center, our flagship hospital, for several reasons: 1) to take advantage of the convenient location (fronting I-20) for most patients of the Ark-La-Tex, 2) to take advantage of the medical and surgical expertise of the large number of physician sub-specialists with offices on this campus, 3) to ensure the continued operation of our inner-city hospital in its existing location through referrals from outlying facilities and 4)

Pictured are the centers of excellence located on the Willis-Knighton Medical Center campus. Top: WK Cancer Center; second row, left: WK Heart Hospital with emergency services on first floor; second row, right: WK Eye Institute; bottom: Bicknell Outpatient Surgical Pavilion.

The pioneer physicians that were most instrumental in the establishment of our centers of excellence on the WK Medical Center campus were: 1) cancer institute and hospice programs – Michael Moore M.D., 2) heart institute – Michael Futtrell, M.D., Stanford Shelby, M.D. and Tommy Brown, M.D., 3) eye institute – William Steen, M.D. and Donald L. Hall, M.D. and 4) outpatient surgery – Albert L. Bicknell, M.D.

Kathy Walker A.R.R.T., a thirty-year employee of WK has directed all activities of the catheterization labs at WK North, WK Bossier and WK Pierremont.

Additional centers of excellence located on the Willis-Knighton Medical Center campus. Top: WK Rehabilitation Institute, as it originally appeared. The three-floor addition was retrofitted to provide a waiting room and a full range of therapy services on the first floor and 60 patient rooms on the second and third floors. Middle: WK Spine Institute and the WK/LSU Center for Reproductive Health. Bottom: WK Extended Care Center for acute rehabilitation.

The WK Rehabilitation Institute was planned and operated by Ronald S. Wehlander, physical therapist. Ron served in this position from 1983 until his death in 2007. This outstanding rehabilitation program was named in his memory.

to take advantage of the proximity and expertise of the subspecialists of the LSU Health Shreveport School of Medicine.

Strategy 14:
Satellite Hospitals (Our Spokes)

If you have built castles in the air, your work need not be lost; that is where they should be. Now put foundations under them.

Henry David Thoreau (1817-1862)

Introduction to the Concept

A game-changing event in the life of Willis-Knighton Memorial Hospital occurred in 1983 with the opening of its first satellite campus, South Park Hospital. It was the first satellite to open in Louisiana and the forerunner of things to come as inner-city hospitals began developing ways to expand their patient bases without abandoning their existing campuses. A hospital relocating from the inner city often ran the risk of having a competitor fill the void with a smaller, more modern and cost-effective facility. The result of leaving a vacuum of services in the old location often was a loss of patients and physicians to the new competitor.

The idea of closing an inner-city hospital and moving to the suburbs flew in the face of the marketing adage, "Never give up business–go after more." The satellite hospital concept became the best solution: a hospital that remained in its original location could keep its existing market share while entering new markets with smaller facilities and gaining an increased patient base. This strategy proved to be a way for Willis-Knighton to have its cake and eat it too: enter new markets while continuing to serve its old neighborhood.

A synonym for satellite is "follower," which best depicts this type of hospital. Satellite hospitals are adherent to their parent hospitals in ownership, mission and leadership and are generally located some distance from the flagship hospital. The new sites, most often located in residential growth areas, are chosen to permit greater access and convenience to larger numbers of potential patients. They are generally more aesthetically pleasing in architectural design and functionality because they start from scratch on vacant property. The smaller satellite hospital, a mirror image of the parent in management, is less expensive to operate because it shares personnel, equipment and support services with the parent facility. No duplications of highly expensive technology are permitted unless the satellite facility has a patient volume justifying them. Some satellite hospitals have been so successful as to outgrow in bed size and patient volume their parent facilities.

A satellite facility usually serves patients with less critical medical conditions and refers patients requiring a higher level of services to the parent hospital. Emergency services are generally provided at satellite hospitals to ensure rapid transport and treatment of residents in their neighborhoods. When a patient is stabilized by the emergency room staff, the triaged patient is then either kept at the satellite hospital or, if he requires more sophisticated treatment, transported to the larger referral center. The transport of patients requiring highly technical and expensive imaging, therapy and surgery to a tertiary level hospital is handled by the health system's transport team of nurses and paramedics.

The greatest value of a satellite hospital is its location nearer the homes of patients with life-threatening, emergent medical conditions. The shorter the time required for a patient to get to a hospital with emergency services, the better the chance of his long-term recovery.

However, after extolling the virtues of satellite hospitals, I feel compelled to share with you the major downside issue associated with their operations: an absolute requirement for a synchronized and coordinated management behavior that must at all times refrain from submitting to the pressures of the satellites' medical staffs and personnel to unnecessarily duplicate functions on their campuses. Each hospital's staff, employees and physicians must be willing to operate under the premise that they are a part of the larger organization, not its sole operation.

They are not independent operations, free to do whatever their management team and physicians choose, often duplicating system functions at their hospitals (i.e., staffing, marketing, human resources, materials management, finances), causing system-wide operational issues, functional misunderstanding of roles, spreading of discord and forcing unnecessary financial expense upon the system. To be successful financially and in the delivery of health services, satellite hospitals must operate within the over-arching directives of the health system.

After almost thirty years of satellite operations, WK has successfully developed and coordinated the inter-working of all four of our hospitals to a point where our health system's costs of operations are significantly less than they would be if our hospitals operated independently of one another. Architectural designs aside, physicians, employees and patients find themselves easily transitioning from one WK hospital to another. All clinical and non-clinical protocols are virtually identical at each facility. One might say: "If you have been a patient in one WK hospital, you would also feel at home in any of the others."

WK South: Satellite Number One A Lifeline to the Suburbs

One thing at a time, and all things in succession.
That which grows slowly endures.

Josiah G. Holland (1819-1881)

Our first satellite hospital, Willis-Knighton South, was initially named South Park Hospital to define the location of the hospital as being near South Park Mall, then the region's largest indoor shopping mall. It is approximately seven miles from the main hospital campus. This $12 million project included sixty-six beds, a surgical suite of four operating rooms with recovery, laboratory, X-ray, central service, cafeteria, auditorium and an emergency department, large for a hospital of its bed size.

An oversized emergency department was provided because there were no emergency facilities closer than Willis-Knighton and LSU Health Shreveport, both of which were seven miles from households in southwest Shreveport. At that time, before Shreveport's fire department took over ambulance service, private ambulance operators were stationed near downtown.

They were about ten miles from southwest Shreveport, and it took twenty minutes to respond to emergencies in this section of the city. After on-site treatment and stabilization of the patient, another twenty minutes was required for travel to the nearest hospitals. The average response time was almost one hour from the dispatch of ambulance to patient's door to emergency care, longer for transports to hospitals in the eastern part of the city. These long response times for southwest Shreveporters with heart attacks and strokes resulted in death rates higher than those in other areas of the city. Residents in the rural areas south of southwest Shreveport had to travel even farther for emergency treatment. The placement and operation of this satellite hospital, Willis-Knighton South, has resulted in the saving of many lives since its opening in 1983.

Another factor that played into the building of South Park Hospital was the shortage and exorbitant prices of properties around Willis-Knighton Memorial Hospital, which continued to stymie expansion for a number of years. The land for South Park Hospital and the adjacent South Shreveport Medical Plaza was much less expensive than that around the parent hospital, and it required no demolition of buildings. A site was acquired by Willis-Knighton in 1981. Later, additional property which was required by a zoning ordinance for the main hospital entrance, Hospital Drive and Susan Drive, was donated to Willis-Knighton by the owners of the South Shreveport Medical Plaza.

The satellite hospital concept had been on the minds and drawing boards of the hospital's management team since the physicians had purchased the land for their offices. Even then the team believed that, if Willis-Knighton were to remain in Queensborough, an inner-city neighborhood, it needed a feeder hospital to attract referrals from the growing southwest neighborhoods.

However, WK could not afford to build a satellite facility because the major addition to the parent hospital, completed in the late 1970s, impacted its ability to borrow additional funds for expansion for a number of years. WK's management had for years studied the satellite concept, and financial projections reflected that the proposed hospital would be more profitable if operated as a satellite than as a stand-alone hospital.

The six physicians with offices in the South Shreveport Medical Plaza building had large primary care practices but were losing patients to physicians across town who were aligned with specialty physicians with other hospitals. Such defections were prompted by the shortage of physician specialists at Willis-Knighton, which limited patient appointments, rather than to dissatisfaction with their primary care physicians.

This fact was borne out by the large numbers of previously treated patients returning to the folds of these physicians, along with throngs of new patients requiring both primary and specialist care, upon the opening of South Park Hospital. Another issue was the fact that with no hospital in this area, there was little difference in travel time advantages for patients seeking specialty care at Willis-Knighton's Queensborough location over other hospitals.

This continuing loss of patient referrals to our hospital from this burgeoning, but medically underserved, section of the city only served to slow our patient growth and financial success, further miring our hospital in a "catch 22" position. The absence of a hospital in southwest Shreveport meant no future physician or patient growth in this booming neighborhood. It meant no recruiting of specialty physicians, who required nearby hospital services for their patients.

The lack of a WK presence in this area meant the continued loss of referrals of patients to our hospital for specialty care because of our limited number of specialists and travel time disadvantages. Lack of growth of patient admissions at Willis-Knighton would mean a continuing deterioration of our hospital business and financial consequences of devastating proportion.

It became abundantly clear to management and the six physicians in the city's southwest area that the only practical solution to this dilemma was to build a satellite hospital near their offices.

With the shortage of specialty physicians on the main campus of Willis-Knighton and with none practicing in this rapidly growing bedroom community of thousands of employees of the large industrial plants of General Motors, General Electric, Beaird/Poulan, Gould Battery and Western Electric, why did it take it so long for our health system to build South Park Hospital, aside from financial constraints?

The answer lay with the thinking of some of the physician specialists on our main campus, who were benefiting from an exclusive pattern of referrals from the primary care physicians in the southwest neighborhoods. A few of these physicians were concerned that the proposed hospital would attract competitive specialists to the facility at their expense. A few of them became so irate over the subject of a satellite hospital that they made threats, even though most privately agreed the concept was the best growth and survival strategy for WK.

They hinted a medical staff vote of no confidence might be pursued. Some pledged never to work in the proposed hospital, and others threatened to move their practices across town. One of our most respected physicians said that he would not take a public position on the project because of our friendship; he believed the strategy was right, but the timing was wrong. A motion for a vote of no confidence for my leadership was proposed by one of the physicians most adamantly opposed to the new hospital, but he could not get a second to his motion. This was my first, and I hope last, threat of a vote of no confidence in my administration of WK.

When the physicians in southwest Shreveport got wind of these actions, they became quite upset and said they would begin referring their patients to specialists at other hospitals if such attitudes continued. I intervened by convening a meeting of the leaders of both sides of the issue to work out their differences, no matter what impact the situation would have on my continued employment. Cooler heads did prevail, and management moved forward with plans for South Park Hospital after a unanimous vote by the medical staff and trustees. To give the specialists time to make plans regarding their participation at the satellite hospital, management moved the date for its opening back three years.

Dr. Thomas Strain Sr., the oldest and longest-serving physician on Willis-Knighton's medical staff, was the most supportive physician specialist of this satellite hospital strategy. This visionary gentleman was Tri-State Sanitarium's first intern in 1926.

His enthusiastic support for this project was largely responsible for the eventual relocation of his group, the Strain Pediatric Clinic, and all OB/GYN physicians from our flagship campus to the Women's Center on the Willis-Knighton South campus in 1989. This center continues to deliver the largest number of babies in this region and is the center of excellence for neonatology, maternal-fetal medicine, pediatric intensive care and a number of other pediatric subspecialties for the health system.

Shortly after this tumultuous time the local newspaper announced that Highland Clinic and Hospital had optioned a large parcel of land immediately adjacent to the proposed site of our satellite hospital and next door to the offices of our six primary care physicians. This inner-city hospital and clinic, like Willis-Knighton, was located in a rapidly deteriorating neighborhood and had been considering a move to a growth suburban neighborhood for some time.

Highland Hospital's acquisition by a national hospital company gave it financial strength to fund the relocation, which greatly updated its physical plant and placed their operations in the heart of the most prosperous area of the city. This move would have placed a competitor hospital next door to Willis-Knighton's largest group of family doctors, possibly jeopardizing their referrals to our hospital.

However, this announcement from a competitor solidified the support of the entire medical staff at Willis-Knighton behind the immediate building of a satellite hospital, negating their previous request to delay it for at least three years. No hospital administrator has ever had a more meteoric ascent from the outhouse of dissension to the penthouse of praise and support of this satellite strategy than I experienced at that time. Since then, I have never experienced any lack of support concerning satellite strategies for Willis-Knighton's prosperity.[29]

Loy Moore, chairman of the loan committee of the bank I approached about financing the new hospital, told me this: Upon the review of WK's application for a loan to build South Park Hospital, the committee's initial reaction was to deny the request. It was approved only after the bank president said to the others, "If Jim Elrod tells you that WK can repay this loan, he will make it happen." Loy has never told me whether he was that convinced of our credit-worthiness at that time, but he has since become a strong supporter and friend of our hospital.

Our management team worked around the clock for four days and nights to prepare an application for certificate of need approval to the North Louisiana Health Planning Agency; it was granted. That organization's director informed our team that no hospital had ever completed an application in the time frame we did. The design/build concept of construction assisted our team with the cost and time parameters of the project.

WK's application was submitted and approved before the Highland Hospital requested the health planning application documents. The letters of support from the six family practitioners of the South Shreveport Medical Plaza in southwest Shreveport played a major role in securing approval of our application.

This herculean effort on the part of our management team, working around the clock to prepare the applications, is remembered as the greatest team effort in our hospital's history. It is the keystone event of the past thirty years, having a positive impact on the morale of our organization that continues to this day. Strong bonds of camaraderie, friendship and cooperation among our team members continue to permeate and spread over the four campuses of Willis-Knighton Health System and over the offices of three hundred and fifty network physicians.

A few days after the public announcement of health planning approval, I received

29 However, the staff at South Park Hospital had to put up with good-natured jokes about the hospital's former rural setting. One physician at WK, a strong supporter of the satellite hospital, kidded one of his favorite nurses by saying, "The only patients you are going to treat down there will be for sunburn and cow-bites." A number of jokes also circulated referring to South Park as the "pea patch" hospital.

a call from Schumpert's assistant administrator, who asked why WK was building a hospital in southwest Shreveport? My answer was that a hospital was desperately needed in that area to provide faster emergency services and reduce the death rate from heart attacks and strokes. I also admitted that it was a strategic move to grow our market share by recapturing patients going across town for medical care.

His reply was that he was glad that his hospital wasn't forced to build satellite hospitals to retain patients. He noted that his patients' loyalty was so strong that they would walk over broken glass to get to them. I replied, "Well, since our patient loyalty is not that strong, we're going to have to build another hospital to hang on to them." I realized his comment was tongue-in-cheek; however, I had to agree with him that his patient and physician loyalty was exceptionally strong because of his hospital's image and reputation for quality.

Ironically, this dominant, high-quality competitor was eventually forced to purchase three hospitals in Shreveport/Bossier City in an attempt to reclaim patients lost to our satellites, WK South, WK Bossier Health Center and WK Pierremont Health Center. Because of its late entry into these three markets and lack of experience operating cost-effective satellites, only one of the three is still in operation, but with a reduced bed capacity. As I remember the telephone call in 1981, I can only say, "So much for the broken glass theory of patient loyalty!"

South Park opened to great fanfare. Over a thousand people came out on a cold January day to tour it, even though the Pittsburgh Steelers and its quarterback, the favorite hometown son, Terry Bradshaw, were on television in the NFL playoffs. The hospital's emergency room became one of the busiest and most appreciated by its neighbors in the city.

Thanks to the numbers of referring physicians and strong community backing, South Park Hospital ended its first month of operation with a positive cash flow. This financial performance continues. Its cash reserves funded the building of the Women's Center in 1989 and a significant portion of the start-up costs of WK Bossier Health Center in 1996.

South Park Hospital (later Willis-Knighton South) was opened in January 1983. The first satellite hospital in the state, WK South was an instant hit, with both patients and medical staff alike and greatly reduced emergency response times in south Shreveport.

Evolving from humble roots, today Willis-Knighton South includes the following centers of excellence: WK Women's Center, Neonatal Intensive Care Unit, Pediatric Intensive Care Unit, Behavioral Medicine and Hyperbaric Medicine (12-patient chamber). The region's only private maxillofacial surgical clinic is located on this campus.

Willis-Knighton South Center for Women's Health (top) remains the largest birthing facility in the region. Behavioral Medicine Unit (middle), the region's only 12-person hyperbaric chamber (above) is located in the Wound Center (inset). Not shown, the outpatient plaza that includes breast center, imaging, GI lab, urgent care clinic, occupational medicine clinic, maternal-fetal and pediatric clinics.

Some of this success was due to the fact that its Medicare admissions were less than 20 percent of its total, compared to over 45 percent at the main campus and other hospitals in the city. This fact came as no surprise to our staff because our demographic studies of the area reflected that its residents were mostly young adults, many of whom were employed at the nearby industrial plants and enjoyed superior health insurance coverage.

WK South has a high level of morale and the lowest rate of personnel turnover in our health system. Its tremendous success played a major role in influencing our decisions to build two other satellite hospitals, WK Bossier and WK Pierremont, and its profitability was a major source of the finances that funded their construction and operation.

I often reflect on how the future of Willis-Knighton might have been different had this satellite facility not been built. Willis-Knighton would not be the largest medical center in Louisiana, and many highly specialized medical procedures and state-of-the-art technologies would not be readily available to patients in northwest Louisiana.

Without WK South to refer large numbers of more acutely ill patients to Willis-Knighton Medical Center, I strongly believe that our flagship would have suffered financial downturns that would have threatened not only its future of service to Queenborough, but also its continued existence.

Further, LSU Health Shreveport would not have benefited from years of contributions and physician training support from WK, its largest private benefactor. Thousands of northwest Louisiana's underserved residents would not be receiving benefits of health and well-being services made possible by WK's tithe of the bottom line that supports our Duties of Conscience.

Finally, southwest Shreveporters owe a debt a gratitude to Drs. Russell Rigby, John Leopard, John Hall, J. E. Smith and Walter Asseff (family physicians) who had the foresight to acquire the land and patiently wait so many years for the building of our mutual dream, WK South.

In closing this section on WK South, I would like to share a heart-warming story of a patient whose life was saved, thanks to the hospital's location in southwest Shreveport and its highly competent emergency room staff. A physician's wife took an overdose of sleeping pills while in her automobile in rural DeSoto Parish.

The physician said to me, "When you announced the building of WK South in 1981, I was in practice in a competing clinic and hospital across town and thought at the time that this hospital wasn't needed in our community and would be a waste of money. Only after this tragic event in the life of my family did I realize that WK South is the essential emergency lifeline, not only to southwest Shreveport, but also to a large rural area south of our city. The sheriff's deputies found my wife in her auto with no detectable vital signs some twenty-eight hours after I discovered her note telling our family of her intentions. Upon the arrival of the EMS vehicle and crew, a decision was made to take her to WK South, the closest hospital by at least fifteen minutes, even though she appeared to have succumbed to a medication overdose. Upon the arrival of my wife at the ER, the ER physician and nurses at WK South also could not detect any signs of life, yet decided to perform an all-out attempt for resuscitation and cardiac stimulation. These last-ditch efforts on the part of the ER staff were rewarded by the return of my wife's vital signs and breathing and no permanent brain damage. The ER physician commented that he doubted that my wife would have survived the fifteen or more minutes of time required for transport to the next closest hospital. Jim, I am here today to thank you and your staff for having the vision, almost thirty years ago, to provide this life-saving facility for southwest Shreveport. In my heart, I know that my wife would not be with our family today were it not for WK South's marvelous emergency and intensive care services. I can never thank you enough for WK South being there in our time of need."

WK Bossier Health Center: Satellite Number Two The Battle for Bossier

A riddle wrapped in a mystery inside an enigma.

Winston Churchill (1874 -1965)

For almost thirty years prior to making the decision to build WK Bossier Health Center at the intersection of Airline Drive and I-220, I observed the operations of the Bossier City General Hospital and its successor, Bossier Medical Center (BMC). I had come to view the hospital as a mystery as I watched its revolving door lineup of administrators and studied its declining patient admissions. I failed to understand why BMC did not seem to garner greater public acceptance and growth. How could citizens so strongly support their city and its growth while being less enthusiastic and supportive of their city-owned hospital? The build, buy and boost Bossier City mentality was not foremost in the minds of patients and families when it came to support for their hospital. Why were the city fathers unaware of, or unwilling to accept, the fact that Bossier City patients would continue the trek across the river to Shreveport's physicians because of their hospital's financial inability to maintain state-of-the-art medical technology that was required to recruit an adequate number of physicians, particularly those in medical specialties? Another question was why city council members were not willing to accept the fact that BMC, under city control, would continue to post financial losses that would eventually have to be funded by taxes on Bossier City residents? One councilman stated in a public meeting, "I personally would like to see us sell the hospital. The city no longer belongs in the hospital business." Yet nothing happened!

I continued to believe the Bossier parish population of 1993 could support a hospital of twice the bed capacity of BMC. This projection was based on the condition that large numbers of physician specialists were recruited to Bossier City to practice. Further observations and opinions are as follows:

1. BMC opened in 1966 in a new physical plant and had undergone few major changes since that time, other than an emergency, outpatient surgery and one patient bed addition. The hospital equipment's level of technological sophistication was not on par with that of Schumpert or Willis-Knighton. Its campus location, three blocks from the I-20 interstate highway, was accessible, but the volume of traffic on streets around the campus presented enormous problems. The increased numbers of businesses locating around the campus were beginning to land-lock the hospital, limiting future expansion.

2. In my opinion, the sale of hospital-owned properties on Doctor's Drive as individual lots for the building of single-physician specialty offices had been a mistake. Multi-floor physician buildings would have made better use of the land, providing more office space and a much higher level of provider density (number of physicians on the same ground space). This utilization would have given BMC a larger base of physician support and enticed additional specialists to practice in Bossier City.

3. The financial condition of BMC, after the city's confiscation of a portion of its profits and without further city-bonded indebtedness, would be inadequate to finance the future needs of the hospital: physical plant expansions, next-generation technology, manpower-intensive services and land acquisitions.

4. One BMC physician publicly stated, "In the last two or three years, I've seen a constant decline in the care of patients because of budgetary decisions. I don't want to see that anymore" (*Shreveport Times*, August 26, 1994).

5. The medical staff of BMC, though it had few physician specialists, was of high quality, in the opinion of WK's physicians. Bossier City was fortunate, in my opinion, to have on its medical staff Dr. Jake Miciotto, one of the most respected and hardest working OB/GYN specialists in the region. Until retirement, Dr. Miciotto provided obstetrical and gynecological services, free of charge, to medical students, residents and their spouses. During his career, Dr. Miciotto delivered more than 900 babies one year and over 17,200 in his career, which was about one-third of Bossier City's population in 1990.

6. The BMC medical staff was supportive of its hospital, but concerned about the political football role it played with some of the city councilmen and mayors. In earlier years, its operations and finances were often undermined by politically influenced hiring practices and the periodic confiscation of its income for the city's uses. Some elected officials' unwillingness to permit the hospital's administrator to run the facility was the root cause of the heavy turnover of administrators.

7. Another concern of the BMC physicians was the inability of the hospital to recruit enough specialists. They were placed, all too often, in the position of having to call on Shreveport physicians for subspecialty support. Bossier City physicians and BMC routinely lost patients to these specialists and Schumpert Hospital, which caused BMC to lose admissions. Bossier City physicians often referred to these physicians as opportunists, but were forced to utilize them as there were no other referral options for specialists.

8. BMC's inpatient admissions had been declining for nearly a decade. Between 1983 and 1993, over half of BMC's previous inpatients were seeking medical care elsewhere, as the hospital's admissions dropped from 8,349 to 4,137 (source: 1983 and 1993 American Hospital Association Guide). This redirection by Shreveport specialists of referred Bossier patients to their preferred primary care physicians in Shreveport continued at an alarming rate. According to 1991 Medicare data, the most current at that time, 58 percent of Bossier City's Medicare patients sought care at Shreveport hospitals, not at BMC. Sixty-two percent of the charges for Medicare services to Bossier City senior citizens were incurred at hospitals in Shreveport. Of every dollar spent on healthcare for senior citizens in Bossier City, sixty-two cents went across the river to Shreveport hospitals.

9. To this day, I cannot understand why the city planners did not attempt to get to the root cause for their decreases in patient support. This fact alone should have prompted the city council to support the plan of Willis-Knighton, or some other hospital system, to bring a full-service tertiary level hospital to Bossier City through a management arrangement, lease or purchase of Bossier Medical Center. This action would have enabled BMC to recruit the additional primary care and specialty physicians needed to ensure its future growth and survival.

10. In the mid-1990s BMC's personnel expenses were out of line compared to those of other hospitals in the region, as some councilmen used the hospital's jobs for political favors. This political cronyism routine of pressuring BMC's management to hire their constituents, regardless of the needs of the hospital, produced a ratio of full-time employees per patient day that was more than double that of WK. At the same time inpatient admissions were in decline between 1983 and 1993, the number of BMC employees increased by 129 percent, more than doubling. BMC's net income plummeted from $4,147,908 to $1,417,143. It should be pointed out that its patient admissions and income were declining years before WK's entry into Bossier City.

11. Ignoring BMC's declining financial position, a long-tenured city councilman said, "This is a dead issue. The council has made up

their mind that the hospital is fixable," while another stated "the city no longer belongs in the hospital business" (*Shreveport Times*, August 25, 1994). Five years later, upon the receipt of continuing devastating financial information that led eventually to BMC's sale to Schumpert, the first councilman said, "We accepted [financial] information as true. We didn't worry. That's why we have auditors. What's to make us think that what was being said wasn't true?" (*Shreveport Times*, April 14, 1999)

12. Requests from the BMC medical staff to the city council were frequently dismissed as trivial or unnecessary. Physicians were often treated by the council with open and hostile disdain rather than with the respect and appreciation they deserved. Numerous media articles by physicians were published over the years in an effort to discourage the politicians from interfering with BMC's operation and looting the hospital's treasury. One councilman said, "If the thirty-five doctors choose to not refer or practice at BMC any longer, that would be fine with us; and if the other two are disgruntled, maybe they should consider transferring to Willis-Knighton. Contrary to their belief, they are not the only doctors in town" (*Shreveport Times*, August 26, 1994). However, I must point out that the thirty-seven disgruntled doctors were over two-thirds of the BMC active medical staff members with offices in the city. Two of the council members, Colonel Reginald Adams, a retired Air Force officer, and Dr. Jimmy Rogers, a well-known dentist in the city, were exceptions to that behavior. Both of these respected citizens were supportive of the BMC physicians and its administrator, willing to listen to and objectively consider any of their requests.

13. A few medical staff members had political clout and the ear of some of the elected officials. Some were involved in financial deals with the hospital and received what was, in my opinion, out-of-line compensation as medical consultants and hospital-based physicians. The contracts of these politically connected physicians were at much higher rates than those of the same positions at WK, a hospital with much greater volume.

14. Bossier City and Bossier Parish were in a growth mode unsurpassed in the state: many new residents moved from Shreveport because of land availability and the large numbers of new houses offered at reasonable prices. It appeared that Bossier Medical Center did not have the financial resources to build facilities and add new services for the expanding population. Its campus was landlocked in an area that was rapidly becoming a nightmare of traffic congestion. As the city moved north of Interstate 220 and farther from the BMC campus, I saw an inducement for a competitor hospital to enter the Bossier market. The farther the growing population moved (in distance) away from BMC, the greater the interest of competitors to enter the market.

15. I have been told that a question deep in the recesses of the mind of patients at a politically controlled hospital is: "Is my privacy as closely guarded in a city-owned hospital as it would be in a private hospital?" Some politicians have enemies or those they choose to keep in line; would a patient's private health information be held confidentially or divulged under pressure of politicians or the media? Often, hospital personnel who owe their positions to political favoritism feel a duty to the politicians.

16. On a number of occasions I was, officially and unofficially, requested by previous BMC boards, without compensation, to assist in their search for administrators through recommendations and contacts with candidates. I was also asked to review radiology and pathology contractual relationships of the hospital and make recommendations to the board. This small involvement on my part raised the hackles of some politicians and a few contractually favored physicians. They made it clear that they wanted no Shreveport hospital administrator involved in any way in BMC's business.

17. WK's management team was aware that the physicians in Bossier City wanted to support BMC, if possible, but to their ire some city councilmen were often heavily involved in the hospital's operations. We also knew that the older citizens of Bossier City would continue to support a home-town venture over a Shreveport hospital entering their market. But we also believed this prevailing hometown attitude would shift, in time, to one favoring more hospital and physician choices as more out of town residents moved there. These new residents, many former Shreveporters, were accustomed to having more healthcare choices of hospitals and physicians.

18. WK's management team believed that at the end of the day politics would continue to rule. At that time our team was not interested in going up against the political machine in Bossier City's government, which could make our lives miserable through issues of zoning and building permits, fire and safety inspections and others. If we built a hospital in the city, we were never fully convinced that requests of emergency patients choosing to be transported to our facility for emergency care would be honored by the fire department's EMS (this fear later materialized at the time WK Bossier was opened). History had shown that some Bossier City politicians would do everything within their power to keep a Shreveport hospital, or any other, from moving onto their turf. They viewed healthcare in their city as their right to an inherited market, without threat of competition (and certainly not competition from across the Red River).

Considering those observations, with special emphasis placed on the last concern, the highly charged political environment in the city, our management team made the decision in the late 1980s that Willis-Knighton would stay out of the Bossier City market for the time being. For several years WK chose to confine its activities to enhancing the healthcare services for Shreveport's inner city and neighborhoods in west and southwest parts of the city to the exclusion of Bossier City and its parish. By 1993, WK had achieved parity with Schumpert in patient volume and market share for the first time in history.

However, it was difficult to just sit idly across the river and watch the slow demise of Bossier Medical Center, which I believed was not due to the actions of its physicians. In my opinion, the city council's dictatorial management style, acts of political favoritism and periodic confiscation of BMC's assets were responsible for the hospital's declining finances and patient volume. A majority of councilmen continued to treat their hospital's physicians with contempt, never hesitating to publicly rebuke them as well. The physicians became the public whipping boys of some politicians while the hospital's patient admissions continued to decline from the early 1980s to the mid-1990s. Few new doctors wanted to enter practice there.

Never Say Never

In late 1993, a physician claiming to represent a large number of the physicians on the BMC medical staff contacted me to request a meeting. Shortly after, a delegation from BMC met with WK's chief financial officer, medical director and me in our board room.

The physicians expressed their frustration with the city's long-time political manipulation of the affairs of the hospital and their concern that their hospital would never reach its full potential as long as these conditions existed. The physicians extended an invitation to our health system, coupled with their pledge of support, to enter the Bossier market. Two of the physicians said that some of BMC's management team should be replaced. I made it quite clear that I would not agree to request the resignation of David Bird, BMC's respected administrator, or Ellen Kyle, BMC's nursing director, going so far as to say that if such terminations were required for the physicians' support, then that demand was a deal-breaker. In my opinion, these BMC officials were only acting at the behest of the city council and were qualified and experienced hospital executives, and BMC was lucky to have their services.

The physicians recommended that WK enter the Bossier City market by assuming the operation of the hospital through some business arrangement. Three ideas for WK's involvement were discussed:

1. A management agreement with the city paying WK $1 a year
2. A lease of the BMC plant and operations from the city with WK paying $1 a year
3. A purchase of the BMC plant and operations from the city

   (Proposals 1 and 2 ensured that all profits from the operation would be shared with the city with income guarantees that greatly exceeded BMC's current profitability.)

After a review and discussion of the pros and cons of those courses of action, one of the Bossier Medical Center surgeons threw a verbal grenade into the group's discussion by posing a course of action that would start a hospital war in Bossier City if agreed to by WK representatives. If the city council and mayor rejected the three options, the grenade was this:

4. Willis-Knighton would enter the market by building a new hospital in Bossier City, provided there was assurance by a majority of the BMC physicians that they would support the move through public endorsements and relocate their offices to the proposed facility. It was a consensus of the group that this option should not be publicly announced, for it would wave a red flag of threat in the faces of the city council and mayoral staff.

That night the WK representatives understood that no matter what was proposed, we would be opening a Pandora's box of potential political conflicts with Bossier City's government. Once any of the first three strategies was pursued, there would be no turning back. Any of the first three proposals, if accepted, would turn control of the city-owned hospital over to an outside party, wresting political power from the grasp of the council and other city officials. At the same time the fourth option, building a new hospital, would be in the back of the minds of the council members, as it is impossible to keep such information confidential. This would be a call for all-out war with the city council and other government representatives of Bossier City. Imagine the gall of a Shreveport hospital, even with the endorsement and support of a majority of Bossier physicians, proposing to cross the Red River to take over BMC, and, if offers were rejected, threatening to compete in Bossier City with a new hospital: there would be war!

WK management had no problems with the first three business arrangements because, if approved by the city council, there would be no great political groundswell of opposition to WK's presence in Bossier City. A few diehards might dislike the arrangement at first, but they could be won over by positive financial outcomes offered through WK's more efficient and cost-conscious management of BMC. There was plenty of "low hanging fruit" of savings that WK could harvest. By merely reducing the ratio of employees to patients through the elimination of politically motivated hiring practices and the renegotiating of contracts of hospital-based physicians and other consultants, the hospital's financial health could be greatly improved. All three proposals would result in BMC no longer being a political hot potato and financial drain on the city coffers, but a windfall of additional funds for the Bossier City taxpayers. How could the city leaders see it any other way?

Upon the unanimous support of WK's medical staff and unanimous approval of the WK Board of Trustees, management began preparing the legal proposals for presentation to the Bossier City Council that would be required to manage, lease or purchase Bossier Medical Center. At this point, we hoped that some arrangement could be worked out to the satisfaction of the physicians in Bossier and the city officials. Even though some of the physicians were making verbal threats to city officials of a new hospital being built in the city, our management team refrained from discussing anything related to that possibility. It was our desire to manage, lease or purchase Bossier Medical Center. It made no sense for WK to taunt the city council. However, we were prepared to honor our commitment to the Bossier physicians by moving to the fourth option if our offers were rejected.

Thirty-nine physicians on the active medical staff of BMC signed a petition to the city council urging that an arrangement be worked out with WK. Early in this process of entreaty, several BMC physicians openly discussed relocating their practices to Willis-Knighton Medical Center in Shreveport, but our staff discouraged them from doing so. At no time in the deliberations were threats used in an effort to intimidate the non-signing physicians or council members. No efforts were in play to build a competing hospital in Bossier City before all avenues to partner with the city hospital were exhausted.

Three of the physicians who had initially supported some WK involvement in BMC's operations were offered attractive bonuses and compensation packages to stay with BMC. No one could fault them for accepting these generous offers.

After some time of waiting for an official acceptance or rejection of our offers from the city council and after hearing of the bonuses being paid some physicians by BMC, WK's management decided to play it safe by approaching the owners of several large parcels of land fronting I-220 and Airline Drive, to see what land might be available to us. No legal action was taken. The owners of the land also hoped that the city council would accept one of WK's offers for partnership. All hopes were dashed when it was verbally relayed to us that the city council had no intention of considering any offers from WK. We were never granted the courtesy of presenting our proposals to the council.

It was reported that, with the exception of Colonel Reginald Adams and Dr. Jimmy Rogers, the Bossier City Council was angry at WK and unwilling to consider our offers to manage, lease or purchase BMC, which forced our fourth option into action: the purchase of land on I-220 and the building of a new hospital in Bossier City. It was inconceivable to me that the city council was not willing to even consider our first two offers, which would have guaranteed the city more profits than had been generated by BMC in its best years. Even more unbelievable was the unwillingness of the city council to meet with WK's management team or the BMC physicians at any time to review our offers. The WK team was quite disheartened with the turn of events.

Looking back with a more objective eye, I see that the city council's rejection of

WK's offers was the best thing that could have happened to our health system. Working with the city council under a management or lease arrangement would have been a nightmare. Political pressures would have continued for job placements and confiscations of revenue through forced renegotiations of contracts. We knew the price we offered for BMC, $37 million for land, buildings and equipment excluding BMC's cash, accounts receivable and inventories, was greater than its true value. It was hoped that this gesture of a generous offer would encourage acceptance of WK's operation of BMC from the owners of the hospital, the taxpayers, and a feeling of goodwill with the city leaders. So much for unrealistic thinking!

In an effort to open a new hospital at the earliest date, WK administrators took most of the Bossier physicians who had committed to a move to WK Bossier on trips to Baton Rouge to tour and evaluate Baton Rouge General Health's new Bluebonnet satellite hospital. The design was well received by the physicians. Willis-Knighton Health System purchased the plans for the Bluebonnet hospital from General Health for a most reasonable price, made possible by Chris Barnette, the administrator. WK engaged the architect of record of the Baton Rouge hospital to manage the project and to make required design changes. The low bidder on the project was the contractor that had built the Bluebonnet project. These actions accelerated the project.

During the construction of the new hospital, there were constant public barrages of false and misleading information from some city council members as if they were in denial of the fact that WK Bossier Health Center was going to be a reality. On July 14, 1996, the $90 million WK Bossier Health Center campus opened after a construction time of eighteen months. An attached four-story medical office building was totally leased by physicians at the time of opening. The WK Wellness Center on the east side of the campus had been opened to the public in January of that year.

At the time of opening of WK Bossier, I prepared an inventory of the favorable things that were now available to residents of Bossier City as a result of the city council's refusal of our offers.

Willis-Knighton Bossier (top), opened in 1996 and serves as the only full-service acute care hospital for the 116,000 citizens of Bossier Parish. Rivaling that of a luxury hotel, the atrium at Bossier (above) set a new precedent of aesthetic appeal for Shreveport/Bossier City hospitals.

Even as the foundation cured and steel was being erected naysayers on the Bossier City council continued to profess that no new hospital was being built, because Elrod's "bluffing" (Shreveport Times, *October 7, 1994).*

WK Bossier Medical and Surgical Pavilion (top left), at 140,000 square feet, is the region's largest outpatient facility. It houses physician offices, outpatient surgery, lab, imaging and rehabilitation facilities; WK Bossier Wellness Center (top right), was the first facility to open on campus (January 1996). The expansive WK Bossier Medical Center fronts Interstate 220 from Airline Drive to Benton Road, two of Bossier City's busiest traffic corridors (bottom).

1. WK Bossier Health Center opens a new, aesthetically pleasing building with a modern functional design on a large, highly visible campus fronting on I-220.

2. Traffic around WK Bossier's campus flows well, and drivers have rapid access from I-220, Airline Drive and Benton Road, major local thoroughfares.

3. WK Bossier is closer than any other hospital to the fastest growing residential neighborhoods north of I-220.

4. There is space on the WK Bossier campus for future growth of the hospital, physician offices and other services.

5. WK Bossier's equipment is of the latest generation.

6. The cost of this new hospital building is not much greater than WK's offered price to purchase BMC plus the additional land purchases and renovations that the existing BMC building would have required.

7. WK Bossier Health Center, a new hospital, will not have to rid itself of BMC's negative image as related to city politics.

8. There will be no involvement of Bossier City's government in the daily life of WK Bossier and, more importantly, no confiscation of its assets.

9. WK Bossier opens with employees from other WK hospitals and new recruits without ties to the city-owned hospital and its poor work ethic (prompted by political cronyism). Only a handful of former BMC employees have sought employment with our hospital; our game plan was not to target that hospital's employees.

10. The WK Bossier Wellness Center, a state-of-the-art facility and an added feature of the new campus, would not have been possible to place on the crowded BMC campus. This is the city's first hospital health and fitness complex.

11. The only competitor hospital in the city is BMC, unfortunately a hospital with a limited future. This is attributable to the limited vision of a majority of the city councilmen's lack of knowledge of hospital operations, absence of respect and admiration for physicians, a desire to continue "good ole boy politics" and a desire to continue meddling in BMC's daily operations.

WK Bossier Health Center, our second satellite hospital, enjoyed a tremendous outpouring of support from the citizens of Bossier City and Parish in spite of the negative attitudes of some city politicians. This support was the catalyst for the hospital's growth and success in recruiting of primary care physicians and specialists. From the first month of its operation, WK Bossier posted a positive cash flow, and financial successes continue.

As BMC admissions and profitability waned and as employees were losing their jobs due to the opening of WK Bossier, I made the decision to again approach the city council. This request was in the interest of WK's acquisition of BMC for the express purpose of converting it to the region's first free-standing, full-service rehabilitation hospital, and hopefully saving hundreds of jobs. The council was unwilling to even entertain this offer while BMC employees were being terminated in large numbers.

Years later, after Schumpert Medical Center purchased BMC, I was even more thankful that the Bossier City Council had rejected our offers. Why? If Willis-Knighton had succeeded in securing some arrangement with BMC, our health system would now be locked into the multitude of negative conditions and issues that now face the BMC campus as an acute care hospital. In its present location and present configuration (replete with numerous ill-planned additions and outdated nursing units) the old BMC campus was not ideal for running a modern and efficient medical center. And I venture to guess that Schumpert, or some other competitor, would now be ensconced on our present campus or somewhere else in north Bossier—much to our consternation—while we would be pondering how to keep the forty-five-plus-year-old BMC hospital open.

I remember my parents' advice: "Sometimes God answers your prayers by not giving you what you prayed for." In the case of BMC, God certainly had something much better in mind for WK.

WK Pierremont: Satellite Number Three The Death Star

Man's mind, once stretched by a new idea,

never regains its original dimension.

Oliver Wendell Holmes Jr. (1841-1935)

In the late 1960s, shortly after my arrival in Shreveport, I had dreams of one day building a WK hospital on the cotton fields of southeast Shreveport. As neighbors and friends in this area told me that they would like to support me by going to WK, but that it was too far across town, this vision became more pronounced. However, our hospital was in dire financial straits at that time and unable to undertake this venture. I shared my dream with Dr. Albert Bicknell, one of my best friends, a loyal and visionary physician at Willis-Knighton, and we kept it alive in our hearts and minds over the years. On one occasion we shared this dream and discussed possible locations with WK's board chairman.

Believe it or not, the property that is now dominated by the massive, nine-floor WK Pierremont Health Center and Tower, the WK Pierremont Medical Arts Building and the WK Portico Medical Mall was my original choice of sites for the campus. At that time, this and surrounding properties fronting on Highway 1 were farmed for cotton and soybeans, with few businesses nearby.

As residents of southeast Shreveport, Dr. Bicknell and I recognized the need for a full-service hospital in this area and its potential for success. At that time there were no physician specialists with offices in this section of the city. The distance from these neighborhoods to the nearest full-service hospital, Schumpert, would assure the success of a full-service, acute care hospital with emergency services supported by physician specialists. We believed that only our lack of money stood in the way of a successful WK hospital in southeast Shreveport.

Some twenty years later, Highland Hospital and Clinic made the move to this medically underserved area. Dr. Bicknell and I were confident that this new hospital and clinic would be extremely successful. We were disappointed that WK could not be the first hospital out there, but we were happy that the area would now have a hospital. We shared the strong belief that the only shortcoming of the newly announced project was the clinic's reluctance to encourage physician specialists, other than those wishing to join their clinic to practice at their new hospital. It was well known that physician sub-specialists preferred to partner only with other physicians of their specialty, rather than join a multi-specialty clinic, such as Highland, with higher shared overhead. Keeping this concern in mind, our management team chose instead to concentrate on our locations in central and southwest Shreveport and eventually in Bossier City. But our dream was never forgotten.

Shortly before the official opening of WK Bossier Health Center in 1996, rumors began to surface that a joint venture between Schumpert Medical Center and the Highland Hospital and Highland Clinic, with a staff of approximately forty physicians, had been consummated. This rumor was substantiated by a *Shreveport Times* article alluding to both Schumpert's and Highland's determination to remain the dominant market forces in southeast Shreveport.

This joint venture, the North Louisiana Hospital Physicians Organization (NLH-PO), with increased numbers of physician participants from the Highland Clinic, was successfully, albeit not wisely, executing managed care contracts at below market reimbursement rates, which reduced the physicians' annual earnings. At the time, Schumpert held a commanding market share of approximately 70 percent of southeast Shreveport's hospital admissions. Combined with Highland's 13 percent, the new venture's market share would further enhance and secure their dominant position (WK's paltry market share was 13 percent).

It was believed this joint venture and its below-market reimbursement contracts were the strategies Schumpert was using to counter the scheduled opening of WK Bossier Health Center and its anticipated losses of patients previously referred to Schumpert by Bossier City physicians. Any further loss of patients by Schumpert would impact their existing parity of patient admissions with WK, further reducing their market share. Highland Hospital's owner, Columbia-HCA, had announced plans for the construction of another medical office building at the intersection of 70th Street and Fern.

After learning of this joint venture, WK's chief financial officer, medical director, physician network director and I were granted a meeting with the executive committee of Highland Clinic. Our team voiced puzzlement about why the clinic was planning to partner with its only active competitor in the area. Schumpert had operated an urgent care clinic and a multi-specialty physician office building a block west of the Highland Hospital for a number of years.

It was widely known in the medical community that Schumpert specialists, upon referral of patients from the clinic, made every effort to keep those patients at their inner-city hospital. We pointed out that WK had never attempted to compete with the clinic, going so far as to encourage our employed network physicians with offices in southeast Shreveport to refer patients to their clinic and the Highland hospital (in the interest of not having their patients travel greater distances for care at a WK facility). Dr. Bicknell told the committee that this concession was not well received by all staff physicians of the WK hospitals, but that it was the right thing to do.

The clinic representatives, while cordial, informed us that they had no interest in working with our health system because of their close personal and social relationships and frequent golf outings with the Schumpert physicians. We thanked them for their time and departed via a route that took us to the present WK Pierremont site. Dr. Bicknell said, "Jim, maybe it's time our dream became a reality."

One question continued to plague me: why had Highland Hospital, with its quality Highland Clinic physicians, not been more successful in its prime southeast Shreveport location? I concluded that the hospital's slow growth (only 13 percent market share after a number of years in this area) could be attributed to its image—that of a less than full service acute care hospital without a full spectrum of physician specialists and subspecialists with offices on campus. The hospital's for-profit mentality and operation did little to fortify its image. In my opinion, the hospital's less than stellar growth over a decade had to be intricately tied to the unwillingness or inability of the clinic to grow its physician membership and not attributable to their location. On the contrary, our team believed the hospital and clinic locations were ideal.

However, I was certain of one thing: the building and operation of the Highland Clinic in this area of the city had turned out to be a unique opportunity for WK. Highland Hospital's presence, though not a full-service facility, had served to lull the management of Schumpert into believing that as long as it continued to be Highland's partner and referral hospital, no other hospital would dare to compete by locating in this area.

Schumpert authorities believed they would not have to expend millions of dollars to build a full-service hospital in the neighborhood because the agreement with Highland Clinic and Hospital would keep another full-service hospital from entering the market. For years, Highland Clinic had discouraged other physicians from locating in southeast Shreveport. A higher ratio of patients to physicians existed in the area than other parts of the city. Further impacting these emergency care scenarios was the fact that there was only one fire station (without EMS services) in this area. (Later, the construction of WK Pierremont prompted the opening of new stations. The Port of Shreveport-Bossier fire station was financially supported by the Willis-Knighton Health System.)

The overwhelming fact that this affluent and educated section of the city was a medically underserved area accompanied by the continuing time delays for access to acute emergency care (cardiac and neurosurgery) were primary drivers of WK's decision to build a new hospital in southeast Shreveport–hence the genesis of WK Pierremont.

Returning to my office, I listed the following reasons that WK should enter the southeast Shreveport market with a new hospital:

1. There was a shortage of physician specialists and sub-specialists with offices in southeast Shreveport. Patients seeking this care often had to travel to midtown or farther.

2. The small number of physician specialists in the area restricted the ability of the Highland Hospital emergency department to treat patients requiring some specialty and subspecialty care in a timely manner. As this fact became known, residents continued to seek care at Schumpert or, to a lesser degree, at WK facilities. We believed these facts would create a groundswell of support for a WK full-ser-

vice, acute care, not-for-profit hospital in the area. (Former Highland primary care physicians stressed that their patients often needed to be transported to other hospitals for physician specialty care.)

3. The response times of the city's EMS to residents of southeast Shreveport were longer than to most areas of the city because the nearest response team was at a fire station in the midtown area.

4. The lack of a significant WK presence in southeast Shreveport was the reason for our low market penetration in inpatient hospital admissions and occupational medicine contracts.

5. Residents of this area displayed a geocentric mindset toward other sections of the city and were therefore reluctant to cross town to WK hospitals for healthcare. This unwillingness hurt WK's ability to recruit physician specialists to this area because their patients would resist traveling to the distant WK sites for hospitalization.

6. Southeast Shreveport was the only remaining major population growth area without a significant WK presence. This area had favorable demographics of population growth, income levels, education and age distribution.

7. The requirement of managed care companies to include Highland Hospital for the convenience of their enrollees, due to lack of other hospitals in the area, was prompted by the requests of large numbers of the city's business owners and managers who resided in southeast parts of the city. Sometimes these requests cut WK out of HMO contracts altogether.

8. A WK hospital near Louisiana State University-Shreveport would have opportunities for synergistic linking with the university's health administration program.

9. The recruitment of physicians from Schumpert would be quite successful because of some physicians' disillusionment with their hospital's loss of direction and momentum and "revolving door" administrators. The overhead of the Highland Clinic would entice some of its physicians to relocate to the new WK hospital and the WK Physician Network.

10. A large senior citizen residential and nursing home population within minutes of WK Pierremont's proposed site offered opportunities for senior initiatives in the community.

11. A hospital in this area would provide better access for the growing numbers of military retirees and their families living in south Bossier and southeast Shreveport. At the time WK was not a participant in the Champus program. Champus had an exclusive arrangement with

the Schumpert/Highland NLHPO, due to our lack of a hospital and an adequate number of physicians in that area of the city.

12. A new WK hospital in southeast Shreveport would have little impact on the present business of WK hospitals or its physicians due to travel distances between them.

13. Without a WK hospital in southeast Shreveport, a potential buyout or merger of Schumpert with Highland Hospital, or vice versa, would give either of our surviving competitors a distinct market advantage as the only game in that part of town. This scenario came to fruition with Schumpert's purchase of Highland Hospital in 2000. WK refrained from making offers to purchase Highland Hospital due to the potential evoking of anti-trust issues.

14. WK Pierremont would constitute an offensive move on our part to gain new market share while forcing defensive moves on the part of Schumpert and Highland to retain theirs.

15. WK's high profile image of philanthropic giving to worthy causes and community services would assist in developing acceptance and support for its new hospital from residents of this civic-minded community in southeast Shreveport.

16. The presence of a Willis-Knighton hospital in southeast Shreveport would benefit the growth and enrollment of WK's managed care products.

17. WK's employed network of physicians would be provided an entrée into this section of the city with convenient office locations and support from a full-service emergency department with subspecialist physician coverage.

The Death Star is Coming!

Upon the announcement of plans for WK Pierremont, there was a great deal of discussion about the impact it would have on the health of residents of southeast Shreveport, most people saying that the new hospital would be an exceptional asset to the area. Even physicians and employees of competitors in the area said that the "death star" was coming, for they believed it would have a devastating impact on other city hospitals, especially Schumpert and Highland. I was characterized as Darth Vader, because I had chosen to build a facility to provide care for this medically underserved section of our city and dared to challenge the market dominance of other less responsive hospitals.

In 1997, less than one year after the opening of the WK Bossier Health Center, unanimous approval was given by our board of trustees, supported by the executive committee of the medical staff, to build our third satellite hospital in southeast Shreveport. I approached the owners of the property we had chosen at the intersection of Highway 1 and Bert Kouns Industrial Drive. They were in the process of negotiating its sale to a strip mall shopping center developer, but had not finalized the deal. Our plans for the property were presented to them. The owners then agreed to sell it to Willis-Knighton because they believed our project would have a far greater impact on the quality of lives of the residents of southeast Shreveport than a strip shopping center. Another party excited about this project was our next-door neighbor, Louisiana State University-Shreveport.

On a napkin at Don's Seafood Restaurant, I drew the basic conceptual design of the proposed hospital, which included a massive lobby with escalator, water features and mezzanines connecting a physician office tower to a hospital patient tower.

My wife encouraged me to take a portion of the first floor of the physician office tower, near the lobby, for an exercise center with swimming pool to convey a sense of health and wellness. This off-lobby wellness center and physician offices on the same floor as hospitalized patients were features seldom found in hospitals.

The major mistake I made in planning this hospital was to undersize it by limiting the number of beds to seventy-five on four floors and the physician tower to five floors, which I had to correct during construction. The success of our physician recruiting efforts made the changes necessary.

The financing for WK Pierremont was made possible by the strong financial performances of WK Medical Center and its satellites, WK South and WK Bossier, which had exceeded our expectations by generating strong cash flows.

Our board chairman asked what I planned to name the new facility. I told him that I thought WK Pierremont Health Center would be a great name. This life-long resident of Shreveport laughingly said, “But, Jim, that area of the city is not thought of by Shreveporters as Pierremont.” I answered, “After this beautiful hospital is opened, it will be.” Today, it is viewed as the heart of Pierremont.

WK Pierremont was at first undersized based on the number of physicians we were recruiting. Our expectations for the recruitment were far exceeded, as large numbers of Schumpert and Highland physicians were interested in relocating their offices to the new hospital.

The health system’s physician network of employed providers was a strong catalyst for physician relocations. Many of the recruited physicians were disappointed with their chosen hospitals, for a multitude of reasons. The Schumpert physicians, many of them employed providers, were disillusioned with their hospital’s loss of mission, heavy-handed corporate tactics and turnover of administrators; but most of all, they were irritated because they had been forced to accept the below-market reimbursement rates of Schumpert’s NLPHO, which had reduced their incomes by as much as 30 percent with no increase in patient volumes.

The soaring numbers of physicians recruited to WK Pierremont forced management to rethink its size and services. Architects were instructed to double the hospital’s bed capacity by building an eight-floor patient tower and to increase physician office space by taking the five-story office building up to nine floors. This revamp of the hospital plant and increased square footage dictated a need for additional parking places, which in turn forced a movement of the hospital’s original footprint back an additional two hundred feet from Youree Drive.

Further complicating this move was the bentonite wall, a 3-foot-wide, 75-foot-deep water retention barrier to control ground water around the underground basement and parking garage. This wall, the first in the area, was required because it was discovered while drilling piers for the foundation that the hospital was being built over an underground tributary of the Red River. Luckily, the barrier wall had not been completed on the east and west sides of the project, so design changes did not slow the project.

One fly in our ointment concerning the enlargement of the hospital was the requirement for land to permit additional parking and perimeter streets around the hospital. The problem: the land we needed was in the process of being donated by two wonderful gentlemen to the LSU Health Shreveport Foundation. The Feist brothers, Malcolm and Carroll, owned the land, which they had farmed for decades. They were two of the most generous philanthropists in the state, and after the death of Malcolm, their estates were being left to the LSU medical school and its Feist-Weiller Cancer Center.

Sonny Moss, one of our administrators, was a good friend of Carroll Feist and arranged a lunch with him. Our team, Robert Huie, Dr. Albert Bicknell, Sonny Moss and I met with Feist and presented our plight, the need for additional land to accommodate our expanded hospital. He listened to our offer to pay the market rate for twelve acres of his land. In a most gentlemanly manner, he informed us that he did not have any land for sale, but that he would consider our request.

This wealthy gentleman added, "Jim, this delicious steak you served me is entirely too large for my lunch. May I have a doggie bag to take it home?" A few days later he informed Sonny Moss that he wanted to help our cause by selling the land to us. He did not mention a price, just related that it would be reasonable, so we held our breath that it would be at or near market value. He offered the land to WK well below the price of comparable land selling in the area and less, much less, than we had anticipated. On a number of occasions after that transaction, Feist told me that he could think of no better use of his land than the site for our hospital in southeast Shreveport.

At this point in the story, I must admit that both Dr. Bicknell and my wife had championed the idea of taking the building up to a minimum of twelve floors to accommodate the second and third waves of physicians who would eventually desire to practice at WK Pierremont. They had great faith that this hospital was going to be more successful than I had dreamed possible. And they were proven right!

In our defense, Robert Huie, CFO, and I were not short on faith regarding the hospital's success; we were just being pragmatic about the money needed to enlarge the project. Honestly, in the back of our bean-counter minds, we knew we could always go back with an addition to the hospital if it were that successful, and we did so a year later.

Willis-Knighton Pierremont (above at right), opened in 1999, is located on one of the busiest intersections in the state. The nine-floor, full-service acute care facility is a landmark in southeast Shreveport. The medical pavilion is seen in the background and the Portico Medical Mall is seen at left. Each of the WK facilities is on a major intersection.

As seen from the Medical Arts Building, the pediatric pavilion (center) at WK Pierremont was built to meet an increasing need for pediatric care in ever-growing southeast Shreveport.

Willis-Knighton Pierremont atrium (above) and tower addition of 2002 (below, center).

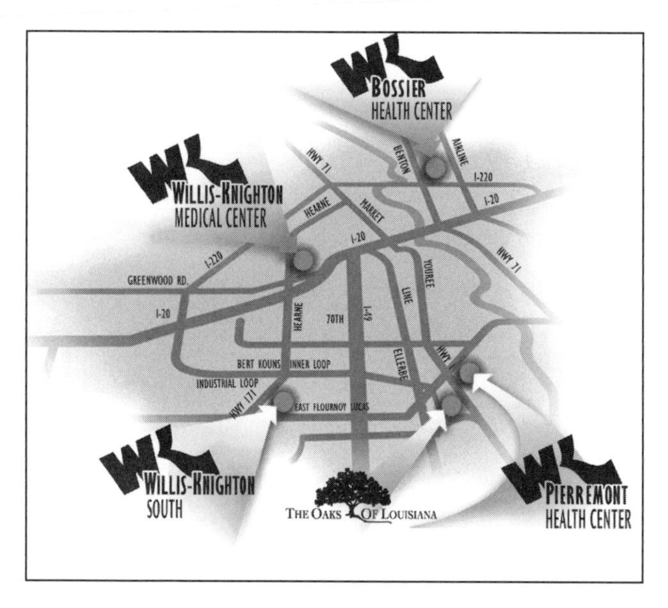

There is a WK emergency room within 8 minutes of every household in Shreveport Bossier City. All of these emergency rooms operate under the competent leadership of Susan Cash, R.N. a 30-year veteran of WK.

The six-floor tower at Pierremont was built to connect to the main hospital elevator core for seamless traffic flow. The tower opened in 2002 to accommodate 80 additional beds, two cardiac catheterization labs, ICU, GI lab and an infusion therapy unit. Since opening, WK Pierremont has never failed to be profitable. Its phenomenal growth has placed it in a position to one day rival WK North, our flagship hospital in admissions. Pierremont's emergency department continues as one of the busiest around, attesting that prior to its opening, southeast Shreveporters were underserved in emergency situations.

A Field of Dreams: We Built Them and They Did Come

The three satellite hospitals of the Willis-Knighton Health System have proved to be the right strategy for us, as they continue to serve metropolitan Shreveport/Bossier

City. They are feeder hospitals for referrals of tertiary level patients (those requiring a higher degree of medical and surgical sub-specialists' care) to Willis-Knighton Medical Center, the flagship hospital, that enable it to remain in its inner-city neighborhood, providing not only quality patient care but also jobs within walking distance of several inner-city neighborhoods. At the same time WK satellites are providing emergency and inpatient care for their respective suburban neighborhoods.

There is a WK hospital, with full emergency services, within eight minutes of every resident of Shreveport and Bossier City. These "hub and spoke" hospitals provide a sophisticated and coordinated lifeline of health services not often found in cities of our size. In addition to eliminating unnecessary duplication of services, these hospitals reduce healthcare costs through access to a multitude of cost-effective practices, thereby providing healthcare technology and services seldom found outside of nationally recognized university teaching hospitals.

Thankfully our major competitor had spent over 25 years relying on their "broken glass theory of patient loyalty" and missed out on chances to have continued their over 40-year dominance as north Louisiana's largest hospital.

Rural Hospitals Support the Satellite Model

During the period of 1983 to the present another important component of our satellite (hub and spoke) model was the inclusion of rural hospitals. A first for our region, WK took over management of an area hospital, the DeSoto Regional Medical Center in Mansfield, Louisiana, at the invitation of its trustees and medical staff. Later, the North Caddo Medical Center in Vivian, Louisiana, and the Springhill Medical Center in Springhill, Louisiana, joined our network of managed hospitals. Each of these hospitals serves as a critical access facility with referral patterns to WK.

Anecdote:
A Crystal Ball or Just Plain Lucky?

A story of clairvoyance or just plain luck is that of our director of nursing at Willis-Knighton Medical Center. It began in the early 1980s.

Upon the announcement of the building of our first satellite, South Park Hospital (WK South and Women's Center), Debbie Olds, R.N. (nursing supervisor), approached me and asked to become involved in the planning and opening of the new hospital. Thinking that Mrs. Olds lived near our existing campus, I commented that the distance from her home to the new hospital campus was several miles. Her response was, "I moved a few years ago to a subdivision near the site of the planned hospital." I granted her request.

In 1994, upon the groundbreaking of WK Bossier, Mrs. Olds approached me with a request to become involved in the planning of WK Bossier Health Center. Thinking that she still lived near WK South, I mentioned that the distance from her home to the new hospital was over twelve miles. Her retort was, "Three years ago, I moved to a subdivision adjacent to the site of the new Bossier hospital." I agreed to her request.

A year after the opening of WK Bossier, we announced the building of a third satellite hospital, WK Pierremont Health Center in southeast Shreveport. For the third time, Mrs. Olds approached me asking to become involved in the new facility. Thinking that she lived near WK Bossier, I commented that the distance from her home to our planned hospital in southeast Shreveport was over twelve miles. Her retort was, "After completing my assignment at the Bossier hospital, I moved to a subdivision near WK Pierremont." For the third time, I agreed to reassign her to a new satellite hospital project.

After these three experiences, one would surely think that Mrs. Olds' clairvoyant power of perceiving the locations of Willis-Knighton's satellite hospitals before management did was at an end.

Not so! A public announcement was made that Live Oak Retirement Community was being donated to our health system. This prompted Mrs. Olds to approach me with a request to become involved in the transitioning of these facilities and the addition of hospice and home health services to this campus. In an attempt to add humor to this request, I responded, "Don't tell me that you have moved again." She answered, "You won't believe this, but about two years ago I moved into a new subdivision adjacent to the Live Oak property." Again, I agreed to her temporary assignment to the project.

The lesson I learned from these experiences was that sometimes real-life events are more bizarre than fiction. And the health system could save a bundle of money on market research the next time we contemplate an expansion of services. Perhaps we should just ask Mrs. Olds where she is living at the time, since all of our satellite locations have been exceptionally successful. It should be pointed out that none of those projects were on our radar screens of planning, much less on the drawing boards of our architects, at the times Mrs. Olds was relocating.

Strategy 15:
Recycling at its Best

Skylight the hell out of it!

James K. Elrod (author)

I have been married to a "tree hugger" for many years, and recycling is a way of life in our household. The separation of paper, glass and plastic items is a daily chore. What our health system has been doing for over forty years is in essence the recycling of bricks and mortar. At WK, we believe a little love and a lot of skylights go a long way to dress up an old building.

WK has long been in the business of converting commercial properties into physician offices and other health delivery services at a fraction of the cost of new construction. By remodeling, we eliminate costs of water, sewer and electrical infrastructure, parking and other expenses of new construction projects. An added benefit of older remodeled properties is the lower property appraisals by tax assessors compared to values placed on new facilities of the same sizes.

The lower investments associated with renovations permit rents that are more economical for both solo practitioners and groups. To a physician this rental expense may provide savings of 20 to 40 percent over new construction rates, which lowers office expenses.

The purchase of the 820 Jordan Building in the mid-1980s gave us a new idea for the leasing of physician office space: we buy recently vacated commercial and retail space, and sewerage and water, utilities and parking are included at a cost of pennies on the dollar. After renovation these spaces can be leased for less than the rates of new buildings. These lower rents have been a major attraction for recruiting physicians to our Physician Network, which was then in the planning stages. The retrofitted Bone and Joint Building on Line Avenue is about equidistant from WK's four campuses, making it the perfect spot for the central business offices of our network of over 350 physicians. A former physicians' office on Line Avenue, near downtown, was a convenient and high-profile location for Health Plus.

Most of the recycled buildings were located on our expanding campuses or within a block of them, with the exception of those near the campus of our major competitor. The 120,000 square feet of the 820 Jordan Building gave Willis-Knighton an opportunity to open offices for physician specialists near our competitor's primary care physicians, thereby garnering referrals to our health system. This building is a five-floor structure: the east wall faces Line Avenue, a main artery, and is a perfect backdrop for a large lighted sign to advertise Willis-Knighton with a WK logo.

To share a little humor, I have been accused of buying church properties so I could have my own church, or bully pulpit, from which to pontificate. At least I hope the folks were joking. Fortunately for WK physicians and employees, all of the purchased church sanctuaries have been razed.

The Willis-Knighton Construction Company

WK's wholly-owned construction company, under the directorship of Nila Willhoite and Jerry Ivey, licensed engineer, has handled the majority of the recycled building projects and a growing number of new buildings on our five campuses. This licensed construction company offers the health system a significant savings on the costs of building projects.

Willhoite, Senior Vice-President, joined the WK management team in 1981. Her keen eye for detail and cost-cutting ability in engineering projects has served our health system well, ensuring a quality product at the lowest possible price. No one is better organized when directing a construction project from conception to completion and occupancy. Since her arrival, Nila has assumed the responsibilities for all construction projects of the health system, including renovations and new construction, totaling in excess of $600 million. Her projects have spanned the gamut: from a single physician office renovation, to two new satellite hospitals (WK Bossier and WK Pierremont) with cancer, heart and eye institutes and a 270-apartment independent senior living facility in between. One of her most interesting challenges was the building of a 200-foot-long concrete bridge (two lanes with pedestrian walkway) spanning a wide bayou on the campus of The Oaks of Louisiana. Nila has now embarked on the construction of a $40 million addition to the WK Cancer Center to provide the region's first proton beam therapy unit, scheduled for installation in 2014. The following projects detail our primary recycled buildings.

Willis-Knighton Medical Center (WK North)

In the early to mid-1970s, the surrounding neighborhoods began a transition from single-family, well-maintained dwellings to multiple-resident, rental and poorly kept units, thereby becoming less attractive for businesses. It was the best of times for purchasing commercial properties, but the worst of times for the image of the neighborhood. News stories on the changing of the neighborhood created a growing perception of crime and unrest in the neighborhood.

We decided then to begin buying as much neighborhood property, commercial and residential, as the hospital could afford and using it for outpatient services and non-patient activities. This would accomplish two objectives: 1) Remove the blighted elements of the area by demolition or remodeling, which would have a positive impact on our image and 2) Save money by converting commercial structures to our use, which is less expensive than adding to the hospital. And they already had parking space (a problem since my arrival in 1965). Among the changes we made were these:

1. The campus land acreage was increased from three acres in 1965 to 165 acres by 2012.

2. A physician office was purchased to permit a cardiologist's move to one of our new condominium physician office buildings. The vacated building was remodeled for our system's human resources department. It was a block from the hospital and had a parking lot. This has been an excellent location for the health system's human resources department because its location keeps job applicants out of the hospital and off our crowded parking lots.

3. A wholesale electrical supply building became our first WK Wellness Center.

4. An A&P grocery store building became the health system's first WorkKare occupational medicine clinic.

5. A Gulf Oil service station became the system's WK Motor Pool and Service Garage for maintenance of a fleet of approximately one hundred vehicles.

6. St. Theresa Elementary Catholic School became the education building, accommodating system-wide orientations, in-service education and college courses conducted by Louisiana State University-Shreveport.[30] The church's sanctuary was razed.

7. The Pioneer Bank building with a fireproof walk-in vault became the system's central business office and storage for valuable papers of the vice president of finance.

8. Dunlop Presbyterian Church became a central pathology and reference lab.

9. A former café on campus was converted to offices and meeting space for the Queensborough Neighborhood Association, a neighborhood

30 One day I received a call from Bishop Friend, informing me that the diocese was intending to close and sell St. Theresa School. He offered the property for $1.3 million. I countered, "Yes, we are interested, but the most we would be willing to pay is $650,000." He replied instantly that "we had a deal." Inquisitively, he asked me how I knew he would settle for half the asking price. I replied, "I looked you up and found out that you were a banker in Miami before becoming a priest." He said, "That's right, you found me out!"

enhancement program under the auspices of the City of Shreveport. Fire and police emergency courses are conducted in this building. WK charges no rent for use of the building; it is included in our community benefit program.

10. A physician-owned surgery center on campus was purchased and converted into the WK Spine Institute and WK/LSU Fertility and Reproductive Center.

11. Bacon and Edwards sporting goods store became the system's paint and carpentry shop, with record storage in a portion of the building.

12. Glad Tidings Assembly of God sanctuary became an auditorium, and Sunday school classrooms were used for human resources, home health and hospice until the building was razed to accommodate parking expansion required for the WK Heart Hospital and outpatient surgery parking.

13. A restaurant appliance dealer's building became an expansion of the WK WorkKare clinic and storage.

14. A garage and service station immediately across the street from our original main entrance on Virginia Avenue became the system's first materials management facility.

15. About sixty houses near the original campus were razed to accommodate the D&S Building, Progressive Care, Medical Arts Building, Physician Commons, Cancer Center, Extended Care Unit, Heart Hospital and Institute and numerous additions to the original plant and parking lots.

16. Dozens of residential properties were purchased and razed to provide a green belt for aesthetics and security.

Willis-Knighton South and Women's Center

Canterbury Square Shopping Mall was recycled into outpatient services to relieve pressure on the crowded WK South campus. One restaurant and two fast food operations were left to provide food service for employees and patients' families within a short walking distance of the hospital. The former mall also houses outpatient physical, occupational, hand therapies and a wound care center with a twelve-patient hyperbaric medicine chamber. Physician office space on Flournoy-Lucas Road was purchased and replaced with a full-service retail pharmacy for preparation of special IVs for all of our hospitals, Quick Care, Work Kare, home health and hospice departments.

WK Pierremont Health Center

1. Youree Center Office Building (originally a commercial office building) was converted to a two-floor medical office building to accommodate twelve physicians and offices for WorkKare and Quick Care (this building is diagonally across an intersection from WK Pierremont Health Center).

2. Portico Shopping Mall had a large grocery store, a number of retail stores and a restaurant (14 acres across a main thoroughfare from the main entrance of WK Pierremont Health Center). This is now a medical mall with convenient parking for physicians and patients in storefront offices and a 144,000-square-foot Orthopaedic and Sports Medicine Clinic with orthopaedic surgeons, MRI, X-ray, lab and outpatient surgery, and physical therapy and rehabilitation with pools and indoor track plus equipment. The seven-year-old mall, including land, brick buildings and parking, was purchased for less than we paid for the same amount of vacant acreage next to our new hospital a few years later.

820 Jordan Building

This 120,000-square-foot office building with a bank on the ground floor with drive-in windows was purchased during the worst part of the oil and gas downturn in our area. IBM, the building's major tenant with approximately 20 percent of the space, was scheduled to relocate to a new office complex outside of the downtown area. The building is next door to the beautiful First Presbyterian Church of Shreveport with overflow parking available to both our building visitors and the church's congregation. The building was purchased for a fraction of its original land and construction cost. The price of the facility provided an opportunity to purchase, renovate and rent office spaces for very favorable rates compared to competitors.

Because of the high level of visibility of this building, our health system took advantage of a marketing opportunity by erecting large lighted signs with the health system's logo on the Line Avenue, Jordan Street and Stoner Street sides.

Bone and Joint and OB/GYN Clinics on Line Avenue

The 11,000-square-foot Bone and Joint Clinic building on Line Avenue was converted into a central office complex for the WK Physician Network's financial operations. This building became available upon the relocation of three orthopaedic and sports medicine physicians to the WK Bossier Health Center's Orthopaedic and Sports Medicine Center.

A former office of OB/GYN physicians on Line Avenue, a major thoroughfare to downtown, was purchased for Health Plus of Louisiana, WK's wholly-owned HMO. This office space in the heart of business and other commercial operations is central to the populations of Shreveport and Bossier City.

Pierre Avenue Clinic and Wellness Center

This early 20th century former laundry and dry cleaning building is a cornerstone of the historic St. Paul's Bottoms, a neighborhood listed on the National Register of Historic Places. Its rare original saw-tooth windows on the rooftop of the laundry processing plant on the north side of the building are reflective of lighting designs of the turn of the century. The facility was divided to accommodate three functions: medical clinic, a wellness center with exercise equipment and a computer lab for children of the neighborhood.

The wellness gym with indoor track was one of the first exercise facilities of its kind in the country to be operated in an indigent health clinic. This clinic and wellness center were built and operated by our health system at the request of a number of the churches in this inner-city area.

A few of our recycled buildings: Top left—Canterbury Square (hyperbaric medicine and physician offices); top right—820 Jordan (physician and ancillary offices); middle left—Bone and Joint Clinic (WK Physician Network); middle right—Youree Center Office Building (WorkKare and Quick Care); bottom: Portico Medical Mall (sports medicine, lab, imaging, outpatient surgery and rehabilitation).

WK's Hospice

A home on the edge of the 312-acre campus of The Oaks of Louisiana was purchased and converted to the main office of our health system's outpatient hospice service. This location is ideal because of its proximity to the largest independent living, assisted living and skilled nursing home developments in this region. This facility provides office and supply space for the entire staff. They provide end-of-life support to patients in their homes and skilled nursing homes at a lower cost than inpatient hospice units.

The Manor—Cultural and Education Center

A beautiful mansion of English Tudor design, built in the early 1920s, was renovated as a center for cultural and educational events. The three-acre grounds are centrally located to LSU Health Shreveport, Schumpert Medical Center and Willis-Knighton Medical Center. The facility is often used to entertain elected officials who are in town to hold news conferences. Not-for-profit organizations are eligible to use the facility. A number of WK's administrative residents have been housed in the carriage house apartment.

This central-city facility was purchased for $245,000 and renovated for $120,000, and the health system has been offered more than $1 million on a number of occasions for its use as a private residence. It has been the feeling of the health system leaders that this historical treasure should remain in the domain of public ownership, protection and use.

A beautiful English Tudor residence dating to the 1920s, the manor has been transformed into a multi-use community meeting, education and cultural center. Interior renovations were done with a careful eye to preserve the original charm and opulence of the structure.

Strategy 16:
Flight Services, Our Time Machine

Waste of time is the most extravagant of all expenses.

Theophrastus (371-287 B.C.)

In 1985 Willis-Knighton Aviation Services was created with the purchase of a Piper Navajo twin-engine aircraft and the employment of Ed Rafferty, an experienced pilot/ flight instructor with several thousand hours of flight time. I must admit that this addition to our health system was born out of my love of flying as well as the lack of commercial flights to our capital, Baton Rouge. Also, the fact that there was no interstate highway (only two-lane state highways) connecting Shreveport and Baton Rouge played a part in the creation of this service.

This aviation service permits our hospital personnel and physicians to travel to educational and other professional meetings within six hundred miles of Shreveport with returns to their homes the same day, thereby eliminating the necessity for overnight stays. This program has added much to the quality of life of our staff, and its existence encourages more of them to participate in career-enhancing programs. Another benefit is a reduced level of production loss from these employees, because they spend less time away from their day-to-day duties. According to meticulous accounting of the costs of the flights by our chief pilot Rafferty, also a certified public accountant, the overall costs of our flights are equal to or less than that of travel by commercial airlines. However, the quality of life advantages this service offers our staff over land transportation continues to be priceless!

In 1990, upon the establishment of the WK/LSU Organ Transport Program, our aviation service assumed an additional responsibility, retrieval and transport of donor organs (heart, liver, pancreas and renal) from areas within 600 miles of Shreveport. In an effort to increase our travel range and reduce the time of organ transports, an eight-passenger Beechcraft King Air F-90 replaced the Navajo. Our pilots are airline transport-licensed with thousands of hours of flight time and have what they refer to as

Willis-Knighton's King Air (above) and Bonanza (inset) aircraft.

the best job in the world: they make several flights a week while their non-flying time is spent in administrative and financial duties.

The flight service has supported the WK/LSU organ transplant program since its inception. It also provides transportation for recruitment of physicians and clinical staff for WK and LSU Health Shreveport, professional educational sessions and transfers of acute patients to specialty centers such as St. Jude, Mayo Clinic and Cleveland Clinic.

In the late 1980s, our health system opened WK Air Rescue, a helicopter ambulance and transport program to provide emergency patient transports to hospitals in Shreveport. Later this service was merged with Schumpert's helicopter flight service in the interest of eliminating unnecessary duplication of services and reducing operating expenses for both institutions. Savings are utilized to defray the costs of the uncompensated flights provided for patients of LSU Health Shreveport.

CHAPTER 6

More Than a Hospital

Twenty years from now you will be more disappointed by the things that you didn't do than by the ones you did do. So throw off the bowlines. Sail away from the safe harbor. Catch the trade winds in your sails. Explore. Dream. Discover.

Mark Twain (1835-1910)

Strategy 17: Wellness Centers

Those who do not find time for exercise will have to find time for illness.

Edward Stanley, Earl of Derby (1826-1893)

Willis-Knighton's first wellness center was envisioned in the mid-1980s as a cardiopulmonary outpatient facility. At that time, few hospitals were becoming involved in preventive healthcare by owning fitness and exercise facilities. Some hospitals were reluctant to invest in them because there is no insurance coverage for preventive healthcare. The concept for the Health and Fitness Center on our main campus was broadened to include a full-service medically based wellness program, the first of its kind in the region.

Views of WK Wellness Centers, listed top to bottom: WK Bossier Wellness Center; WK South Wellness Center; WK Health and Fitness Center; WK Pierremont Wellness Center; The Tower at The Oaks Wellness Center salt water pool, and Pierre Avenue Wellness Center (not pictured is the one at WK Homer).

All members were required to be over eighteen years of age and medically approved for exercise activity by a physician.

Since that time, our health system has opened six more facilities of this design to the public. They are state-of-the-art wellness facilities complete with strength, cardio and aquatics on our hospital campuses in Shreveport/Bossier City, a facility attached to an indigent medical clinic in an underserved inner-city neighborhood and a small wellness center in a clinic in Homer, Louisiana. The newest wellness unit is in the Tower at The Oaks, a vibrant life style complex for seniors. An aquatics program is also available to the residents.

Since our 1988 entry into this preventive medicine modality, our membership has grown to approximately ten thousand members, and the centers are credited with enhancing the health of our community. Ken Paulovich, R.N., a thirty-eight year veteran of the health system, has directed this program since its inception.

Strategy 18: Partnering with the Medical School

Coming together is the beginning;
keeping together is progress; working together is success.

Henry Ford (1863-1947)

LSU Health Shreveport School of Medicine opened in 1969 with the admission of its first class of medical students. This program became the third medical degree-granting program in Louisiana, joining LSU Medical School and Tulane Medical School, both in New Orleans.

Since the post-war period of the late 1940s, Shreveport physicians, business and governmental groups had lobbied the Louisiana legislature for the establishment and funding of the school, which was to become affiliated with Confederate Memorial Medical Center (the present LSU Health Shreveport Medical Center), a state-owned hospital.

The hospital was the state's second largest teaching hospital with a large bed capacity and highly rated intern and residency training programs. These programs were directed and supervised by local medical and surgical specialists in voluntary service.

The primary mission of this new medical school was the education and training of primary care physicians (family practice, internal medicine, pediatrics and obstetrics/ gynecology) to address the critical shortage of these specialties in rural and suburban settings. At the time, Louisiana was experiencing one of the worst rural physician shortages in the nation.

Why a New Medical School was Needed

The major impetus for a medical school in Shreveport was the failure of the two medical schools in New Orleans to produce enough primary care physicians opting to practice in rural settings. But Louisiana was also experiencing an acute shortage of primary care physicians in some urban areas. In my opinion, there were several reasons for these failures: 1) the two schools' enrollments were not adequate to produce enough primary care physicians and specialists to satisfy the state's healthcare needs, 2) the location of LSU and Tulane schools in New Orleans, a large metropolitan area, was not conducive to enticing students to select rural practice locations after they became acclimated to the cultural benefits of city life, 3) there were blatant attempts by the faculty to direct students to careers in specialty medicine, 4) students were taught by specialists and supported by the highest level of technology, which did not adequately prepare them to treat patients in rural settings without such backup and 5) Tulane, a highly ranked private medical school, recruited large numbers of out-of-state medical students who had no intention of remaining in Louisiana after their training.

Shreveport's dream of having a medical school became a reality with the appointment of its first dean, Dr. Edgar Hull, a highly regarded faculty member of the LSU Medical School in New Orleans, and the acceptance of its first class. Most of the city's medical community fully embraced the new school, and many private physicians volunteered to participate in intern and resident training. For years prior to the appointment of full-time faculty, chiefs of a number of medical and surgical departments were private physician specialists of the community.

For the first few years after its opening, in spite of the fact that some of our physicians were active adjunct faculty members at the school, there were few relationships between Willis-Knighton's management and the medical school. Reasons for this situation were: 1) our hospital was continuing to labor under the financial burden of undeclared bankruptcy, doing well to merely exist, with little time for outside relationships, 2) at that time, the medical school was not forced to seek financial support from the private sector because it was adequately funded by the state, 3) the medical school had embraced the New Orleans *modus operandi* of providing medical care and training of residents only within the walls of the teaching hospital, seldom venturing into the community and 4) most of the local physicians appointed as chiefs of departments practiced primarily at T. E. Schumpert Memorial Hospital. Since most of the chiefs were unfamiliar with the workings of other hospitals or the talents of their physicians, they were not inclined to consider projects with WK or other hospitals in Shreveport. More surprising was the fact that few resident training programs were ever initiated with their hospital, Schumpert, seemingly a natural partner, one offering critical mass and the most impressive facilities around. (Please do not misconstrue this comment as a criticism of the physician chiefs of services' credentials, competence, ethics or actions. These part-time leaders were among the most respected and talented physicians in this region and deserving of their appointments. I must also add that at that time there were no other hospitals than Schumpert with the facilities, services or finances to support the school).

A Symbiotic Relationship Evolves

WK became involved with the medical school in a limited way upon the appointment of Dr. Ike Muslow, the school's highly respected chief of medicine, to the office of dean of LSU Health. Years before, Dr. Muslow had been in private practice at WK as the director of the system's renal dialysis unit. He was aware of our health system's growth and vision and wanted to involve our management and medical staff in support of activities of LSU Health Shreveport, especially in the area of off-campus clinical training sites for the school.

It was during the administration of Dean Muslow that medical students and residents of the school's medical and surgical departments were encouraged to spend time in clinical rotations in the offices of private practice physicians at WK. Dr. Muslow also played a major role in the formation of the joint-venture WK/LSU organ transplant service, granting Dr. John McDonald, chief of surgery, permission to take the medical school's surgical expertise outside the walls of LSU Health Shreveport to the community. This public/private cooperative community health program will always be credited to the visions of Drs. Muslow and McDonald.

In 1990, the surgery department of LSU Health Shreveport joined with our health system to provide the second organ (heart) transplant program in the state, under the directorship of Dr. McDonald, a nationally recognized transplant surgeon, and his team of expert surgeons. It was envisioned that LSU Health Shreveport surgeons would provide the required surgical expertise while WK provided the specially equipped operating rooms, anesthesia, supplies, specialty care units and outpatient clinics for the program. All expenses of the program were to be borne by WK. No patients were rejected based on their inability to pay.

The heart transplant program was an extension of the health system's cardiology and cardiac (open heart) surgery programs. These programs had experienced remarkable growth under the directorship of Dr. Mike Futrell, chief cardiologist, and Dr. Stanford Shelby, the region's most active heart surgeon, who had moved to WK in the 1980s.

Dr. Futrell became our system's first cardiologist upon relocating from across town in 1978. Much of the credit for WK's growth and reputation as our region's largest heart program is attributable to his medical skills, vision, humble leadership style and unselfish nature. His actions in leading our heart program to prominence were always undergirded by his willingness to share the limelight and credit for accomplishments with fellow cardiologists.

Some of the achievements of WK's cardiology department include:

1. WK was the first hospital in the region to surgically implant a pacemaker.

2. WK was one of the first hospitals in the nation to surgically implant a micro-chip pacemaker that measures the patient's ventilation and adjusts the heart rate according to the patient's individual physiological requirements.

3. The first mechanical heart device in the region was implanted by the organ transplant team at WK Medical Center.

4. The first free-standing heart institute and hospital was opened on the WK Medical Center campus. The three-story building includes a lobby, expanded emergency department and a hybrid surgical suite on the ground floor, heart and vascular catheterization labs on the second floor and offices for the cardiologists on the third floor. More heart catheterization procedures are performed in this facility than in any other hospital in the region.

5. The region's first 64-slice CAT scanner for heart studies was installed in the heart hospital.

6. In 2009, Willis-Knighton was recognized on ABC TV's "Good Morning America" as the hospital with the nation's lowest death rate of patients with heart attacks. This honor was based on Medicare statistics from almost six thousand hospitals.

To this day, Dr. Futrell continues to work diligently and without fanfare to enhance the program while regarding it as a work far bigger than himself; he always shares credit with his fellow cardiologists.

The first initiative of the WK/LSU joint venture surgical program was a heart transplant under the surgical supervision of Dr. Moshin Hakim, a surgeon recruited from the Mayo Clinic in Rochester, Minn. Dr. Hakim received his heart transplant training at Papworth Hospital in Cambridge, England, the world's largest heart-lung transplant program and the one with the highest survival rate. On June 4, 1990, with enthusiastic and extensive media coverage, the first heart transplant in the region was performed at WK Medical Center. (The entire staff of the hospital was hopeful and silently prayerful for a successful outcome for our first patient and for the many to follow. Our prayers continued to be answered as 10 patients received successful heart transplants in the first six months of operation).

An Unanticipated Game-Changer

Never could we have foreseen the effect this surgical achievement would have on our health system: a public out-pouring of support and recognition by the media of the program's impact on the health of our region and increased referrals of cardiac patients to WK cardiologists and cardiac surgeons. The increase in cardiac patients forced our two WK cardiology groups to immediately recruit additional physicians to their practices. This success rate was driving a perception on the part of the public that "If WK physicians can transplant a heart, they can certainly take care of all my heart issues."

This phenomenal positive image of our hospital and its capable physicians began to transcend our care of hearts, flowing over into other medical and surgical specialty referrals and prompting increasing numbers of patients to seek treatment at WK. Our inpatient admissions grew by 10 percent from 1990 to 1993; WK's admissions equaled those of Schumpert Medical Center for the first time in history.

The health system took an extraordinary gamble in undertaking the heart transplant program because: 1) any potential adverse patient surgical outcomes could negatively impact the hospital's reputation, 2) the number of medically underserved, high-risk patients in our region was higher due to our partnership with a state charity hospital, 3) the health system was required to provide non-reimbursed (non-billable) organ transplants for a trial period of three years and 4) the program's future ability to receive Medicare reimbursements would be determined, at the end of the three years, by patient outcomes and a number of other conditions. Thankfully, at the end of our three-year probation and of no reimbursement for procedures performed, our heart transplant program was approved. However, at no time has a transplant patient been turned away for lack of ability to pay.

Shortly after our heart transplant service was undertaken, the renal, liver and pancreas transplant programs were implemented in 1991 with great success. In 1992, the first living donor renal transplant was successfully accomplished. Dr. McDonald's surgical team for these programs included Dr. Gazi Zabari, a Johns Hopkins-trained transplant surgeon, and Drs. Robert McMillan and Donnie Aultman, faculty members of the LSU Health Shreveport surgical department.

In 2012, WK had clinical affiliation agreements with LSU Health Shreveport for twenty-six residents and eight fellows. In addition, there are seven hospital-based clinics on our campuses, jointly operated by WK and LSU Health Shreveport. WK's family practice fellowship, located in Vivian, Louisiana, and designed to entreat residents to enter practice in rural settings, is one of only a handful in the country. Drs. John Haynes and Steve Taylor have directed this program since its inception. WK's laparoscopic surgical fellowship, robotic surgical training and maxillofacial residency programs continue to train surgeons from across the region.

Strategy 19: WK's Physician Network

Alone we can do so little. Together we can do so much.

Helen Keller (1880-1968)

When the Willis-Knighton Physician Network opened in 1990, I never imagined the magnitude of the role this small operation would one day play in saving our health system from the financial disaster described in the chapter, "The Perfect Storm." The network was initially formed at the request of a few solo practicing physicians at Willis-Knighton to help them improve the management and profitability of their practices. It was believed that consolidating the business side of their practices would result in reduced practice expenses.

Management took their request and the concept of a provider network of physicians to the medical staff's executive committee for approval. At that time the network was to be operated basically for the benefit of primary care physicians because there was little desire on the part of management or our medical specialists for them to be included in the network's membership. After a unanimous vote of the WK executive committee, the request was presented to the entire medical staff where it was also approved.

The main goal of the network was to provide the support necessary to extricate a physician from the operational and financial issues of a practice, so he or she could concentrate on the practice of medicine. Solo and other small physician groups were the first targeted for support from this new service.

As fate would have it, the Highland Clinic was closing its off-campus primary care clinics in an effort to reduce operational expenses. Their support staffs were being discharged. Three clinic physicians called me to recommend the former manager of the remote clinics, Peggy Gavin, for a position with WK. She was employed and in training for another position when we decided to start a physician network. Not to get too far ahead of my story, I am pleased to relate that this terrific manager went on to become the director of the clinical operations of our network of over three hundred and fifty providers and manager of approximately one thousand employees. Interestingly, the three physicians who recommended her later joined our physician network and continue there today. Her husband, Greg, a computer technology consultant for medical clinics, joined our staff in 1993 to manage the network's financial operations.

The most critical decision made by our hospital leaders was to design a clinical and financial support system for physician offices that did not operate within the hospital organization. The benefits from this separate model were actions that were more focused, responsive, interactive and cost-effective than could be attained through a hospital-involved model.

In the beginning, the physician network relied on a number of outsourced services but eventually brought all services in-house. The first network-wide computer system was fully operational in 1994; it was the first tier in our decentralized model that placed decision-making autonomy in the hands of our providers. In addition to our employed primary care physicians, a special category of non-employed providers was incorporated as vendors in the network operations. This special designation permitted non-employed physicians to enjoy many benefits of the network by not having the headaches of financial operations (computer billing, collections, filing of insurance benefits and accreditation) in their offices.

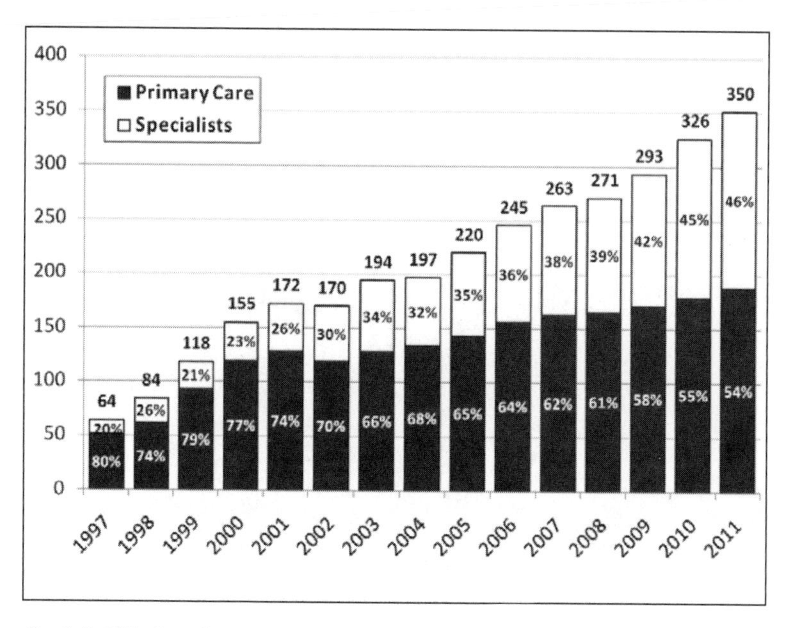

Graph 3: This chart shows the growth of the physician network from a majority (80 percent) of primary care specialists in 1997 to near parity, 54 percent primary care vs. 46 percent specialists in 2011). The network has grown to include 350 providers as of 2011.

Contracts were not boiler-plate. They were adaptable to the unique issues of each physician specialty and approved by outside national legal and compensation consultants. Local attorneys assist in this process to ensure compliance with all federal laws and regulations. At the outset, a decision was made to prohibit the network from purchasing physician practices (accounts receivables and good will). Only hard assets are purchased, upon appraisal, from physicians joining the network.

Network physicians and WK enjoy numerous benefits:

1. WK Physician Network providers receive a higher reimbursement on average for professional services from managed care companies than other area physicians, due to the critical mass of providers in the network, both primary care and specialist.

2. WK hospitals receive higher reimbursements from HMOs than hospitals without employed physicians. Our profits are reinvested in health system improvements: physical plants, equipment, services and personnel.

3. The critical mass of physicians in the network means less angst and mental pressure during negotiations with managed care companies.

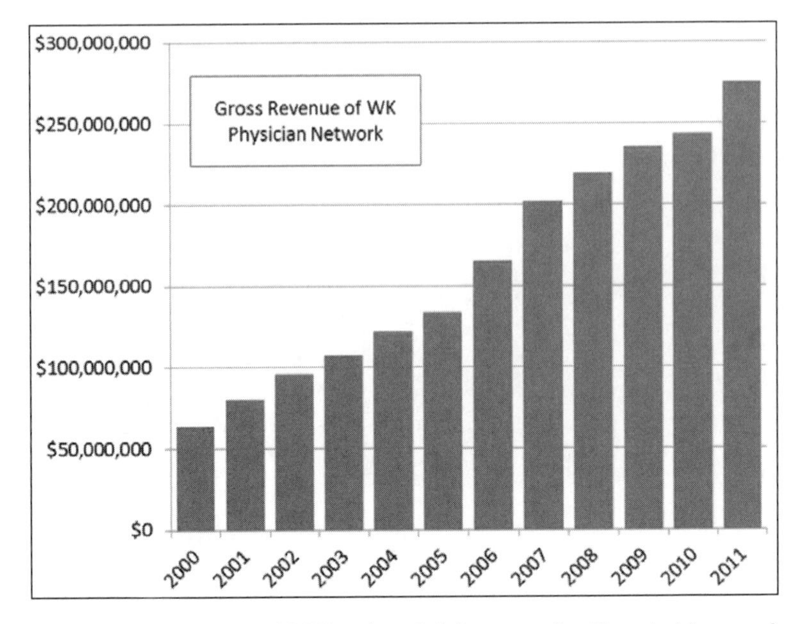

Graph 4: Ninety-one percent of WK inpatient admissions are attributable to physician network providers (either through direct admissions or referrals to other aligned physician specialists and subspecialists).

4. Physician networks are viewed by credit rating agencies (S&P and Moody) as a major stabilizing factor in determining an institution's future financial success and credit-worthiness.

5. WK's multiple hospitals and centers of excellence, reputation for quality of care, and dominant market share (a result of the number and quality of providers in its physician network) have enabled the health system to secure a very favorable financial rating.

6. If global payments (combined hospital and physician billings) become the standard reimbursement method for Medicare and other programs, WK's physician network will be well-positioned to convert to these changes with relative ease.

Willis-Knighton Health System has significantly benefitted in a number of ways from its large physician network, including, but not limited to:

1. Patient access: Our primary care physicians have enhanced the health system's patient volumes, inpatient and outpatient and referrals to specialists. They have also provided referrals and medical resources to the system's senior initiatives, including independent living,

assisted living, skilled nursing (with and without hospice care) and rehabilitation units.

2. Revenue enhancement: Hospitals rely on high volume, reimbursement revenue from orthopaedic, urology, gastroenterology, cardiac services and other surgery specialties, and physician networks of primary care physicians drive such referrals.

3. Centers of excellence: Only hospitals and health systems with a large base of primary care physicians, ensuring high volumes of patient referrals, can afford to become recognized centers of excellence. The costs of physical plants and technological equipment are prohibitive for low patient volume institutions.

4. Clinical trials for pharmaceuticals and treatment protocols: With a base of more than 350 physicians, primary care and specialists, the numbers of participating physicians necessary for clinical trials and research will be more easily amassed and coordinated.

Strategy 20: Health Plus of Louisiana (HMO)

If you can't run with the big dogs, stay up on the porch.

Anonymous

The history of health maintenance organizations (HMOs) in Shreveport/Bossier City was one of failures until Health Plus of Louisiana, a wholly-owned subsidiary of the Willis-Knighton Health System, arrived on the scene in 1995. These were the major events:

1. In 1984 Cigna Health Plans contracted with Highland Clinic and Hospital to offer the first full capitation plan of health coverage in this region. A capitation plan reimburses an agreed-upon amount to the physicians and hospitals paid by the HMO for any required patient services within a stipulated period based on prescribed benefits. The agreed amount for a physician included the reimbursement for office visits, lab, X-ray and supplies. This plan was unpopular, eventually eliminated from the market place.

2. In 1985 physicians of Shreveport/Bossier City came together to invest in Physicians Health Plan, the first physician-owned HMO in the

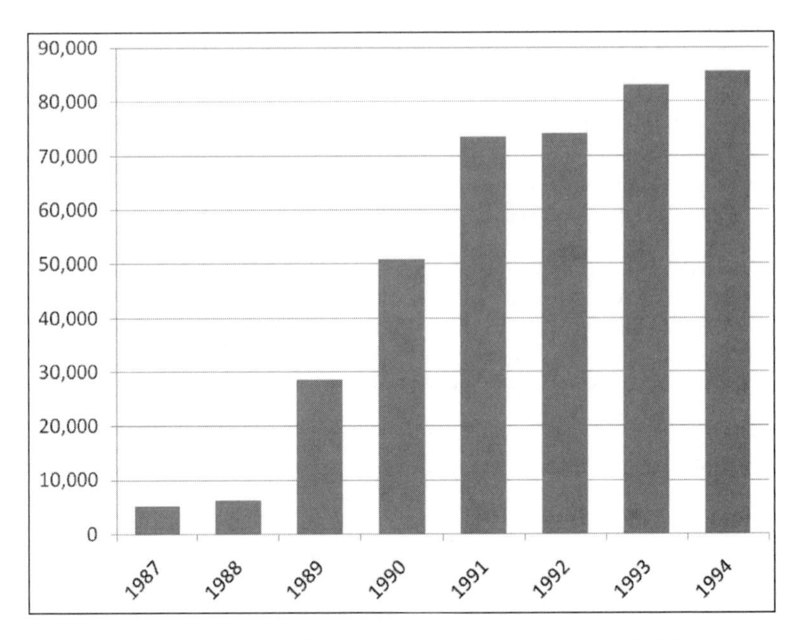

Graph 5: The Willis-Knighton Health Plan (PPO) enrollees from 1987-1994. Despite tremendous growth in enrollment, the program was deemphasized due to an innate lack of control over the utilization of patient services.

region.[31] Its operation was under the control of a board of physicians who imagined a physician specialist healthcare market with little or no input from hospitals or other healthcare providers. Its demise was preordained, for it paid considerably higher reimbursements to specialists than to primary care physicians and exercised no controls over utilization. No appreciation for the role that primary care physicians played in the delivery of healthcare was evident in its ill-conceived operation.

3. At the requests of a number of regional businesses for a Preferred Provider Organization (PPO) to provide discounted health services to their employees, the Willis-Knighton Health Plan was organized in 1986. The enrollment of the plan grew from 5,065 enrollees in 1987 to 85,701 in 1994, but did little to curb the overuse of health services.

4. In 1987, Blue Cross/Blue Shield entered a joint venture with Willis-Knighton Health System for a managed care product administered by Blue Cross. The prior experience of Cigna had a profound impact on the life of this product. Neither Blue Cross/Blue Shield nor WK

31 Several physicians who invested in this ill-conceived HMO plan ribbed me about the fact that I did not discourage them from investing in this short-lived plan, leaving them with thousands of dollars of debt. They frequently noted "Jim, you know doctors generally aren't good business men."

was experienced in this form of healthcare coverage; this product was withdrawn from the market after a short period.

5. Schumpert Health System and Highland Hospital/Clinic formed the North Louisiana Health Providers Organization (NLHPO) in 1994. Its purpose was to wrest market share from Willis-Knighton Health System, which was anticipated to grow rapidly upon the opening of the announced WK Bossier Health Center. WK's admissions increased 65 percent from 1996 to 2000.

6. The failure of North Louisiana Health Providers Organization played a major role in the recruitment of Schumpert and Highland physicians to the WK Physician Network for office relocations to WK Bossier Health Center and WK Pierremont Health Center. Schumpert leaders negotiated managed care contracts at reimbursement rates of 30 plus percent discounts off the average market rates, which reduced their physicians' incomes while offering no promise of additional patients. This less than astute business deal was viewed by many of the Schumpert physicians as the last straw in their relations with their hospital, and they sought out WK for better options.

These unsuccessful performances by HMOs in the region inspired jokes about HMOs, such as the following:

"You know you've joined a cheap HMO when...

1. ...your physician is wearing the pants you donated to Goodwill last year."

2. ...the answering service message is, take two aspirin and call me in two months."

3. ...your physician uses a popsicle stick for a tongue depressor."

Considering the gloomy history of managed care in Shreveport/Bossier City, people have asked me why WK's leadership made the decision to offer an HMO product, Health Plus of Louisiana, to the public. My answer is that we believed that Health Plus was the right product for the time to level the local playing field of competition by lowering premiums for managed care products, while it also helped grow the WK Physician Network through the use of exclusive contracts.

WK benefitted as the physician network was successful in recruiting new providers...but we accepted that every product has a life cycle and that a day would come when Health Plus might have to be pulled from the market. Until that day, Health Plus would give the health system a head start in garnering additional market share through an ever-enlarging network of employed physicians. As our network grew, so would our bargaining power with other health insurers. This advantage of market dominance through our multiple hospital locations and critical mass of providers would continue with other HMOs even if Health Plus were closed.

Let me be perfectly clear: while I always think in terms of products or services having life cycles, I did not anticipate that Health Plus would be closed to the public as soon as it was. We did not foresee how soon so many Shreveport/Bossier City businesses would, through buy-outs, become owned by national companies with existing health insurer relationships. The five local casinos were sold to larger corporations with contracts with insurers from out of the area. A number of other locally owned companies and the region's four largest banks followed suit.

Prior to the start of this buy-out movement, Health Plus of Louisiana, under the capable leadership of its president, Patrick Bicknell, and its medical directors, Drs. Bendel Johnson and Carey Allison, had attained a membership that placed it in a financial position of profitability as the second largest HMO in the region. This profitability had three causes: a membership large enough to provide actuarially sound utilization data, physician oversight of utilization and our extremely low administrative expenses. I must mention that in spite of our low administrative expense, Health Plus provided member services of the highest quality, as verified by the state's department of insurance. Brokers referred to Health Plus as the kinder and gentler health maintenance organization that paid claims faster than others.

All Products Have a Life Cycle: Our Health Plus Was No Exception

In my opinion, Health Plus of Louisiana was the right product for its time as it played a crucial role in the growth strategy of the Willis-Knighton Health System. Since its opening in 1995, Health Plus provided the following benefits:

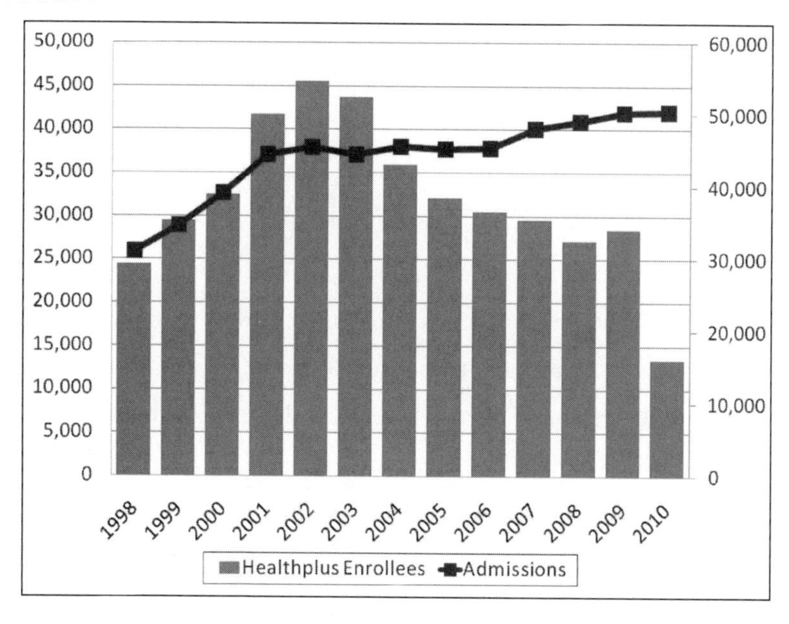

Graph 6: Health Plus of Louisiana's number of enrollees per year, 1998-2010, correlated with inpatient admissions per year. The trend line reflects that Health Plus's continued operation was not necessary to sustain patient volume after 2003.

1. Support for a patient gateway to market dominance as WK grew by 30,982 inpatient admissions (147 percent) between 1995 and 2010.

2. Assistance for the growth of the WK Physician Network from a small number of primary care physicians to 350 providers today, primary care and specialists, through the offering of exclusive contracts.

3. Serving as a catalyst for the recruiting of a multitude of physicians who relocated from other hospitals and were the foundation for the opening of WK Bossier Health Center in 1996 and WK Pierremont Health Center in 1999.

4. Provision of a TPA (third-party administrator) capability that remains in place to administer the healthcare reforms of the future, at savings to WK and its employees.

However, an analysis of Health Plus's future impact showed losses from operations (utilization spread over an inadequate actuarial base of membership) would begin to negatively impact the health system's position as its enrollment decreased.

The above graph, which compares system inpatient admissions overlaid against the growth of Health Plus enrollees, reflects that the system's inpatient admissions continued to grow even as the number of Health Plus enrollees declined. This loss of enrollees was primarily due to ownership changes of a large number of our region's larger businesses to national companies.

This realization prompted WK's management to explore the best and worst case scenarios concerning the continued operation or closure of Health Plus. What fallout would occur from a closure or sell-off of Health Plus, the region's most applauded HMO? Any potential negative impact on WK's image in the eyes of the public was of major concern to us. After privately consulting with key physicians (both network and non-network), trustees and a number of business leaders around the city, we decided to close to the public Health Plus of Louisiana, one of the most admired and praised HMOs in the state. In 2008 HealthPlus was named by Goldline Research as one of "The Ten Most Dependable Insurance Professionals" of the central United States.

While every product has a life cycle, in the case of Health Plus, it was a product dear to our hearts and the community. In 2010 it became the first service of WK to shutter its operations since my arrival. A compensating benefit of this decision was that Health Plus's TPA continues in operation to serve our employees and their families. Two of our most loyal and respected physicians, Drs. Bendel Johnson and Albert Bicknell, board members of Health Plus, played major roles in the life and success of this community service. Their sacrifices of time and service for Health Plus will be remembered by the WK family.

Should Health Plus be Sold to Another HMO?

After deciding to exit the managed care business, WK's management initially pursued the sale of Health Plus of Louisiana to other health plans. However, that was not the best option for these reasons:

1. National health maintenance companies (HMOs) were backing away from the purchase of provider-owned health insurers, not offering previously attractive prices for a number of reasons. One negative effect was the disadvantages associated with such ownership, which was being considered for inclusion in the looming national health reform plan.

2. If Health Plus could not be sold for a price adequate to justify the risks inherent in publicly endorsing any HMO over others, then why make the sale?

3. WK management was reluctant to endorse any health plan to employee groups and members, as the health system would have no control over the buyer's ongoing operations, including product pricing, underwriting and member services. We believed that this would be a contractual requirement for any sales contract.

4. Our management was reluctant to commit long-term, below-market rates to a purchaser HMO, considering the large numbers of Health Plus enrollees.

5. There was value in utilizing Health Plus's third party administrator (TPA) license for a continuing program of providing health benefits to the employees of the health system at rates under those in the market. Most of the prospective purchasers insisted on the inclusion of our TPA as a part of the Health Plus sale.

6. Arrangements with our preferred providers (WK physicians) would not be subject to exclusivity.

Before closing Health Plus, we told brokers, employer groups and members of our plan in An Open Letter to the Community: Clarifying the Changes at Health Plus, carried in a number of press releases and paid advertising that gave the rationale for its change of business model. WK employees were informed of their benefits to be derived from the future operation of Health Plus's TPA.

After the closure of Health Plus's managed care operation (HMO), the plan continued to operate as a third party administrator (TPA), providing benefit coverage and payment of claims for WK's employee health plan. The health plan's more than 10,000 members continue to receive outstanding health benefit coverage with lower than market rates due to its strong utilization oversight programs. This successful program of our TPA has continued under the direction of the former Health Plus medical director, Dr. Carey Allison. Exclusive contracting with the health system and its physician network continues.

Update on Divestiture of Health Plus of Louisiana

Benefits of the immediate closure of the HMO operations of Health Plus were these:

1. Release of $2 million in state insurance reserves.
2. Release of net assets of the plan of approximately $17 million.
3. Greater reimbursement from other HMOs for former Health Plus member enrollees of approximately $12 million a year.
4. Elimination of liability exposure.
5. Stopping losses incurred by Health Plus's below-market rates. These savings are better utilized for community benefits.
6. Reassignment of a cadre of exceptional former employees of Health Plus to other departments of the health system.
7. Release from WK's obligation to monitor relationships among physicians, the hospital and the state Department of Insurance, thereby eliminating compliance issues.
8. Ending the threat of federally mandated HMO benefits (such as pre-existing conditions, public options and portability).
9. Though operating in a different role, Health Plus of Louisiana (TPA) continues to promote the growth and success of the Willis-Knighton Health System. It remains as a gift that keeps on giving by virtue of its third party administration capability, which continues to dutifully serve the WK family of employees and physicians by keeping their health care benefits costs at a minimum, when compared to other plans on the market. This TPA arrangement permits exclusivity of our employees' admissions to WK physicians and hospitals.

After having been in the HMO business I have come to accept as factual the following notion: When small provider-owned HMOs get in competition with large national HMOs, they must decide whether they are the fox or the chicken in the coop. In our situation we became the chicken as our actuarial base eroded.

Strategy 21: Serving our "Greatest Generation"

While one finds company in himself and his pursuits,

he cannot feel old, no matter what his years may be.

Amos Bronson Alcott (1799-1888)

Given that the mission of the Willis-Knighton Health System is "To continuously improve the health and well-being of the people we serve," our management team believes the undertaking of non-medical projects that benefit our senior citizens is well within our stated mission.

Virginia Hall Becomes WK's Progressive Care Center

WK's first venture outside its walls to enhance the well-being of senior citizens was the purchase of Virginia Hall Nursing Home in 1985. This one-hundred-fifty-bed skilled nursing facility had been in operation since 1969. Its location fronting on the east side of our pedestrian mall from WK's original main entrance made it not only a nursing home but also a relief valve for the growing inpatient numbers and always overcrowded bed conditions of the financially struggling WK Memorial Hospital.

Our hospital's growth was a result of successful physician recruiting efforts made possible by the public's enhanced perception of our hospital. Yet our hospital's poor financial picture limited its ability to undertake the building of additional beds to accommodate the growing numbers of patients. Virginia Hall, later renamed WK Progressive Care Center, became the referral facility for Medicare patients who required some inpatient care but not acute and critical care nursing. Patients transferred from the hospital to this extended care facility received the nursing care they required at a substantially lower cost and kept their inpatient hospital days allowed under Medicare from being exhausted. Shortly after its purchase, a portion of the first floor wing was renovated to

Willis-Knighton Progressive Care Center (formerly Virginia Hall), a 131-bed skilled nursing facility, provides highly skilled sub-acute care at a significantly lower cost than a traditional acute care hospital.

accommodate the hospital's renal dialysis unit, which had twice outgrown its space on hospital property.

The sterling reputation of Virginia Hall and its successor, WK Progressive Care Center, was due primarily to the tireless efforts of two people, Rosalind Foster, administrator, and Maude Ward, R.N., director of nursing, both of whom had served since its opening. It seemed that these dedicated professionals had no set hours for work, as they were always on their jobs, day and night. These two ladies demonstrated the love, caring and compassion that one expects in any ministry of healing. Their residents and families loved them for the many ways they showed their loving concern. The only time they ever took me to task was when I made the comment that they were not expected to continue purchasing clothing and toiletries for residents out of their own pockets. I told them the facility would provide such funds if needed. In a kind and most ladylike way they informed me that it was none of my business how they chose to spend their salaries. Needless to say, that was the first and last time I mentioned the subject over the thirty years that I was privileged to know and love these two humble servants of their fellow man.

Willis-Knighton Enters a New World of Service

Prior to embarking on projects related to the lifestyles of our senior citizens, a detailed staff analysis was conducted of the future needs of the WK Health System. This study of our northwest Louisiana market revealed that WK had optimized the number of hospital locations and acute care beds that the area would require for a number of years, given the region's present population trends. Our goal was not to supplant other community not-for-profit healthcare providers. We believed that WK's image would be enhanced by meeting a critical family-sensitive need not undertaken by any other healthcare organization in Louisiana.

In 2007, the health system purchased a 200-acre tract of land on the LA 3132 corridor in southeast Shreveport with a futuristic retirement center development in mind. This beautiful pastoral land that fronts a limited access highway on both sides was purchased for significantly less than the price of adjoining land.

Our adjacent neighbor, across Sand Beach Bayou, was the Multi-Faith Retirement Community, commonly known since its opening in 1982 as Live Oak Retirement Community and Nursing Home. I decided that it would be an act of common courtesy to invite the board of Live Oak to lunch to inform them of our land purchase and to assure them that WK had no plans that would compete with their present operations. The purpose of the meeting was to express our sincere desire to be a good neighbor. Live Oak board members at that meeting were interested in exploring possible joint ventures with WK.

A few days later I was informed by the chairman of their board, Jim Bolin, that they were serious about the exploration of a partnership or merger. It was after this call that I entered the Live Oak complex for only the second time in my life. What I discovered behind the wooded entryway was a wonderful, caring ministry with a spirit unlike any community I had ever known. Mrs. Winona Ward, a visionary, along with a number of determined supporters, had performed a miracle in the late 1970s by securing contributions to fund the design and building of the most advanced concept at that time for a retirement community in the state of Louisiana. The land for its 110-acre campus was donated by the Alta and John Franks family, one of Shreveport's most generous philanthropic families, who also funded a community center for the residents.

Live Oak needed financial support from WK to renovate and refurbish the existing twenty-five-year-old facility of one-hundred-twenty cottages and apartments for independent living, the one-hundred-thirty-bed skilled nursing home and the Franks Community Center. It had also been a goal of Live Oak to add an assisted living facility to the campus to complete the continuum of senior living. Live Oak Retirement Community was soon donated to WK, and we made a commitment to provide $25 million for the desired changes and additions. The WK project team decided that a campus beautification program and a new bi-faith (Christian and Jewish) chapel should also become a priority. The health system's office for hospice services was relocated to the campus from WK North to permit ready access to the Live Oak Skilled Nursing Facility.

Little did I realize at that time the magnitude of impact this unique retirement community would have on this region and our WK family. Our health system was entering a new phase of service to our community, a life style change in independent living for seniors. A steep learning curve was required for our staff to successfully venture into this new world of daily living for seniors. Where would we find a model for our future development?

While the required renovations and refurbishing of the existing independent living and skilled nursing facilities were made, the WK team traveled to the heartland of premier independent living facilities in this country: the southeast and mid-Atlantic states. What we discovered were retirement concepts totally unlike anything in our region. Our team realized that we had entered a new and fascinating world: one of active and exciting senior living.

The best ideas gleaned from our visits to several retirement communities were photographed and cataloged. We asked their management teams for advice on building and operational issues. Their staffs were graciously willing to take time to assist us in learning more about their revolutionary senior housing concepts. We learned that few hospitals had ventured into this business because of the cost of such projects and that professional focuses of workers in retirement centers differ from those of a hospital. A hospital patient stays for four or five days while a retirement resident resides in a seniors' community for a number of years; therefore a different relational mindset must exist with employees.

While there are some differences between the operations of a retirement center and a hospital, there are also a number of cost-cutting benefits that a hospital can offer a retirement center under its ownership. These benefits result in lower expenses derived from: 1) savings from the health system's quantity discount prices of foodstuffs, paper products and nursing medical supplies, 2) lower property, liability and directors and officers insurance costs, 3) lower employee health and life insurance benefits, 4) lower operational expenses as a result of the sharing of personnel (dietary, maintenance, security, business operations, human resource, social service and management), 5) lower vehicle maintenance expenses through hospital motor pool operations, 6) reduced utilities expenses by virtue of volume hospital (high user) discounts and 7) shared personnel and other operations of the wellness and fitness facilities. In our case, The Oaks of Louisiana benefits from the operation of the WK Construction Company, which provides new construction and renovations at less than market prices.

My wife Margaret was assigned a leadership role partly because of her strong background in the areas of fitness and wellness as well as the humanities. This project became dear to our hearts as we both were in the process of recovery from the losses of our mothers a few months earlier, at the ages of 90 and 95 respectively. They had both resided for a number of years in WK's Progressive Care Center.

Margaret continued to oversee the operations of WK's wellness centers, WorkKare and WK Quick Care (urgent care) clinics and the marketing department, while at the same time she became both physically and emotionally immersed in the development of this futuristic concept of senior living.

Why is WK Moving into Senior Developments?

Man cannot discover new oceans unless he has the courage to lose sight of shore.

Anonymous

According to the U.S. Bureau of the Census, our population age 65 and over will grow by 83 percent between the years 2010 and 2030. Baby boomers are starting to retire at a massive rate, and they expect in retirement to have active lifestyles in upscale settings without reminders of aging.

Today's senior consumer is: 1) more youthful, 2) more affluent, 3) well-traveled, 4) more likely to be married, 5) well-educated, 6) more communicative, 7) accustomed to options and variety and 8) more accustomed to quick response/change than seniors of fifty years ago.

Focus groups disclosed the following: There was a need in Shreveport and Bossier City for attractive senior housing with opportunities for on-site lifelong learning, cultural programs, wellness and healthcare services. One of the keys to the success of a seniors' project is its ability to offer a range of products and prices to the market. There was pent-up demand in the middle, upper-middle and high income senior markets in Shreveport.

What Are Seniors Looking for in a Community?

Research shows that retirees are looking for a mild climate plus: 1) affordable housing, 2) job opportunities (especially military retirees who retire at young ages), 3) access to quality healthcare and 4) safe and quiet neighborhoods. Shreveport easily provides the first three requirements while The Oaks of Louisiana, with around-the-clock security service, ensures the fourth factor (a sense of safety and security) in concert with the law enforcement agencies of the city and parish governments.

Seniors are also looking for a broad continuum of service levels in retirement communities to preclude their having to move to another facility as health conditions dictate. The desired range of facilities and services seniors expect to have available on one campus are: 1) independent living, 2) independent living with concierge services, 3) assisted living, 4) skilled nursing, 5) skilled nursing with post-acute rehabilitation services and 6) skilled nursing with outpatient hospice services. WK's Oaks of Louisiana is the only retirement community in the state that provides all of these levels of services plus a multi-faith chapel, clubhouse, MarketPlace (gift, accessories and convenience store), indoor wellness facility with a natatorium, aerobics studio and senior-specific resistance equipment and specialized exercise stations along outdoor walking paths. Tranquil pastoral settings with water features and an abundance of wildlife are attractive and therapeutic accouterments of a retirement community.

How does Shreveport rate with retirees? In 2006 CNN *Money Magazine's* website rated Shreveport as a great place for seniors among cities our size. The Shreveport/Bossier City area is among the top ten most popular retirement communities for retired military personnel. Helping to ensure this ranking is Barksdale Air Force Base with its services: commissary, Base Exchange, golf course and officer, non-commissioned and enlisted persons' social clubs.

The Economic Impact of Transferring Retirees

Mark Fagan, a researcher at Jacksonville State University in Alabama reports: "A typical retired couple has the same economic impact of 3.4 manufacturing jobs (money plus spending) when you consider the economic incentive packages granted to attract industry and paid by taxpayers (land, utility infrastructure, tax credits, low interest loans, the high costs of recruitment and the negative environmental impact of remaining 'brown fields' when industries exit our city after tax incentives and accelerated depreciation are exhausted)."

An extensive study conducted by our WK team revealed the following information:

1. Americans age 50 and over: a) control 77 percent of all personal assets, b) own 80 percent of all money in savings accounts, c) own their homes at a rate of 70 percent, d) purchase 48 percent of all American-made automobiles, e) spend 70 percent of tourism dollars, and f)

support cultural, charitable and educational activities at a higher rate than other age groups.

2. The national averages for retiree households are as follows: They a) hold $400,000 in total assets, b) have annual incomes of $40,000 a year (non-cyclical), c) spend 85 percent of their dollars locally and d) pay more in taxes than they cost in public services.

3. Relocating retirees to Shreveport brings new money (retirement dollars earned elsewhere plus tax revenues) to our economy, yet they do not strain social services, school systems and criminal justice systems, and they create few environmental problems. Population and growth in cities with strong tourism and retirement industries have outdistanced the growth in cities that depend on manufacturing, mining and agriculture.

4. Retirees relocating to Shreveport do not require the high financial inducements (at the taxpayers' expense) necessary to attract business and industry, and they are an experienced pool of talent and committed volunteers.

5. Retired military personnel bring substantial retirement income and an asset base that isn't always reflected in demographic data.

After considering all of the above data, which not only qualified, but also quantified the real value of a retirement community investment, our management team determined that our health system should rapidly move forward to take advantage of this positive and encouraging data to benefit our seniors.

A Pictorial Look at The Oaks of Louisiana

A review of The Oaks of Louisiana, which includes the former Live Oak facilities, the new Tower at The Oaks, the Savannah Assisted Living facility, the bridge to a 200-acre nature preserve and pecan grove and the North Pavilion addition to the Live Oak skilled nursing facility follows on pages 234 and 236.

In concluding this discussion of the strategy of WK projects that enrich the lives of our senior citizens, I share a letter written in 2010 from the executive director of The Oaks of Louisiana to the board members of Live Oak Retirement Community. Her passion for the residents and their home is best described by her own hand. The intent for this letter was to assure the board members that WK's promises for Live Oak had

Views in 312-acre gated campus of The Oaks of Louisiana:

Top–The Tower at The Oaks (independent living); middle left—Savannah at The Oaks (assisted living); middle right—Chapel at The Oaks (multi-faith worship center); bottom—entrance gate (staffed 24 hours daily).

been fully realized. In turn, these board members have continued to faithfully serve their new dream, The Oaks of Louisiana.

Dear Board Members:

Over the years, Live Oak has been blessed with the expertise and devotion of its board members who have provided leadership to help it navigate through good times as well as challenging times, and I want to extend my personal admiration and thanks for your contribution and undying loyalty and devotion to the Live Oak dream. We are very grateful that you have chosen to give your support to this organization even during a time of tremendous transition and, indeed, transformation in partnership with Willis-Knighton Health System. Together we have achieved a complete renovation and revitalization of Live Oak and witnessed its integration into a master-planned community, The Oaks of Louisiana, built on the foundation laid by Live Oak's visionary leaders and the faith and commitment of our board members.

The development and transformation of the campus continues to be a truly phenomenal project. Appropriately, our first new construction endeavor was to provide The Oaks with an inspirational venue for worship and prayer and thus Chapel at The Oaks became a reality. Residents as well as staff find a place for quiet contemplation as well as celebratory worship in this beautiful structure, reminiscent of a church in the English countryside. Meanwhile, as the total remodeling of Live Oak itself took place, MarketPlace and Clubhouse at The Oaks were added to the campus and now provide an enjoyable and convenient shopping experience as well as a comfortable, cozy place for residents and friends to congregate.

In the fall of 2010, the Tower at The Oaks opened its doors and presented our community with a premier residential concept unequaled in the state of Louisiana, complete with multiple dining venues and fabulous wellness center. In about two months, Savannah at The Oaks, an assisted living residential facility, will welcome residents, similar in design and décor to the Tower, but providing those extra care services that many come to require. A few months hence, the North Pavilion at Live Oak will begin welcoming residents as well. It will be a beautiful thirty-bed all-private-room total care and skilled nursing addition to Live Oak's existing health center.

At the same time that exciting physical changes have been taking place at The Oaks, we have also worked diligently to expand, enhance, and enrich the lifestyle opportunities for our residents. Every day is a new and exciting day at The Oaks!

We are excited about the future and The Oaks' expanded options for Shreveport area seniors and their families. We look forward to your support as we launch new phases of services and residential options as well as your presence for activities and events on the property. You have helped us achieve great things and we look forward to an exciting future with your continued guidance.

—Margaret

The Oaks of Louisiana is situated on the largest pastoral tract of land remaining undeveloped in urban Shreveport. A natural bayou featuring a covered bridge, bandstand, pecan grove, three lakes and numerous fowl and wildlife grace the setting. The North Pavilion (top) houses thirty private, up-scale skilled nursing rooms. The Clubhouse at The Oaks (center) features the MarketPlace and a club room. Inside the Tower, a beautiful serenity wall (second from the bottom) graces the approach to the Spa and Wellness Center. Residents and guests gather at Grumpy's (bottom left), named in honor of the author, whose lighted caricature (bottom right) marks the entrance to the Tower residents' favorite 'library of libations'.

Strategy 22: WK's Spiritual Life Program

You may already know that WK offers the finest healthcare in the region. But did you know that since our mission is the well-being of the whole person, WK addresses the spiritual needs of our patients and their families as well?

Brochure of the WK Spiritual Life Services

The Spiritual Life Services staff is responsible for the following services and benefits for our patients:

1. The WK Prayer Line is provided for prayer intentions and requests on voicemail. Contact numbers for this service are posted in patient rooms and printed in patient handbooks. Prayer requests may also be sent by email.

2. A Spiritual Life Committee assists the director with planning and implementation of programs. The committee is instrumental in providing services at all WK Campuses.

3. Spiritual Life Volunteers, after undergoing training and supervision, assist the clergy staff in ministering to patients and families.

4. A number of multi-faith religious services are held at the Chapel at The Oaks. These services are open to the public as well as residents of the retirement community. Active participants in the multi-faith services represent the Jewish, Roman Catholic and Protestant faith traditions. Spiritual services at Live Oak have been under the faithful and dedicated leadership of Mrs. Mickie Cowan for nearly three decades.

5. Chapels and serenity rooms are available to families of our patients at all WK hospitals and The Oaks of Louisiana. They are good places for clergy to gather for prayer or to counsel family members.[32]

32 The hospital's first chapel was made possible through the generous gifts of two of the hospital's trustees, one an Episcopalian and the other a Presbyterian, in memory of one of our finest physicians, also an Episcopalian. They told me that they would prefer that I not be on the chapel design committee. I asked why. They laughingly answered, "Jim, we know you are not an Episcopalian, and we would prefer not to have a chapel with concrete floors and folding chairs."

6. Upon request, identification badges are provided free of charge to all members of the clergy in the area. The badges allow our staff to quickly recognize designated clergy so that we can offer them assistance.

7. Free parking near entrances to all WK hospitals is provided to the clergy.

8. A webpage provides suggested prayers from different faith traditions for healing, comfort and solace. Additionally, three-minute videos by local ministers of different faiths offer care and spiritual support.

9. WK's in-house television channel (WKTV) includes spots on the spiritual services offered by WK and two worship services rebroadcast from the Chapel at The Oaks.

10. A number of spiritual events and resources for employees are offered, including a Nurses' Week Florence Nightingale Pledge and Blessing of Hands for all personnel, a *Book of Blessings* available at Christmas near each cafeteria entrance for employees to write about how God has blessed their lives this year, and messages to all employees about the spiritual aspect of their mission. WK hosts breakfasts and luncheons for the clergy of the region, held in both Shreveport and Bossier City hospitals, twice a year to update them on the activities of the Spiritual Life Committee and engage them in this ministry. This effort has been widely acclaimed by the clergy of all faith traditions.

The following letter is included in the admission process for patients:

> *The spiritual concerns of patients at Willis-Knighton are very important. As we fulfill our mission to continuously improve the health and well-being of the people we serve, we realize that this ministry of healing includes body, mind and spirit. A hospital stay, and particularly a serious illness, can be a pivotal time in a person's spiritual as well as physical life. Especially at those times, many of our patients and their families need spiritual support and care.*
>
> *WK is not owned or operated by any religious institution. However, the spiritual component of our mission is very important. The mixture of faith traditions among our patients and staff is quite diverse. We use the word "spiritual" care because we believe it is a broader term that encompasses all faith*

The Chapel at The Oaks of Louisiana (top), a multi-faith facility serving the residents of the vibrant seniors' campus. Interior of the chapel (bottom). Not visible are the organ, altar and piano.

traditions. Our policy is to respect all faith traditions and encourage people to use their spiritual faith as a source for healing.

We hope this brochure will help you become better acquainted with the spiritual services and support available to our patients. Our team of trained employee volunteers and I are ready and willing to help address the spiritual needs at WK. I invite you to call on us if we can be of help to you or a patient under your care. We also welcome your suggestions and look forward to sharing in God's work with you at Willis-Knighton.

—Rev. Andrew Comeaux

Strategy 23:
Proton Beam Unit in WK Cancer Center

Technology is a gift of God. After the gift of life it is perhaps the greatest of all gifts. It is the mother of all civilizations, of arts and of sciences.

Freeman Dyson (b. 1923)

A 300 percent growth in patient encounters at the Willis-Knighton Cancer Center in the past eleven years has afforded our health system the opportunity to provide cutting-edge technologies not often found in community hospitals. Willis-Knighton has scheduled for 2014 the installation of a proton beam (pencil guidance) therapy unit, currently the most advanced radiation therapy technology available. At the time this order was placed, there were only nine units in the United States (most are located in university medical teaching institutions).

The advantage to using proton beam therapy is that the protons emitted from the device stop at a very specific depth within the patient's tissue instead of penetrating all the way through the body. This allows the physician to create a treatment plan where the tumor receives a very high radiation dose, but the surrounding healthy tissue receives

Architect's rendering of the WK Cancer Center, which is highly visible from Interstate 20. The volume of patient encounters has tripled since 2000. No one has contributed more to WK's cancer program than Michael Moore, MD, our first oncologist to join the medical staff in 1980.

Architect's drawing of the building, left, that will house the proton beam vault and control rooms, patient waiting areas, staff offices and a spacious conference area. (At right is the north side of the Cancer Center) Patients and visitors will be greeted by a serenity wall (falling water feature) and bistro to accommodate food service.

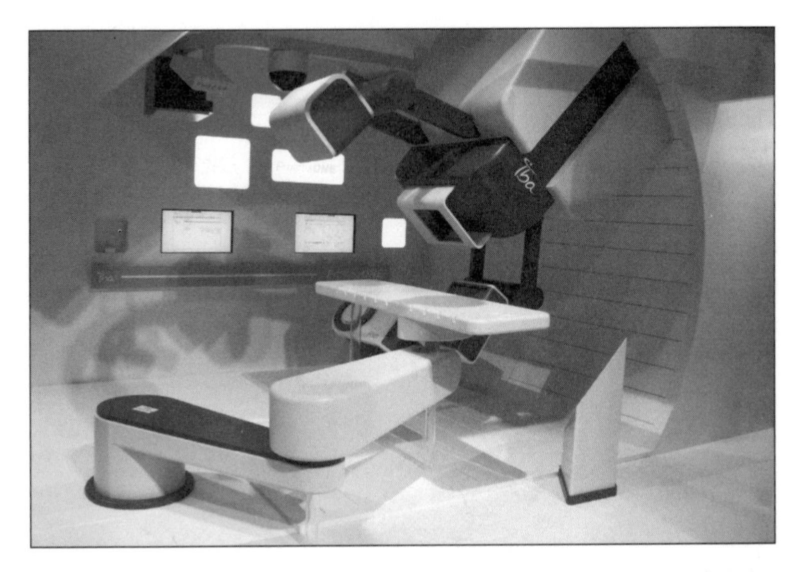

WK's proton beam therapy modality features precision pencil beam guidance, which revolutionizes the treatment of a variety of cancers.

very little radiation. WK's device, the first to be installed in the U. S. (*Miami Herald*, October 3, 2011), will utilize the most advanced type of proton beam therapy, pencil beam scanning, which uses extremely small beams of protons to radiate the tumor with microscopic precision. This is such a new technology that it has proven difficult to find radiation physicists with the training required to operate the device. In the interest of assuring that we will have enough trained radiation physicists, WK co-funded the start-up of the state's first medical physics residency, a joint program with Mary Byrd Perkins Cancer Center in Baton Rouge.

Housing the proton beam unit will require an extensive addition to the Cancer Center. The unit itself will require a 3,700-square-foot vault built with nine-foot thick concrete walls and large enough to wholly contain two average American homes. Total costs for the purchase, installation and housing of the unit is expected to reach $40 million.

The proton beam unit will be staffed by Drs. Lane Rosen, Sanford Katz, Michael Durci and supported by H. Terry Wu, Ph.D. In addition to the proton beam unit, the expanded cancer center will provide offices for hematologists, oncologists and radiation therapy staff.

As a community hospital, WK is proud to offer the latest in cancer-fighting technology to our region. Although it is too soon to generate a precise financial *pro forma* for the facility, we expect the survivals from cancer to more than justify this terrific expense.

Strategy 24: Respite at The Oaks of Louisiana (An Old Dream Comes True)

Rest is a fine medicine.

Thomas Carlyle (1795-1881)

The Willis-Knighton Cancer Center is the largest and most active treatment center for cancer in this region, presently offering radiation and chemotherapy treatment. The center's tomo-therapy program is one of the most active to be found in a community hospital in the nation. The radiation therapy unit is under the medical supervision of four radiation oncologists, supported by a team of radiation physicists and technicians.

A major influx of patients from a larger geographical area is anticipated with the introduction of the region's first proton beam therapy modality (with beam guidance and pencil beam scanning) in 2014. The nearest proton beam facility is in Houston, Texas.

The Issue

Chemo, radio and proton therapy patients require an average of six to eight weeks of onsite treatment, often five days per week. This rigorous schedule of treatments is especially difficult on out-of-town patients and their families. Our system of arranging discount lodging at local motels and hotels, while the best that we can do at this time, is less than optimal due to the lack of a supportive and aesthetically pleasing environment for patients and families. A small room on an upper floor of a motel with only a view of a parking lot and no in-room meal service is less than ideal and places another burden on the patients and their weary families. Transportation is an issue as many of the out-of-towners are unfamiliar with our city, and their families require the family automobile to get to work during patient treatments.

The Answer

The Respite at The Oaks consists of a number of cottage apartments at the Live Oak Independent Living Complex at The Oaks of Louisiana that have been furnished for the use of patients and their families during treatment. It is not a hospice but a place of healing and peace for the family during a patient's chemo, radio and proton beam therapy, where routines of daily living are possible in an out-of-town setting. The Respite offers these advantages:

1. The cottage apartments are ADA accessible and have a combination of attractive hard surface and Krypton carpet floor treatments and modern kitchens.

2. Regular and dietetically prepared meals may be delivered to the patient's cottage by the dietary staff of Live Oak. Family members may also purchase meals.

3. Guests will be charged a minimal fee for lodging and food (less than hotels).

4. Transportation to and from the WK Cancer Center, physician offices or to run light errands will be provided at no charge by The Oaks of Louisiana/WK personnel.

5. Guests will have access to the in-cottage Oaks of Louisiana television channel featuring special campus activities and spiritual life services at The Oaks multi-faith chapel.

6. Program participants requiring home care services will have them from the WK Home Health service at their cottages on The Oaks campus.

This program is another demonstration of the willingness on the part of WK personnel to go outside the walls of our hospitals to provide a hospitality-based program of care. The Respite at The Oaks of Louisiana works closely with the Caddo/Bossier

Cancer Foundation League, an organization of cancer survivors, to educate the public about the disease and to solicit funding from other cancer survivors and philanthropic donors to provide non-medical necessities of patients in treatment.

CHAPTER 7

The WK Way

Individuality is either the mark of genius or the reverse.
Mediocrity finds safety in standardization.

Frederick E. Crane (1869-1947)

Strategy 25: Resist Chasing the Fads in Health Care

Only dead fish swim with the stream.

Anonymous

Our management team was determined to resist mindlessly chasing all of the fads in healthcare. We stiffened our resolve against trendy concepts or projects just because they were in vogue by adhering to the following beliefs. Blindly following some healthcare executives into highly speculative and untested "hot ticket" deals is akin to swimming with the lemmings at sea, no lemming dares to break ranks by swimming off alone. A trendy concept that violates laws of business and experience could impair an institution for years to come. No two hospitals are exactly alike, nor are their markets exactly the same. The old saying, "when you've seen one market, you've seen one market," is profoundly true. "New and improved" is not always better than "tried and true."

We chose to go our own way. Have you ever noticed that many successful investors have the greatest financial successes by investing against the conventional wisdom of the stock market, choosing to trust in their own instincts and knowledge? They sometimes are buying when others are selling or selling when others are buying. Today, some health systems that defied conventional thinking by investing in owned HMOs and employed physician networks are in an enviable financial position compared to those that were divesting themselves of their physician networks or limiting membership to primary care physicians only.

In my opinion, since every market is different, the best offensive strategies to stave off the financially devastating impacts of reduced reimbursements, competitive physician entrepreneurial ventures and unlevel playing fields caused by monopolistic HMOs are timely (proactive) custom-tailored responses to market needs and changes, not fashionable "cookie-cutter" solutions.

Our health system has often chosen to buck trends by initiating services when other systems were getting out of the business or vice versa. A few examples of this behavior:

1. Including a tithe of our profits to fund our humanitarian Duties of Conscience in the annual budgets of our health system for over thirty years.

2. Starting a health maintenance organization (HMO) at a time when many systems were divesting their operations.

3. Employing primary care physicians when many health systems were dismantling their employed physician networks.

4. Adding employed medical and surgical specialists and sub-specialists to our physician network.

5. Refusing to purchase an existing physician's practice (no remuneration for goodwill and accounts receivable) to grow our provider network. WK established this policy long before the implementation of the Stark Laws.

6. Rejecting overtures from physicians wishing to joint venture (co-own) outpatient services with the health system (an arrangement that would have given a financial advantage to a small number of medical staff physicians over other physicians who support Willis-Knighton Health System and ensure its future services to the community).

7. Making the painfully difficult decision to compete with the physician specialists on our medical staff who invested in ventures in direct

competition with our health system. We replaced them on our medical staff by employing new physician specialists in their stead.

8. Discouraging the exclusion of relatives during the hiring process for new positions. WK does not believe in discriminating against our family's (employees') talent pool. Believing that "the fruit does not fall far from the tree," some of our finest employees have been recruited from the familial ranks of existing employees.[33]

9. Refraining from mandatory retirement ages. We believe that our senior employees have much to contribute in empirical knowledge and experience.

10. Building two new hospitals in new markets in a span of four years, when national media were declaring an overabundance of beds in our country; that was not the case in our market (where misdistribution was the issue).

11. Resisting the national trend to grow our system by merging with other hospitals outside our markets. One proposal was to merge WK with hospitals in Alexandria, Baton Rouge, Lafayette and Lake Charles. Our philosophy is that healthcare is more responsive when provided by hospitals whose operations are under the ownership and control of local medical staffs and governing bodies.

12. Avoiding a "top-heavy" approach to administration and departmental management. WK believes that the place to be "heavy" in staffing is in clinical areas and bedside care.

13. Abstaining from paying extra for physician call coverage to respond to specialty needs of our emergency rooms, thanks in part to the strength of the physician network and the willingness of WK physicians to support the health system's patient safety net responsibility.

14. Avoiding a "silo" mentality among our workforce by assigning employees multiple jobs and tasks to stimulate their personal and professional growth. Many healthcare organizations have eagerly pursued the fad of forcing their employees to specialize in a specific area of operations. While there are valid reasons for a high degree of specialization in some areas, system-wide specialization creates a singular focus among staff members that often prevents the attainment of organizational goals. We believe that the most successful organizations are those that have many employees who are adaptive and possess skills beyond a narrow specialty. Most importantly, employees who have a myriad of responsibilities show a far greater level of engage-

33 Over the years I have approached many of our employees with exceptional work ethics to inquire whether they had any siblings or children that might be interested in working for WK. The four Hutto girls (Danita, Dora, Doretta and Dorothy), in particular, are probably quite tired of me asking if they are certain about not having any other siblings!

ment and interest in their jobs than those that are restricted to the same repetitive, daily tasks.[34] Burnout can be a debilitative condition.

15. Resisting the trend to outsource patient services (outpatient and inpatient).

16. Resisting the trend to outsource maintenance service contracts for medical imaging and technology by virtue of our unique in-house Bio/Rad engineering program.

17. Rewarding employees for regular work attendance by the institution of a program that converts unused sick days into a year-end bonus. WK does not force employees to use time off, nor does it restrict the days accumulated.

18. Refraining from using our health system's not-for-profit tax status to solicit financial contributions or grants, either private or governmental, to support operations or building projects.

19. Declining to sell over $250 million (replacement value) of physician office buildings to enhance our cash position. Since over 350 of our system's employed providers occupy many of these offices, this action would place future rental rates, standards of maintenance of the buildings and parking in the control of outside parties.

20. Honoring our strict conflict of interest policy, voted on long ago by the WK Board of Trustees, enables WK to adhere to its "spread the wealth" mantra whereby the health system utilizes a number of community banks and a multitude of vendors in the region. The "Good Ole Boy" system of only dealing with a few of our management's and board of trustees' friends has never been a part of the WK culture. Special emphasis is also given to local and minority suppliers and contractors as is practical.

21. Refraining from restructuring our corporation into several legally separate corporate entities during the frenzy of the 1980s for such differentiation of integrated healthcare organizations.

---

34 Perhaps our best example of a "non-silo worker" is Sonny Moss. He is a vice president of the WK Health System and administrator of WK Pierremont, is responsible for all land and property acquisitions for the health system, oversees the management of all non-hospital buildings and grounds (more than 600 acres) and serves as a community and economic development liaison. His positive attitude is contagious as he moves around the system playing a vital role in the growth of WK.

Conclusions that Support WK's Strategies for Success

If at first you do succeed—try to hide your astonishment.

Anonymous

Dr. Liam Fahey of Babson College notes that "a crucial test of strategic management is whether the organization is attaining and sustaining marketplace leadership: Is it outdistancing its current and future competitors? Is it regarded by customers as the most innovative and premier supplier or merely as one of the pack?"

At WK, we believe a review of the following quantifiable measures supports the thesis that most of our strategic initiatives have been successful in growing our health system. Questions as to the ability of Willis-Knighton Health System to meet the future challenges of health reform and to sustain our financial, clinical and operational performance must continue to be addressed. And, is our health system optimally structured for the future? I believe it is!

Presently, thanks to strong, stable and long-term leadership on the part of our board of trustees, medical staff and management, our health system enjoys the following qualities and indicators of past and future successes:

1. Provision of high quality care (consistently ranked in top 5 percent of hospitals in the nation).

2. Broadest continuum of services in the state (pre-school immunizations to organ transplantation).

3. Strong brand identity and patron support.

4. Inpatient admissions of 51,343 in 2012 (78 percent share of local, private hospital market), the largest number of inpatient admissions in a six-state area of Oklahoma, Arkansas, Louisiana, Mississippi, Alabama and Georgia (source: 2012 AHA Guide) and 85 percent of births in our local market.

5. Four hospitals with fully equipped emergency departments located in the four quadrants of our metropolitan area.

6. WK's emergency departments rank as the thirteenth busiest in the U.S. (Modern Healthcare, February 27, 2012) Urgent care and occupational medicine services (95 percent market share) are provided at eleven sites.

7. No rejection of patients due to their inability to pay (even prior to the enactment of the EMTALA law).

8. Financial strength of profitability and liquidity above peer hospital systems (2012 operating margin of 9 percent).

9. Access to capital under favorable terms (Moody "A" and S & P "A" ratings).

10. Debt free—cash position exceeds liabilities and bonded indebtedness (with maturity date of 2027).

11. Lower costs than peer groups of hospitals (lower staffing levels, higher productivity, and efficiency wrought by rigorous oversight of all expenses).

12. Charges for patient services less than local competitor (outpatient, 30 percent, and inpatient, 12 percent).

13. Modern and aesthetically pleasing physical plants with a low average age and a replacement value in excess of $1 billion.

14. Highest level of technology in the state: eight MRIs, eight CAT scanners, ten heart catheterization labs, two electro-physiology labs, two linear accelerators, one tomo-therapy radiation unit, a hybrid cardiovascular lab, a PET scanner and a twelve-patient hyperbaric chamber (the only one in the state). A proton beam therapy radiation unit, with pencil beam guidance, is scheduled for 2014.

15. Very low maintenance costs for our technology installation, service and repair when compared to hospitals that outsource such activities.

16. Physician network of 350 employed providers (strong primary care representation ensuring referrals to WK hospitals and specialists and critical mass for HMO negotiations.)

17. Physician network that provides the health system with the vehicle to implement bundling of Medicare charges (hospital and physician), which is a consideration of the new health reform law.

18. Region's largest centers of excellence (cancer, heart, organ transplant, eye, stroke, fertility, rehabilitation, laparoscopic and robotic surgery, neonatal, maternal-fetal and wound care).

19. Network of ambulatory centers (urgent care, occupational medicine, imaging, hyperbaric wound care, and rehabilitation therapies).

20. Largest provider of outpatient services (hospice, home health, emergency, urgent care, hyperbaric and imaging) in region.

21. Owner and operator of eight wellness centers (including cardiac and pulmonary rehabilitation) with several thousand dues-paying members.

22. Health Plus TPA manages the Willis-Knighton employee health benefits program at a fraction of the cost of outside benefit managers with exclusivity of referrals for network physicians. Premium savings derived from its reduced costs of operation are used to upgrade employee benefits above those of competitors.

23. Management team of strong, experienced and long-serving leaders with a willingness to promote innovative concepts.

24. First health system in state to enter the senior living market with a 312-acre campus with continuum of 245 independent living apartments, 48 assisted living apartments and 261 skilled-nursing beds.

25. Support of eight indigent care clinics, several university healthcare programs and hundreds of community well-being services (these Duties of Conscience funded by tithe of 10 percent of system's EBITDA).

26. Medical staff of strongly supportive, competent and engaged physicians with a sense of interdependence upon one another for referrals.

27. Physician and employee recruiting programs that benefit from the system's reputation, image and financial strength.

28. The only hospital in the region with an aviation service to support organ transport, recruiting, patient transport and educational travel for our employees.

29. Joint venture partnership in several initiatives with LSU Health Shreveport Medical School, including several hospital-based clinics for specialized physician services.

30. Management or other support contracts with three rural hospitals in northwest Louisiana that provide specialty referrals to the health system.

31. Strong family feel of the health system, credited with WK's being chosen for an award, Top 100 Hospitals for Nurses' Job Satisfaction by Nursing Professionals magazine in 2009.

32. Employee turnover rate that is lowest in the region and less than one-half of America's hospitals in 2010.

33. WK offers its employees a defined benefit plan (pension) which is unique among community hospitals today.

34. Largest private partnership with the nation's fourth largest nursing school to ensure adequate registered nurse staffing.

35. Our staff's belief that WK has been, and continues to be blessed beyond measure, not as a result of our benevolent actions towards all in whom we come in contact, but rather why we choose to undertake such actions in the first place, a motive for good.

CHAPTER 8

The Perfect Storm: Surviving and Thriving in the Era of Physician Entrepreneurship

When good is in danger, only a coward would not defend it.

Confucius (551-479 **B.C.**)

Most people know I am normally an optimistic person, seldom slowed by negative thinking. My glass may not be overflowing, but it is usually almost full. And they know I am always willing to fight for my convictions. One time however, I permitted events to threaten not only my continued service at WK but also the future of our health system. My failure to think quickly and positively was caused by my longing to hang on to the good old days of physician/hospital relationships rather than bite the bullet and acknowledge the new thinking of some physicians and react accordingly. The resulting adversarial relationships among our physicians, a first in WK history, gave me cause for remorse and personal soul-searching.

In the mid-to-late 1990s WK had committed or spent over $500 million for new facilities: WK Bossier Health Center, WK Pierremont Health Center, WK Cancer Center, WK Portico Medical Mall, Medical Arts Building at WK North and the WK Pierremont Patient Tower. All were open, under construction or in the planning stage. These projects would accommodate huge growth in our patient admissions and outpatient services.

Through the exercise of tight budgetary controls, our new facilities had been built during a period when many hospitals were not expanding because of dwindling margins and burgeoning uninsured patient populations. Inadequate reimbursement levels of government and managed care coupled with severe staffing shortages and growing liability issues were endangering capital acquisition for new technology and infrastructure for hospitals.

By 1999 we had a $900 million fleet of hospitals, centers of excellence, physician offices, wellness centers and senior initiatives (skilled nursing, rehabilitation, hospice and home health services); all were threatened by what I recall as a "perfect storm."

Our storm spanned seven years. Huge problems appeared so fast that no one could have foreseen them. Its forces wreaked havoc on the operations and physician relationships of our health system. All of the five forces were financially challenging, while the fifth and most powerful required changes in our relationships with many medical staff members. Thus it was a highly emotional time.

The fifth force had a devastating impact on physicians who were loyal to the hospital and its leaders. No party (trustee, manager or physician) was spared the fray. Willis-Knighton's continued existence was never in jeopardy, but this force, if not aggressively countered, could have impeded the system's ability to thrive—that is, to continue providing state-of-the-art facilities, cutting-edge technologies and the employment of professionals to man these ventures. Also at risk was our future ability to fund our Duties of Conscience, which supported a multitude of services for the underserved of our community.

The first four forces were primarily financial:

Force One: The Highland Clinic, a multi-specialty clinic of approximately forty physicians, and the Highland Hospital announced their affiliation with the Schumpert Medical Center's North Louisiana Physician-Hospital Organization (NLPHO). While this affiliation did not change many of the referral patterns of the clinic's physicians, it did provide our major competitor's new PHO with a larger panel of physicians and a future potential for expanded and better reimbursed contracts with managed care companies.

Force Two: Schumpert Medical Center's NLHPO began executing contracts with a number of managed care companies (HMOs) that in many cases were at reimbursement rates of less than their cost. Physicians in the NLHPO were encouraged to accept lower payments for their services (some cuts were as much as 30 percent) so that HMOs would negotiate with their organization.

These "low-ball" rates placed pressure on our health system to consider a restructuring of our already lower than market rates at a time when over $500 million had been committed to the expansion of new facilities and services. Our competitor's below-cost pricing was made in an effort to recover from its declining market share, primarily brought on by the success of WK's new hospital (WK Bossier), WK Heart Institute, WK-LSU Organ Transplant Program and our HMO, Health Plus of Louisiana.

However, above all other factors, Schumpert's management was anticipating greater losses of admissions after WK's 1997 announcement of the building of a new hospital in southeast Shreveport, WK Pierremont. This section of the city was heretofore the exclusive patient turf of Schumpert, which enjoyed 70 percent of the local market share. Their concerns were realized; between 1996 and 2002, WK's inpatient admissions grew by 22,120 (or 107 percent).

Force Three: The passage of the 1997 Balanced Budget Act by the U. S. Congress, the storm's third force, had a devastating financial impact, as it was responsible for the reduction of the health system's profits (net income) by approximately 50 percent, or $18-$20 million a year. This reduction forced the hospital to undertake major cost-cutting initiatives, including reduction of our employee workforce by over two-hundred positions. Fortunately, as a result of contingency planning brought on by the need to tighten our financial belts after the impact of the first two forces, management had secured most of the employee cuts through the less painful route of attrition.

Force Four: Health Plus of Louisiana, WK's wholly owned HMO, which had been successful in growing our health system's patient base, was facing insurmountable business challenges. A large number of the area's major businesses with Health Plus coverage were being sold or merged with national or regional conglomerates with established managed care or health insurance contracts. The loss of these large contracts reduced Health Plus's membership and opportunities for continued growth. While Health Plus continued at breakeven or slightly better profitability and its contracts continued to route patients to WK physicians, its membership dipped from almost fifty thousand to thirty-two thousand members. Further, Health Plus's two largest corporate accounts were reducing their work forces.

The Eye of the Storm: Blue Skies of Hope

Like the eye of a hurricane, a period of tranquility and beautiful weather came after the first four forces of our perfect storm. We believed that we were emerging from the destructive storm forces, and our health system leaders began to feel more positive about our financial situation. A spirit of renewed confidence took over, supported by the growth and tremendous success of our two new full-service hospitals, WK Bossier Health Center and WK Pierremont Health Center, and three new centers of excellence, WK Pierremont Portico Medical Mall, WK Cancer Center and WK Heart Hospital and Institute, all of which had remarkable positive cash flows in their first months of operations. During this time, WK Pierremont's high occupancy rate precipitated the construction of an additional patient tower of eighty beds.

The Tower at WK Pierremont was under construction within one year of the opening of the initial hospital. On the surface, things seemed to be heading in the right direction. Little did we know that our greatest test of character was yet to come.

The Fifth Force of The Storm

It is easier to resist at the beginning than at the end.

Leonardo da Vinci (1452-1519)

This prophetic thought proved to be quite accurate in the case of our storm's fifth and most powerful force, a result of national trends brought about by Medicare and health insurance providers' formulas for reimbursements for outpatient services. While the logic behind such reimbursement eludes me, outpatient rates of reimbursement are more profitable than those of inpatients, even though hospitals with large inpatient populations are forced by community health needs to provide many expensive yet unprofitable safety net services (such as around-the-clock emergency, obstetrical, neonatal, behavioral health services and uncompensated indigent care).

Force Five: In the year 2000, a new day of physician entrepreneurship dawned when a large group of physician specialists announced their intent to construct an off-campus surgery center, to be completed in eighteen months. To take advantage of the inequitable outpatient reimbursement rates, some physicians established private facilities, in direct competition with WK, for outpatient procedures. The existing reimbursement formula permitted the competing physicians to "cherry pick" the most profitable patient procedures, while referring the least profitable procedures to not-for-profit safety net hospitals. The fifth and most powerful force was not only destructive financially but also mandated changes in our historical physician/hospital relationships.

These ventures were not only threatening our health system's financial health and jeopardizing its future mission, but also laying waste friendships and relationships of some physicians with WK and one another. We did not foresee that time-tested personal relationships with some of our medical staff members, most of whom I had been personally involved in recruiting to WK, would become intensely adversarial and hostile.

A Milieu of Tension and Mistrust

Better an honest enemy than a false friend.

German Proverb

Dissension within our medical staff ranks became public knowledge around the city, fueled by personal and public attacks on loyal physicians and administrative staff. Our medical staff and management team accepted that the physician entrepreneurs had every legal right to compete for outpatient services in opposition to our health system. However, issues of ethical behavior prompted the non-competitor (loyal) physicians to become upset with the entrepreneurial physicians, who chose to take their referred patients to their privately owned and competitive facilities over the voiced objections of the referring physician. Many of the referring physicians were concerned that the competitive facilities lacked adequate medical specialty support services in the event of a medical emergency. Their complaints generally fell on deaf ears, while the competing physicians referred their no pay or low profit surgeries to WK.

Some entrepreneurial physicians chose to remain in positions of leadership in our medical staff structure, amid charges that they were acting as if they had no fiduciary responsibilities to the health system. Charges of conflicts of interest and disruptive behavior were rampant as medical staff leaders attempted, unsuccessfully, to conduct business in a climate of objectivity, harmony and cooperation. Loyalist physicians and management were pitted against the entrepreneurial physicians.

Much of the progress of the system was grinding to a halt as the battle raged. Until this time our management and trustee relationship with our physician staff had always been one of trust, cordiality and support of mission. No health system had ever been blessed with a greater degree of mutual teamwork, trust and warmth of relationships among these groups.

But change in these relationships was evolving. It seemed there was nothing I, or anyone else, could do to dissuade the competing physicians from undertaking these destructive financial activities. In spite of this action on the part of the competitor physicians, I was somewhat in denial as I refused to accept the reality of the situation. I chose not to fully accept the fact that some of our heretofore loyal physicians would participate in ventures that jeopardized not only the health system's mission, but also the careers of so many nurses, technicians, staff and other physicians who had supported them over the years. In my opinion, the entrepreneurial physicians were acting with seemingly little thought for their responsibility to their patients. A physician always has an ethical responsibility to protect his patients from financial as well as physical harm, not to take advantage of the trust the patient places in him.

Early during this cataclysmic period I prepared a paper titled "'Enronitis' and Physician Entrepreneurship," which outlined my perspective regarding physician competitive entrepreneurial ventures. In this article I attempted to describe a number of ethical issues concerning physician ownership of patient services outside their offices.

I am sad to say that, at the time, the reasoning of this paper was lost on many of our medical staff physicians, competitors and non-competitors alike. Competing physicians rejected such thinking outright, while non-competitor physicians agreed with my reasoning but were unwilling to challenge the physician entrepreneurs.

They had no idea of the financial damage these ventures would ultimately have on their hospitals and their personal practices; therefore many chose to sidestep the issue because of personal relationships and lack of options in subspecialist referrals. No one could fault these loyal physicians for their actions because most of the damage done by the competitor physicians was not fully evident at the time.

The fact that so many of our former medical staff leaders would undertake projects in competition with their hospital, threatening its finances, mission and relationships, was incredible to me. Who would provide the full range of healthcare services required by the community, year around, without regard to the patient's ability to pay, if their hospitals were forced to close due to financial lack of support? Who would then fulfill the vital, and often uncompensated, community safety net services (emergency, obstetrics, neonatal)? Certainly, not their privately owned ventures that operated basically eight hours a day, five days a week with no night services. Continued financial losses would jeopardize virtually all charity care within our hospitals and indigent clinics.

Most of these competing physicians had been recruited, provided offices and supported by the health system; in essence, they had been provided a practice turf on which there was little or no competition in their specialties. These monopolies existed because the health system assisted the continued growth of its specialty groups, rather than encourage the formation of other competitive ones.[35] This *modus operandi* created larger groups that could in turn recruit subspecialists within their specialties while enhancing the life styles of the groups through reducing after-hour emergency call assignments. It was commonly believed the reasons for these actions on the part of the hospital were honorable and in the best interests of all concerned parties.

My angst and frustration were so great that, for the first time in my career, I considered leaving Willis-Knighton. After being approached by a large and well-respected medical center in another state (one with no issues of physician competitive ventures, being a certificate of need state), I wrote down the pros and cons of staying in Shreveport. In my naïve thinking, I debated whether my relocation or retirement, providing WK with a change of leadership, would halt the groundswell of physicians who were starting competitive ventures. Maybe they would have a change of heart and return to the fold of hospital supporters. Maybe cordial relations would be restored, and nirvana would be attained.

But trustees and physicians in whom I confided chided me for such unrealistic hopes. Their rationale was that this new entrepreneurial era was pervasive in the healthcare world and would continue, no matter who led Willis-Knighton. They were right—most healthcare systems in states without certificate of need legislation, like Louisiana, were experiencing the same forces. This reasoning helped me accept some of the harsh realities of the time, and I stopped blaming myself for everything that happened.

35 A wise surgeon once urged me to not "let physicians bunch" by encouraging the formation of large groups of specialists to the exclusion of a number of smaller competitive groups. He advocated greater competition: "Don't put all of your eggs in one basket, Jim. The day may come when you rue that decision."

Physician-owned ventures were not going away, and I had to do what was best for Willis-Knighton, no matter what the consequences were for the competitive physicians.

At the height of the turmoil of this intense, gut-wrenching period, when the personal attacks on me by the competitor physicians were raging, a friend shared a comforting thought by Confucius: "If you are true you will know it. For all the good people in your village will like you and all the others will hate you." As painful as it was, I came to the realization that some change was required. Our status quo was not sustainable and would eventually threaten the future viability of the health system.

Negative Impacts of the Storm

By 2001, a number of competitive physician-owned ventures, including two short-stay hospitals and several outpatient centers for surgery, imaging, endoscopy and radiation therapy, began to hurt Willis-Knighton in the following quantifiable ways:

1. The loss of a large portion of our most profitable outpatient product lines was having a major impact on patient volume and profitability. Losses of procedures to physician competitor facilities are reflected in the following illustrations: Graph 7 (page 222), a loss of 752 urological procedures (63 percent); Graph 8 (page 222), a loss of 1,490 orthopaedic procedures (62 percent); Graph 9 (page 224), a loss of 4,833 gastroenterology (GI) procedures (72 percent) and Graph 10 (page 224), a loss of 485 otolaryngology (ENT) procedures (70 percent).

2. From year 2001 to 2004 the system's EBITDA (cash flow) was reduced by approximately $20 million annually. The net income in 2003 of $92,902 was the lowest the health system had recorded in over forty years, a $30 million reduction from 1998. A comparison of the annual net incomes of the mid 1990s, when the first forces of the perfect storm appeared, to that of 2003 and 2004 reflected a staggering reduction, averaging approximately $25 million each year.

3. However, even in this devastating financial downturn from 1996 to 2002, our annual inpatient admissions grew by 22,120 (107 percent) as a result of the openings of WK Bossier and WK Pierremont, while gross revenue grew by $821 million (209 percent). This continued growth of inpatients and the tripling of gross patient revenue might have given us a false sense of security; if these had been the only indicators monitored, they could have lulled our management team into an attitude of complacency. But not so! An old idiom in business

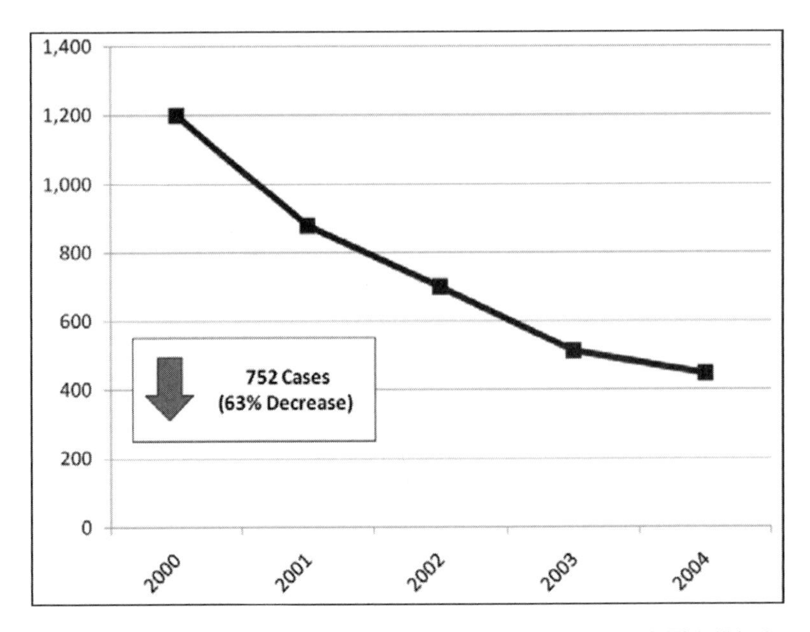

Graph 7: Trend line tracking number of urological procedures performed in WK facilities by competitor entrepreneurial physicians from dates shown.

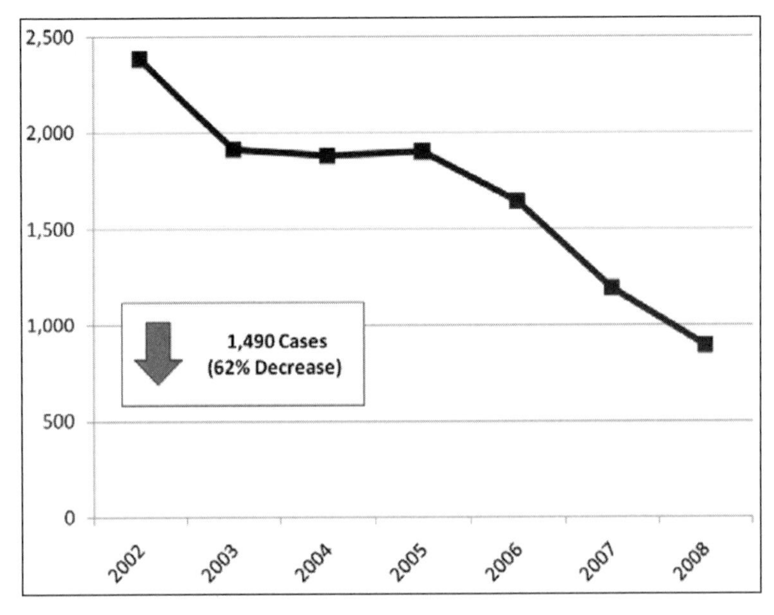

Graph 8: Trend line tracking number of orthopaedic procedures performed in WK facilities by competitor entrepreneurial physicians from dates shown.

states, "you cannot make up your losses by continuing to sell your services at a rate less than your cost of providing those services." Increasing volume becomes immaterial when it comes at the expense of financial performance. A continued decline of our outpatient business would continue to erode our financial position.

4. Many of the health and well-being services offered to the underprivileged residents of the region would have to be curtailed if our health system did not have the financial strength to continue them.

5. Some competing physicians attempted to recruit our hospital employees through offers of attractive perks of no night or weekend work schedules. They had free rein to undertake this unethical behavior as they made patient rounds, performed surgery in the hospital and spoke disparagingly about the health system and its leadership. Employee morale was affected.

6. Discord within our medical staff was fueled by negative remarks about the health system and its activities by some physician competitors. The comments were designed to have a negative impact on the loyal physicians' support of the system, as the detractors hoped to move hospital outpatients of the loyal physicians to their competitive facilities.

7. It became difficult for the medical staff to discipline disruptive and inappropriate behavior on the part of competitive physicians because factions of the competing entrepreneurial physicians served on peer oversight panels that investigated such incidents. Gridlock was the rule of the day as the loyalist physicians and competitor physicians battled over allegations of unethical and disruptive behavior.

8. Two of the largest groups of specialists involved in competitive ventures vacated their offices on the campuses of our four hospitals without much advance notice to their patients. These below-the-radar moves created market confusion, longer response times between inpatient rounds by physicians and slower response times for emergency cases–all of which caused a widely held perception of our health system's instability. Vacant physician office buildings coupled with some of the competitors' slow responses to patient care tended to foster an uneasy feeling that "all is not well at WK."

9. Some of the competitor physicians' longer response times to inpatient needs and emergencies precipitated an increase in their patient lengths of stay of an additional 1.1 days, a 25 percent increase over our average length of stay, with corresponding quantifiable increases in costs to both the patients and our hospitals. These delayed rounds and slower response times by the competitor physicians, coupled with the lack of familiarity of their partner physician's patient conditions,

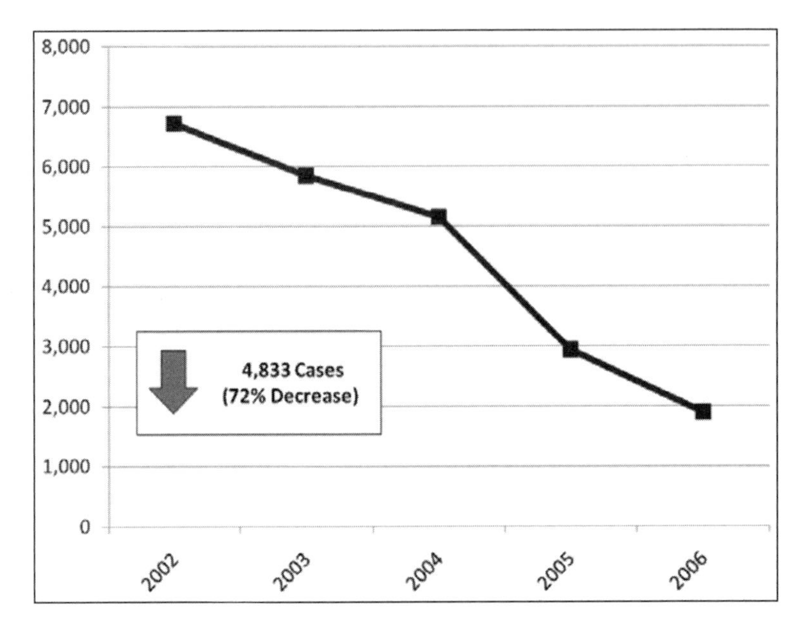

Graph 9: Trend line tracking number of GI procedures performed in WK facilities by competitor entrepreneurial physicians from dates shown.

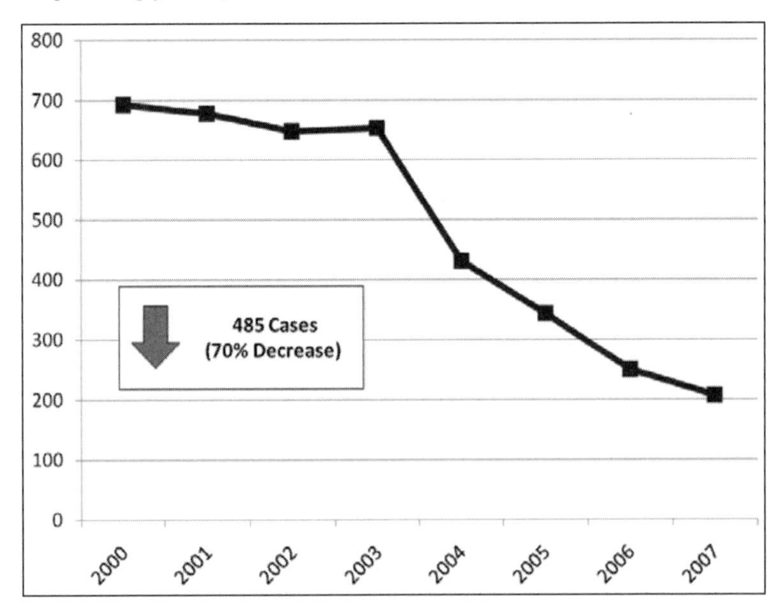

Graph 10: Trend line tracking number of ENT procedures performed in WK facilities by competitor entrepreneurial physicians from dates shown.

> promoted an increase in patient and family dissatisfactions and complaints. Malpractice threats grew substantially. Until it was brought to management's attention, a number of inpatients were transported to the competitors' remote outpatient sites for simple treatments or procedures, such as catheter care. These complaints led to an increase in the number of threatened malpractice claims against the health system and the attending physicians.

As I reflect on those events, which caused such problems to our health system, I see parallels between some of the competing physicians' actions and the behavior of our Weimaraner. Mallory, our adopted pound dog, has this view of all property in our home: 1) "If I like it, it's mine." 2) "If I get tired of it, it's yours." and 3) "If I want it back, it's mine." This analogy applies because we had previously relieved a number of these competing physicians from financial losses sustained through their ownership of an outpatient surgery center on our campus. A number of these new competitors were the same surgeons that WK had bailed out of losses from a previous competitive venture. At that time, many of these financially rescued physicians promised never again to work against the best interests of the health system and its patient community.

What Should the Health System Do?

When life knocks you down to your knees,

you are in a perfect position to pray.

Anonymous

Our administrative staff had been studying the reactions of major health systems around the country to their physician competitive ventures, and we realized that our situation was more complex than theirs. It was exacerbated by our management's routine practice of honoring requests of our large specialty groups to recruit all new physician specialists to their practices, thereby eliminating competition.

This prior naïve *modus operandi* left our mega groups with a monopoly on their specialties. At this time, all the orthopaedic surgeons, urologists and gastroenterologists on the North, South and Bossier campuses were now in competition with our health system for outpatient services. All ear, nose and throat specialists on the Bossier and Pierremont campuses also became fierce competitors.

Our management and medical staff leadership now understood the lesson conveyed by the old expression, "No good deed goes unpunished." This exclusivity of previous recruiting strategies was now working to the detriment of the health system.

Accepting the reality that physician entrepreneurship was not going away, and a new course of action was needed, we came to this conclusion: "We cannot direct the winds... but we can adjust our sails." WK's management, medical staff and physician network leaders determined that there were only four possible courses of action:

1. **Do nothing and hope the situation would go away, possibly through government intervention** (reduced reimbursement formulas for Medicare and Medicaid would reduce the profitability of the physician ventures, or perhaps such ventures would be prohibited). But hoping that such intervention would cause a change of heart and mind and bring the physicians back to the hospital system was not realistic.

As I considered this option, the following admonition by Robertson Davies (1913-1995), a Canadian novelist, came to mind. "The world is full of people whose notion of a satisfactory future is, in fact, a return to the idealized." There could be no turning back to the physician/hospital relationships of years gone by.

To adopt this approach reminds me of the story of a man who went to the fortune teller to predict his future. The clairvoyant looked into her crystal ball and said: "You will be poor and unhappy until you are forty-five years of age." "Then what will happen?" asked the man hopefully. "Then you will get used to it."

2. **Joint ventures with willing physician entrepreneurs** in their outpatient ventures was the most common course of action taken by health systems throughout the country. However, this option presented more than a little heartburn for our hospital leaders, medical staff, trustees and management because of the following concerns:

   A. According to the Harvard Business Review, the average lifespan of joint hospital/physician ventures is seven years, a relatively short term for ventures of this import.

   B. There was no assurance that the competing physicians would entertain a partnership venture with WK, and if they would, at what price of ownership. Without such approval, joint venturing is a moot point, as competition for these product lines continues.

C. If the health system were successful in receiving approval by the investors for a joint venture, WK would be required to continue providing all product service lines and equipment to serve the outpatients of non-joint venture physicians who chose to support the health system outpatient services and patients whose insurance plans were not accepted at the joint venture facilities, including all Medicaid plan enrollees.

D. Historically, hospitals have been expected by physician partners to be the primary buyers of failed ventures at higher than market values. Years ago, we had a similar experience in the buying out of a failed physician-owned surgery center on our main campus. Some of the physicians rescued from that venture were the ones now choosing to again compete with the health system. We had been there and done that.

E. How could we justify partnering with only a small number of our most highly compensated physicians in such ventures to the detriment of the health system and other loyal physicians? We would be creating and supporting a caste system of haves and have-nots within our medical staff.

F. In our case, many of these physician entrepreneurs were "splitters" with multiple hospital loyalties. Those physicians that practiced primarily at a competitor hospital would be reluctant to fully commit to utilize a co-owned venture to the exclusion of their primary hospital. Therefore there would be no guarantee of exclusivity of referrals even with a joint venture to permit accurate volume forecasts and budget projections.

G. Would the financial return from a major joint venture ensure the continued availability and provision of equipment, staffing and programs required by the health system to adequately serve the patient needs of all medical staff physicians, not just the joint venture partners?

H. How could we justify giving away revenues and the profitability of outpatient services that are required to support the health system's mission, without at first attempting to take some forceful action that might preserve the entire profitability for the health system's future?

I. Is joint venturing with the entrepreneurial physicians, which may be done in the interest of maintaining a harmonious relationship with a small number of staff physicians, merely putting off an inevitable decision for stronger competitive action in the future? Sir Winston Churchill warned, "An appeaser is one that feeds a crocodile, hoping it will eat him last."

J. The last, but certainly not the least, concern was that physician joint ventures hinder the growth of hospital networks of employed physicians. Future chances to develop a hospital-owned network of employed physician specialists would generally be made more difficult or possibly lost forever.

This line of reasoning is supported by a thought from Edward Heath (1916-2005), a former UK Prime Minister, who offered, "All of us must rid ourselves of the illusions that we can buy our way out of the problems of today by mortgaging our future."

3. The third option for action was to **take a "head on" approach by competing with the entrepreneurial physicians for all contested outpatient services.** With Dwight D. Eisenhower's admonition in mind, "Neither a wise man nor a brave man lies down on the tracks of history to wait for the train of the future to run over him," we came to the decision that our actions of today would determine our future. There could be no appeasement or capitulation to the whims and demands of the competitor physicians, no matter the cost to relationships. Our trustees, management team and medical staff decided that our best course of action was to compete head to head with the competitor physicians. Our message to them would clearly have to be, "Either support all WK outpatient services or we will be forced to compete with you by recruiting physicians of your specialty." And we had to make it clear to our community that no part of Willis-Knighton, a major community asset, was for sale or would be surrendered without a fight. Our battle flag was raised!

However, for this option to be successful there had to be a herculean effort by the system's management and medical staff to recruit approximately fifty replacement specialists. A strong element of trust on the part of the staff physicians in the health system had to exist for this option to be successful because it is only human nature to embrace the theory that a known quantity is usually better than an unknown one. It was imperative that all recruited physicians be of exceptional quality and training. The recruited physicians also had to be courageous because they were entering a battle zone of heated competition. To promote patient referrals to these new specialists, considerable time would be required to introduce them to the medical staff. Massive marketing campaigns would be required to inform the public of the new specialists' practice locations. Our physicians' trust in the WK recruiters would be critical to the success of this endeavor.

4. The fourth option to WK was to **file a lawsuit in federal court against a group of sixteen practicing surgeons**, formerly

> with offices on most private hospital campuses, who had merged into a single corporation to provide specialty care at only one site in Shreveport/Bossier City. The grounds would be restraint of trade and predatory, monopolistic practices. The sixteen surgeons, 100 percent of the private practicing specialists in their field in northwest Louisiana, had merged their offices at a site considered by many patients to be less than convenient and a great distance from most hospitals in the city.

For the first time, WK's management team faced a force so great that sheer work ethic alone would not prevent the financial harm to our health system. No fine tuning of the organization's economical effectiveness could thwart it. A new and bold *modus operandi* had to be selected, structured and placed into service quickly. Never again would it be business as usual in a traditional harmonious setting of medical staff / management / trustee / employee relationships for our health system.

My Inner-Relational Conflicts

The path of social advancement is [sometimes] strewn with broken friendships.

H.G. Wells (1866-1946)

I must admit that I had a difficult time making the decision required to combat the devastating impact of this fifth force, physician competition for outpatient services. The optimal strategies required the replacement of long-tenured physicians (my long-time friends and members of our medical staff) and the pursuit of legal action against the most egregious entrepreneurial group.

These two strategies caused me remorse and sadness. It was as if deaths were occurring, as most of these physicians were disappearing from my life. It seemed everywhere I turned these events were disturbing a natural rhythm; I was forced to change my family's personal physicians in the specialties of orthopaedics, gastroenterology, urology and ear, nose and throat.

Intellectually, I knew the strategies of recruiting new physician specialists to the WK

Physician Network as employees and filing of an anti-trust lawsuit were the best courses of action, but it was still difficult on a personal level for me. Many of these displaced physicians, I believed, would not accept the health system's right to compete on a level playing field for outpatient services and would act out their anger toward everyone at our hospitals. I was right. The physician dining rooms became centers of discord and bitterness.

At that time, the WK Physician Network consisted of approximately one hundred and seventy physicians, most in primary care. A conscious decision had been made years before that our network would not recruit competition for our loyal specialty physicians but employ primary care physicians, who had been hurt financially by prevailing reimbursement formulas. Referrals of their patients were made to our previously loyal specialists, now our competitors. The system had basically awarded a *de facto* monopoly to our specialty physicians. As it became apparent that the optimal strategy was the recruitment of specialists to compete with all the entrepreneurial physicians, the battle heated up.

After thoughtful deliberation, the board of trustees, upon the recommendation of management and the medical staff's executive committee, unanimously approved the following actions:

Action One: Recruit Specialists to the Willis-Knighton Network

Our "compete, not capitulate" strategy of recruiting specialists to the WK Physician Network to replace the competing physicians was necessary, no matter how distasteful, if WK was to continue to thrive rather than merely survive. "Thriving" required a financially sound *modus operandi* to ensure the continued provision of the latest technology, facilities, programs and staff for giving the highest quality of care. Our humanitarian Duties of Conscience programs for the underserved were also at risk of closure. Merely surviving the storm by returning to the hard fiscal times of our first fifty years was not an option to our health system's leadership. Continuing to thrive was the only option!

The executive committee of the medical staff and trustees also adopted three key policies, recommended by management, that were essential to the success of the system's strategy. These policies addressed the issues of conflict of interest, disruptive behavior and a revised Code of Conduct, applicable to all members of the governing board, medical staff and management. To my knowledge, no health system had ever implemented a more transparent and comprehensive set of rules of behavior. They prohibited trustees and managers with financial and personal conflicts from holding office and any medical staff member with such conflicts from serving in a position of leadership on the medical staff. However, medical staff membership and privileges to practice within the health system were not affected by this policy. To this day, no person in a position of authority in the health system has any financial or personal conflicts of interest that might stymie a climate of positive dialogue and prudent stewardship.

Action Two: Initiate Legal Action

In 2002, Willis-Knighton Health System filed an anti-trust suit against a group of sixteen competing physicians with the United States District Court for the Western District of Louisiana.

This restraint of trade case was settled a few years later. While the terms of the settlement are confidential, I can share some of the positive outcomes for our health system:

1. Patient and family complaints decreased as a result of these changes.
    - A. Response times for inpatient and emergency patient care coverage by the physicians were shortened.
    - B. Unnecessary transports of patients to physician offices for routine hospital procedures ceased, thereby removing transport fees, duplicate charges and inconvenience to patients and families.
    - C. Patient records at the physicians' offices, surgery center and im-

aging centers were made more accessible to hospital emergency rooms; that meant more rapid diagnoses and elimination of repeat imaging procedures.

D. Disruptive and morale-impacting behavior on the part of the competing group toward Willis-Knighton employees ceased.

E. Fewer patients at any one of our four emergency rooms with readily treatable diagnoses are transported to the physician surgery center for outpatient procedures or to other hospitals in the city where the patient has no primary care physician relationship.

2. The lawsuit demonstrated WK's resolve to fight for its right to compete on a level playing field with this medical group of surgeons and any other physicians contemplating such monopolistic ventures.

3. A window of opportunity for WK to recruit competitor physicians was created as a result of the defendant group's reluctance to recruit additional associates during the case (for fear of further charges of anti-trust violations).

4. In the early days of the lawsuit, the system's loyal medical staff members were reluctant to take a public stand on the health system's decision to file suit, primarily because there were no other specialists in the region to whom they could refer their patients. In time, as the climate of competition began to take a toll on the health system's finances and physicians saw the negative behavior of some competitor physicians (both in medical staff meetings and on patient rounds), many of them better understood the actions of management and voiced their support. A climate of respect and appreciation emerged as a result of the courage and convictions of both WK management and trustees as they stood up to physician competition. The medical staff members began to take an active role in the hospital's efforts to recruit new surgeons to the physician network.

Did We Choose the Right Strategies?

It is not the going out of port, but the coming in,

that determines the success of a voyage.

Henry Ward Beecher (1813-1887)

At a recent meeting, a healthcare consultant was presenting strategies to combat competitive physician ventures. A distraught administrator sought advice from the consultant by asking, "What can I do to ensure my hospital's future now that all of the surgeons in my town are opening their privately owned imaging and surgery centers?" Before the consultant could answer, an administrator in the audience gave this sobering advice: "Update your resume and contact an executive search firm."

While the answer was not very diplomatic and simply intended to lighten the mood, the advice was not far off the mark. It has been proven that a hospital has little hope to prosper once a significant volume of its most profitable outpatient service lines (imaging, lab, therapy, radiation oncology and surgery) are lost to competitive physician-owned facilities.

In reaction to the vigorous actions taken by our health system to combat our "perfect storm," you may ask if our management and medical staff took the most effective courses of action. We believe our post-storm data speaks for itself. Not only have we emerged from the stormy barrage, weathered but intact, but in a purely financial sense our health system is no longer merely surviving but thriving beyond our greatest expectations. Its future looks bright, fortified by our large network of employed physicians that ensures our patient volumes.

As the network continues to grow, an increasing number of the region's patient referrals come under the control of our network physicians (80 percent of the primary care physicians in Shreveport/Bossier City) whose loyalty and support of WK, the region's most prominent patient safety net hospital, is steadfast. Their deep-rooted, faithful commitment prohibits them from supporting competitive ventures, physician-owned or otherwise.

I believe our physician competitors will be unable to maintain their present volumes of patients in the future. The increasing starvation of referrals to these rival physicians will eventually mean a decrease in their numbers of office visits. Any diminution in their patient volumes will have an adverse effect on their competitive endeavors. A surgeon hurrying to get to his office once commented to me, "Jim, I have to examine a lot of patients to find the few that need surgery. A surgeon's volume is dictated by his number of office visits."

Without referrals from 80 percent of the primary care physicians in Shreveport/ Bossier City, the competing physicians will be unable to maintain present patient volume and incomes. In my opinion they will be forced to find other sources of revenue to maintain their standards of living. Without the influx of new patients, the competitor physicians may be forced to: 1) increase charges, 2) provide new treatment protocols that are unavailable in the community, 3) overuse ancillary procedures (X-ray, CT, MRI or radiation therapy) or 4) move routine office procedures to their expensive treatment settings (i.e. surgery rooms). No matter what tactic they adopt, one of their biggest challenges will be to compete with the level of WK's outpatient charges, which continue to be the lowest in the region. Patient charges are destined for greater future public scrutiny, oversight and comparison with other providers.

While our health system's future looks bright, I am sad to say that my earlier concerns regarding the loss of friendship with these physician entrepreneur competitors have materialized, for many of them severed their personal and professional relationships with our management and physicians. Advice by Mother Teresa has been etched in my mind and is comforting at times of personal and professional reflection: "If you are successful, you win false friends and true enemies. Succeed anyway." But I do have bouts of sadness as I recall the less trying times of camaraderie, and I will continue to voice my appreciation for many past contributions that some of these now estranged physicians made to the success of Willis-Knighton.

Additionally, I am pleased to relate that a number of the estranged physicians have returned to the welcoming arms of WK, for they are realizing that all parties, including patients, are best served when there is a united approach to healthcare delivery, and a number of the competitive ventures have been dissolved.

Further Evidence of Our Successful Strategy

The health system's reclamation of the lost outpatient procedures is reflected in our present debt-free position and our financial success. The following illustrations (Graphs 11-16 on page 236, 237, and 238) reflect the tremendous success achieved through the growth of the physician network, now some 350 physicians and growing, and favorable credit ratings with Moody's and S&P's support.

A number of hospitals have requested information regarding our competitive strategies; unfortunately, it is probably too late for many of them to be as successful as WK. They have delayed too long in taking actions, lack funding to sustain start-up costs and losses incurred by new network physicians, or have taken joint-venture routes that will continue to plague them with future challenges.

Affirmations of Quality of Care

In the years after the storm, awards of quality affirmation, more than at any other time in our history, resulted from the positive dynamics of our physician network and aligned physicians on the medical staff for the following reasons:

1. Physician Network members and aligned physicians readily identify themselves as system supporters, willingly accepting their duty to protect system assets and support its mission of promoting the health and well-being of our community.

2. Medical staff meetings have become focused on clinical quality and other issues of substance, not petty issues of personal agendas. This fact has been borne out by the most recent surveys of The Joint Commission and national recognitions of quality care.

3. Employees of the health system feel more appreciated when the physicians with whom they work are not ridiculing and undermining their hospital. Such behavior impacts employees' morale and *esprit de corps*. For example, in 2009, *Nursing Professionals* magazine featured our health system as one of the top 100 hospitals in the country for nurses' conditions of employment.

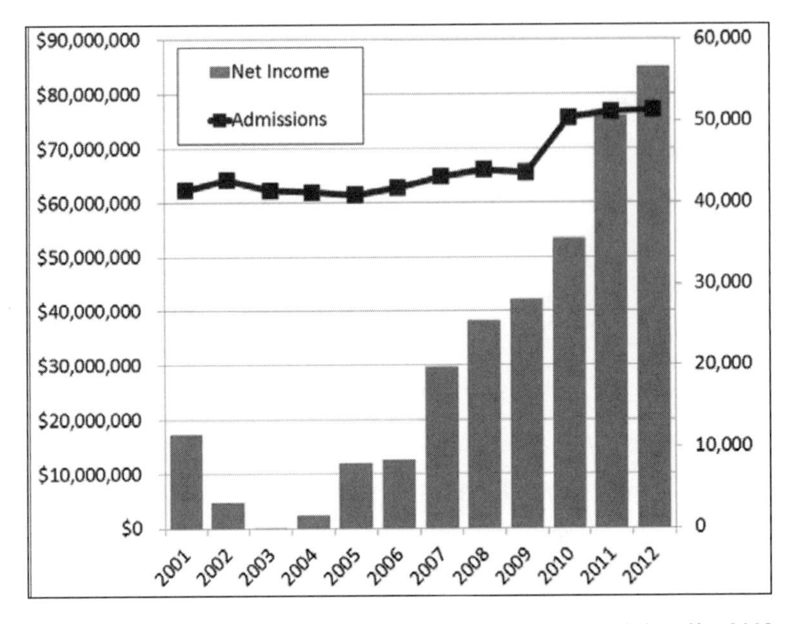

Graph 11: WK's net income, 2001-2012, juxtaposed with inpatient admissions. Year 2003 was the least profitable year ($92,902) since 1965.

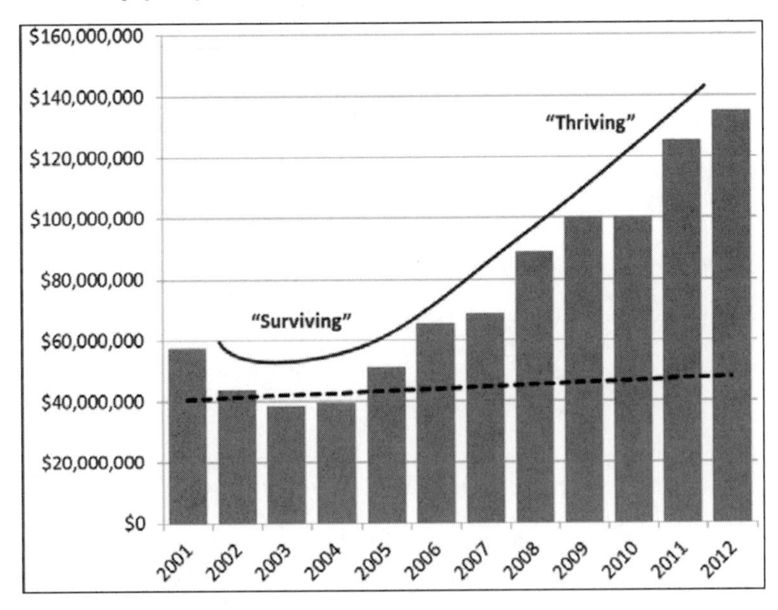

Graph 12: WK EBITDA, 2001-2012. The dotted line (increasing annually from $40 million) denotes the amount of capital the health system must invest annually to cover plant property and depreciation expenses. Enhancements and depreciation in plant and technology are additional.

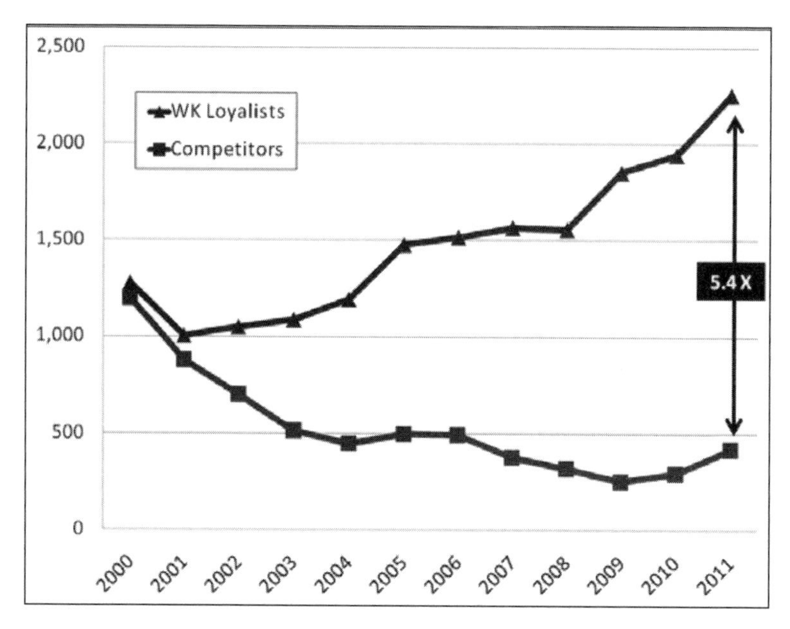

Graph 13: Trend line tracking urological procedures performed in WK facilities after WK chose to compete by hiring new specialists for its physician network. Network physicians now perform 5.4 times the volume of the competitor urologists.

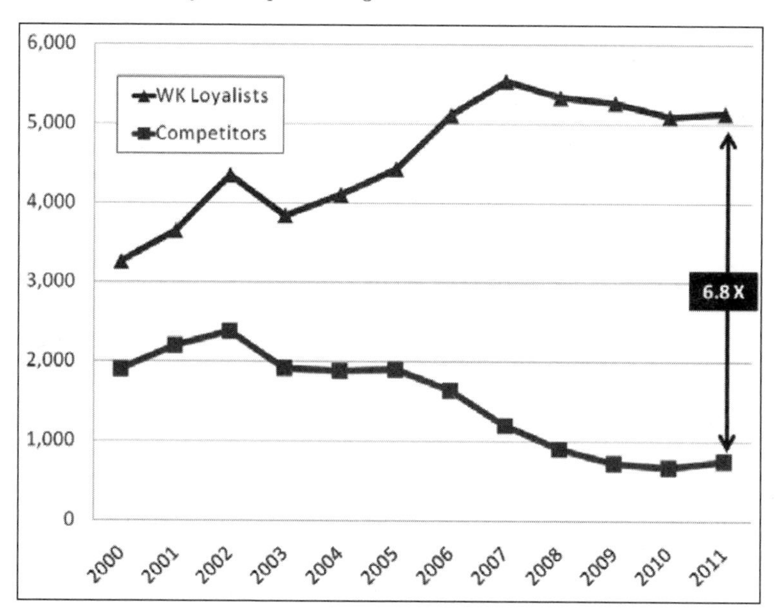

Graph 14: Trend line tracking orthopaedic procedures performed in WK facilities after WK chose to compete by hiring new specialists for its physician network. Network physicians now perform 6.8 times the volume of the competitor orthopaedic surgeons.

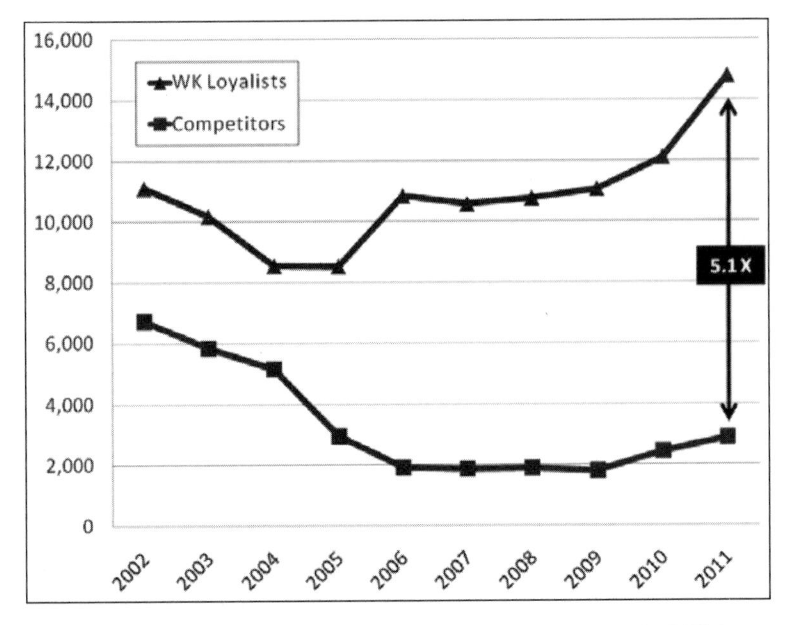

Graph 15: Trend line tracking GI procedures performed in WK facilities after WK chose to compete by hiring new specialists for its physician network. Network physicians now perform 5.1 times the volume of the competitor gastrointestinal specialists.

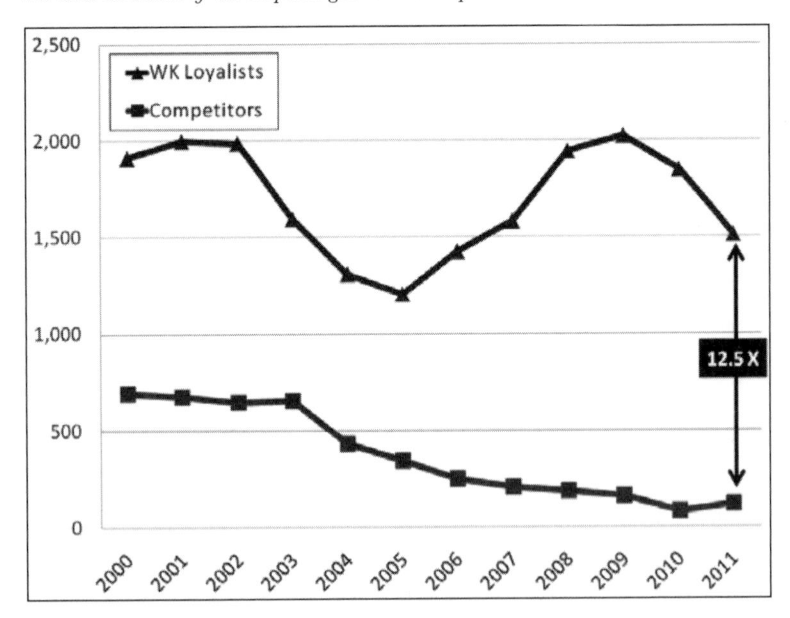

Graph 16: Trend line tracking ENT procedures performed in WK facilities after WK chose to compete by hiring new specialists for its physician network. Network physicians now perform 12.5 times the volume of the competitor ENT specialists.

Reflections on the Perfect Storm

Adversity has the effect of eliciting talents, which in prosperous circumstances would have lain dormant.

Horace (1st century B.C.)

Our decision to compete with the entrepreneurial physicians is further validated in Graph 17 (on page 240), which verifies that a modern hospital cannot survive on inpatient admissions only; outpatient revenue is paramount to fiscal success. The health system's revenue was so negatively impacted during this period that WK was in a perilous position of merely surviving, rather than thriving–a status which is necessary for the health system to remain a key community philanthropic partner and the region's largest patient safety net provider.

As I consider the accomplishments and growth of WK's Physician Network, I can't help pondering the above declaration by Horace, the poet and philosopher. This thought was thoroughly demonstrated by actions of the Willis-Knighton trustees, managers and medical staff leaders as they rose to the task at hand and worked tirelessly to ensure that their health system would not merely survive this perfect storm but thrive in its aftermath.

During our darkest hours, WK leaders did not seek to retaliate, but rather chose to take the high road of conduct. What was in the best interests of our patients and their families was always foremost in our hearts, thoughts and actions as the storm endangered the future services of Willis-Knighton.

But this I know: never again will our health system hesitate to take deliberative action against any forces that threaten its future viability and its mission. Through such actions our institution will remain a beacon of healthcare in the Ark-La-Tex for generations to come, while the short-sighted actions of a few physicians will soon pass into distant and unremarkable memories. WK has been blessed beyond measure as it con-

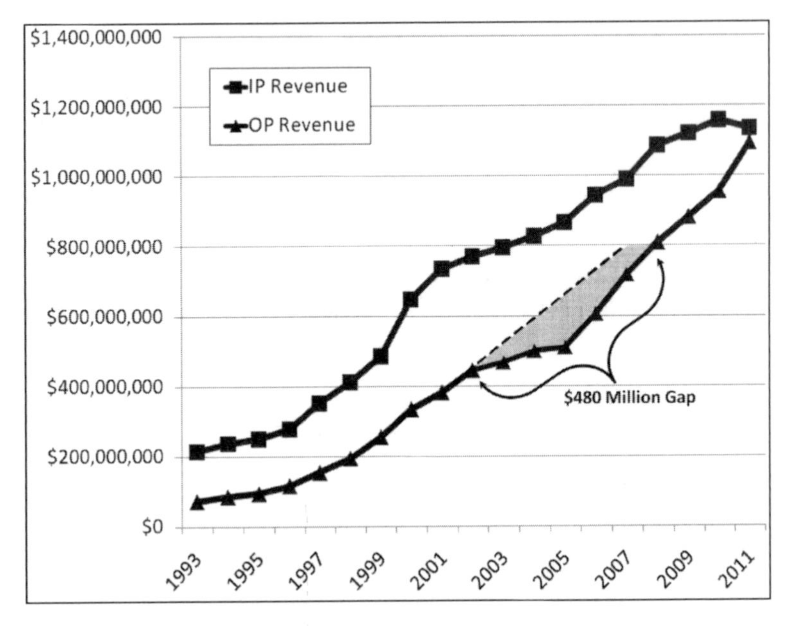

Graph 17: The actions of the competitive entrepreneurial physicians cost the health system an estimated $480 million in gross revenue 2002-2008 (approximately $20 million per year was siphoned from the hospital's net revenue, which correlates to the losses shown in Graph 15). The total loss for these years is reflected in the shaded area below the dotted line.

tinues to afford to plant trees of human kindness under whose shade many of us will never rest.

CHAPTER 9

Learning from Another's Mistakes

Not yet, gentlemen, not yet: when your enemy is executing a false movement never interrupt him

Napoleon Bonaparte (**1769-1821**)

In the above quotation, Napoleon advised his lieutenants in battle never to interrupt their foes as they made imprudent mistakes. The same should be said for your business competitor. I have learned a great deal from our rivals, much from the mistakes they have made.

In writing about another organization's mistakes, I do not want to come across as if I am a hospital administration genius who is overly critical of competitors. After all, I have made my fair share of mistakes as well. That is why this chapter was so difficult to write. But a smart executive carefully watches what competitors are doing...and what kind of responses their actions generate.

Our major competitor has been a wonderful hospital with a great history, and I do not want to denigrate in any way the years of dedication and compassion of its loyal staff. In 1907 the Sisters of Charity of the Incarnate Word took charge of Dr. T. E. Schumpert's 16-room hospital and nursing school in Shreveport. Over the years they set a high standard of care and consideration, and a great example for their talented employees and excellent physicians. When I arrived in 1965, it was apparent just how much they meant to the community.

In 1965 T. E. Schumpert Memorial Hospital was, in my opinion, the best hospital in Louisiana and one of the best in the nation with private and hospital-based specialists of excellent repute. It was revered by health professionals both locally and throughout the state. Their dedication to mission, a Christian ministry of healing, was always at the forefront of the nuns' decisions as they provided care to patients and service to the community, a level of service unsurpassed by any hospital in the region at that time. Also, Schumpert was rumored to be one of the most financially successful hospitals in its order.

A monumental change occurred at the hospital when Schumpert's owner, Sisters of Charity (headquartered in Houston), decided to change its administrative leadership to a lay person in the late 1980s. A new health corporation created by the merger of two Catholic orders in Texas in the late 1990s, continued this leadership model. I do not mean to imply that a lay administrator cannot have the heart for the mission. Certainly, as a lay administrator myself, I believe lay persons can provide effective and competent leadership. But from my outside perspective, I believe that some of the early lay administrators selected by the religious order were ill-prepared or shackled by corporate superiors who were not familiar with our market. It has been apparent that their corporate superiors did not fully appreciate that a strategy that works in one area of the country will not necessarily work in another.

Before proceeding any further, I must clarify one point. For approximately twelve years, this leadership model had much to do with altering the course of this great institution's financial history, but in no way has it impacted the quality of its patient care. Schumpert remains one of the best hospitals in the region as it provides an exceptional level of patient care.

However, the actions of a number of their early lay administrators were the genesis of a monumental transition that continues even today to erode the institution's patient base, former dominant market position, financial health and physician and employee relationships. These debilitating actions sapped the strength and vitality of the institution and were primarily responsible for the eventual relocation of over 125 of their staff physicians to WK and other hospitals. One of the Schumpert lay administrators remarked to me that the ghosts of these less than astute physician-related actions by predecessors continue to haunt their physician recruitment.

Let the Chips Fall

When I said I was hesitant to write about learning from competitors' mistakes, a number of former Schumpert physicians and employees familiar with those mistakes encouraged me to do so. I was even encouraged by academics, whose philosophy was "let the chips fall where they may." They felt an analysis of operational mistakes would be valuable as part of a case study and helpful to other healthcare professionals.

One aspect of this has been very touching. When talking about Schumpert's loss of dominance, former physicians and employees who had dedicated much of their lives in service to the hospital became teary-eyed. They acknowledge that the actions of some of the lay administrators were the cause of their relocation to other hospitals. They say that they would not have left if they had felt the lay administrators exhibited the same sense of ministry, purpose, partnership and fairness that was so lovingly demonstrated by the Sisters of Charity of the Incarnate Word at their hospitals for more than a century.

These former employees and physicians often refer to the spirit of Schumpert under the leadership of the nuns as one that made it an honor to serve, one that fostered a sense of duty and service to a common ministry, healing of their fellow man. Absent this nun-kindled spirit, the void of inspirational leadership was filled by the business-centric approaches of the early lay administrators that failed to win their physicians' and employees' support. To paraphrase a former Schumpert employee, in their attempts to acquire greater prosperity and market domination, they caused the loss of a kind of Divine Being sense of service that made it a privilege to work there.

A Changing of the Guard

The mill cannot grind with water that's past.

George Herbert (1593-1633)

It is only fair to state that I believe in recent years Schumpert's last three administrators, two physicians and a former medical technologist, all of whom had ties to our city prior to their appointments, made greater efforts than their predecessors to restore relationships among their own employees, other hospital administrators and leadership of the LSU Health Shreveport medical school. They were willing to collaborate on worthy projects when their superiors would permit them to do so.

I found them to be persons of character, integrity and veracity. However, since their arrivals, these administrators were consumed with continuous restructuring and downsizing to reduce services and personnel in an effort to turn around the hospital's discouraging financial picture.

So how did a great hospital that was the largest in the state, with a commanding market share of patient admissions and births, and one of the most financially profitable operations in its religious order lose that position in a little over ten years? The mistakes can teach valuable lessons.

Strategies Must Respond to Local and Market Needs

In my opinion, aside from the benefit of group purchasing and access to capital, larger not-for-profit hospitals generally derive few competitive advantages from a corporate affiliation. Distant corporate headquarters often inflict handicaps on local organizations, handicaps that prevent them from responding quickly and effectively to market needs and changes.

A hospital that is free to operate within the needs of the local community and dictates of its medical staff will have an advantage over one directed by a large, often sluggish, corporate headquarters that is far removed from patient care and physician interaction. When the profits of a high-performing corporate hospital are shared with hospitals that consistently underperform, the high performers can become discouraged and the poor performers can become complacent; their innovation, drive and work ethic suffer.

The late speaker of the U.S. House of Representatives, Tip O'Neill, said, "All politics is local." That is also true for healthcare. Hospitals are not franchises selling hamburgers. They are service organizations that "sell" individualized care, and every market is different. Basic standards and performance quality measures can be standardized nationally, but local governance allows hospitals to respond more rapidly to needs in their marketplaces.

In my opinion, as Schumpert became more corporate and less local in direction, it fell victim to a paralysis that appeared to be the result of its detached and uninformed out-of-town leadership, determined to utilize system-wide cookie cutter approaches and strategies for all problems. Prior to 1989, the local administrator-nuns had greater power to make unilateral decisions.

Successful Strategies Reflect the Cultures of a Region

Shortly after the arrival of Schumpert's first lay administrator, several of his controversial programs seemed to fly in the face of local conservative business and cultural traditions.

His first strategy, the well-publicized announcement of the opening of a gourmet restaurant (with lunch and dinner meals offered to the general public) in the lobby area of the new hospital building, met with little public resistance at first, as it was viewed as merely a novel idea. However, the hospital's shortage of parking for patients and families near the lobby entrance prompted voiced concerns about the new restaurant's impact. Another concern was the potential negative impact the restaurant might have on the morale of hospital employees. Lower paid employees would be unable to afford it, yet it would always be within view of their cafeteria and workplaces. For those employees who could afford to dine there, service delays could cause them to exceed their allotted lunch break times (the restaurant's waiter service would be slower than the cafeteria line next door).

When the cost of the décor (elegant furnishings with several large palm trees spaced throughout the restaurant) became known, there was a murmuring of discontent focused on such extravagant expenditures by a not-for-profit hospital. Physicians and employees began to openly criticize the project, questioning its value.

The loudest public outcry against this project occurred when it was learned the administrator was planning to secure a liquor license for the lobby restaurant. Needless to say, as the full scope of the project became publicly known the pursuit of the license was stopped.

I attended another promotion by this administrator, an elaborate open house held to dedicate Schumpert's new administrative and restaurant addition. I heard attendees speculating on the cost associated with serving specialty liquors and *hors d'oeuvres* inspired by themes of Japanese, Italian, Mexican and American cuisine on the four floors of the new addition.

An amenity in the administrative suite of the hospital that evoked much criticism (when many employees were being laid off due to financial issues) was the installation of an elaborate Italian cappuccino machine for use by the executives in their suite.

Recently, the present chief operating officer of Schumpert told me the infamous palm trees that had caused so much controversy some twenty years ago, had been removed from their building. None too soon in his opinion, I gathered.

Longevity Matters

Since the departure of the last nun administrator, Sister Agnesita, a series of lay administrators has appeared at Schumpert. No one knew then that the departure of this wonderful lady was a sentinel event in the life of this great hospital.

A lack of continuity in leadership prevailed as administrators changed frequently, eight in just twenty years. The average tenure of service was less than the national average. What this meant was that they had little time to learn the local markets or bond with employees and physicians. Several displayed a "just passing through on my climb up to a corporate position" attitude. This did not endear them to physicians, employees or the local community. Some failed to get involved in business, cultural or community affairs, often displaying an air of ambivalence. Some were quoted as making negative comments to their associates about Shreveport and Bossier City.

When forced to make employee layoffs, it is rumored that a number of the early administrators chose to target some of the most loyal and experienced employees for termination without regard to their dedication and service. Why? A larger savings on personnel costs can be accomplished by concentrating on the generally higher paid employees. It was also rumored that some who escaped the hatchet of termination were required to provide a letter of resignation to be kept on file for possible use in the next round of layoffs. In my opinion, this procedure would do little to encourage employees to think outside the box for ways to enhance their hospital operations, for they believed that to do so would be to place their names on the next termination list.

Focus on the Mission

The sisters who gave so much to Schumpert had the heart, soul and support of the Shreveport community because everyone knew without question that they were focused on their ministry of healing. Unfortunately, some of the early lay administrators did not seem to fully embrace that sense of mission, choosing to concentrate primarily on business operations. Perhaps they were caught up too much in the stress of daily management (for most it was their first experience as CEO of a major medical center).

Collaborate When You Can for the Good of Others

Hospitals in the same market must be careful not to violate antitrust laws to gain competitive advantage. However, when it is legally permissible, hospitals can and should collaborate for the betterment of the community. Many health-improving projects throughout the country have been the result of collaborative efforts of hospitals. The nuns at Schumpert were always willing to listen and respond to opportunities to benefit our community, but as lay administrators arrived, some of those collaborative efforts were derailed. In my opinion, a climate of isolationism fueled by their unwillingness to cooperate with other hospitals began to permeate the institution, eventually influencing the behavior and decisions of some of their hospital staff.

Acts of collaboration should include timely public announcements regarding elimination of services by a health provider. When a hospital decides to discontinue a patient service, it is imperative that adequate notice be given its patients and other providers of similar services to facilitate the relocation of those patients. Many are life-saving services that must always be available. Several patient services at Schumpert were discontinued during the time of the early lay administrators, who did not give advance notice to Willis-Knighton, the only private hospital in the region with comparable services. Examples include the closures of their renal dialysis unit with over forty patients receiving dialysis three times a week, renal transplant program, pulmonary rehabilitation unit, occupational medicine program, First Care (their urgent care facility) and the obstetrics unit and emergency room at Bossier Medical Center. Management at WK learned of these discontinuations of services as patients called for appointments or presented themselves for treatment at our already overcrowded facilities.

For more than a decade there was little collaboration between Schumpert, the medical school and other hospitals. A number of joint efforts with WK that started under the nuns were discontinued: Financial support for the highly successful Shots for Tots preschool immunization program and the joint recruitment effort with WK for medical school specialists were eliminated.

The biggest setback to collaborative efforts occurred when Schumpert opened Sutton Children's Hospital, competing with LSU Health Shreveport and Shriners Hospital for Children for specialty pediatric patients and with the WK/LSU surgical program for kidney transplant patients. Schumpert's transplant program closed after a couple of years due to a lack of patient volume. Their new children's hospital was not embraced by a vast majority of the pediatricians in the city, who went on record protesting plans for this pediatric hospital and vowed not to support it. Once opened, this hospital reduced the number of pediatric patients seeking specialty physician services at LSU Health Shreveport and Shriners.

Pediatric specialists were recruited from the ranks of the children's services at LSU Health Shreveport and Shriners to staff the new hospital. In my opinion, Sutton Children's Hospital was an unnecessary duplication of services in a market that could not support two full-service children's hospitals; it has experienced problems related to pediatric patient volumes, inadequate reimbursements from Medicaid and subspecialty recruiting issues. It has been forced to rely on the pediatric specialists from LSU Health Shreveport.

Analyze, Then Protect Your Referral Sources

Large urban medical centers have a role to play in the support of rural hospitals. To be effective with their boards, physicians and employees, an administrator must believe that these hospitals play an important role in their community's healthcare delivery. When I came to Shreveport, Schumpert had strong physician relationships and exclusive referral patterns with most of the physicians in our region's rural hospitals, much to the detriment of WK. These patterns of patient referrals began to change as the lay administrators at Schumpert downplayed the roles of rural hospitals and became less than enthusiastic about working with them.

Even though their rural strategies did not work, the lay administrators were convinced that another way to regain lost market share was to acquire urban hospitals. They purchased Physicians and Surgeons (P & S) Hospital, Bossier Medical Center and Highland Hospital. This strategy flew in the face of the adage, "Why buy a cow when the milk's free?" because patients from these hospitals requiring specialty physician care were already being referred to Schumpert on an exclusive basis. Schumpert officials closed P & S Hospital, thinking its patients would simply move down the street to Schumpert. But a number of P & S physicians either retired or relocated to other hospitals, taking their patients with them.

Several services at Bossier Medical Center closed shortly after assurances were given to its loyal physicians and the Bossier City council that no services would be terminated for five years. The turmoil surrounding the premature closures served to further jeopardize the hospital's future causing a number of BMC physicians to move their practices to WK Bossier.

Make Business Friends of Your Doctors

The nun-administrators were well known for supporting their physicians and their willingness to meet any time with physicians and other health professionals for ideas to enhance their hospital's services. Some of the lay administrators did not seem to understand the role that physicians must play in a hospital for it to be successful. Physicians are the patient's primary care-givers and the hospital's customers because they choose which hospital their patients will utilize. An administrator must also never forget that the physician's relationship with his or her patient is sacrosanct. A physician's faith in an administration is extremely sensitive to broken promises and decisions that place financial gain ahead of patient care.

Some actions taken by lay administrators at Schumpert, or its corporate officers, that did not promote feelings of partnership with their physicians were the following:

1. Their corporate-wide marketing program, "Specialists Are Our Specialty," conveyed the impression that they were touting their specialists as their most valued physicians. This was an affront to some of their primary care physicians, who perceived that they were being relegated to a second-class position.

2. Favoritism was shown to some physicians at the expense of others. Physicians routinely had long waits for an appointment with some of the administrators if they were not included among the inner circle of administration. Physicians favored by administration were appointed to positions of hospital leadership, often compensated, without input from the medical staff and without regard to qualifications or the posting of job openings. Loyal, long-serving physicians felt pushed aside if they did not follow the dictates of management.

3. Some of the lay administrators never seemed to grasp the fact that the surgeons removing patients from Schumpert to their personally-owned surgical center were business competitors. Favored treatments (assignment of desirable surgical block times and the provision of expensive robotic instrumentation) were provided to surgeons who openly competed with Schumpert for outpatient services. At the same time they were favoring these competitors, many requests from their loyal physicians and surgeons were denied. Later, the competitors opened a radiation therapy unit that captured a large percentage of the cancer patients previously treated at Schumpert. This loss of volume of radiation treatments eventually led to the resignation of Schumpert's highly respected chief of radiation oncology.

4. In the mid-1990s, a lay administrator negotiated managed care contracts for his physicians that financially threw many of Schumpert's physicians under the bus by forcing them to accept unreasonably low reimbursements. A number of physicians were quoted as saying their administrator worships at the altar of the managed care god, while destroying their livelihoods. Several contracts promoted by management included reimbursement rates that were often well below market rates with little chance of increased volumes for physicians. Market conditions were such that it was public knowledge that the Shreveport/Bossier City market was not in play, as it was largely controlled by existing exclusive contracts with WK's HMO, Health Plus of Louisiana, and its forty-eight thousand enrollees. Schumpert's contracts cannibalized its own physicians' practices, reducing their incomes and causing a large number of them to terminate their relationships with the hospital.

5. Over the years, the most renowned cardiovascular surgeon in this region, Dr. Stanford Shelby, performed the majority of his open-heart procedures at Schumpert. Dr. Shelby was highly skilled and respected, having completed his cardiovascular surgical training under the world-famous Dr. Denton Cooley at St. Luke's Episcopal Hospital in Houston. When Dr. Shelby began to voice concerns about operation efficiencies, the lay administrator's response was to become angry with him and promote referrals from his medical staff to another cardiovascular surgeon. Dr. Shelby would subsequently relocate his practice to WK's fledgling heart program. Within a couple of years after his relocation, the number of open-heart procedures performed at WK exceeded those at Schumpert, due to the presence of this remarkable surgeon. Also, the number of cardiologists practicing at WK grew significantly.

6. Over many years, only a few physician "insiders" were permitted to participate in Schumpert's strategic planning sessions.

7. A number of pediatric physicians were employed at Sutton Children's Hospital at attractive salaries. Tensions ran high among non-Sutton physicians as requests for equipment purchases and new services were denied to them, with many physicians becoming concerned about their futures. The resultant loss of adult patients is reflected in the fact that the St. Mary's campus transitioned to primarily treating women and children (*Shreveport Times*, August 25-26, 2010).

It is only fair to state that long before lay administrators arrived, favoritism toward a group of high-volume surgeons was a daily practice at Schumpert. At the time of my arrival at WK, I was made aware of Schumpert's implausible practice of favoring a number of its high-profile, high-volume surgeons with operating rooms and schedules reserved for their patients at the expense of its other surgeons.

Partiality toward those surgeons stuck in the craw of the new surgeons who were forced to alter their practice schedules (operate around the favored surgeons' schedules) or wait until they released their reserved operating rooms (often, hours after the completion of their procedures). I have been told that there were times when favored surgeons went out of town or forgot to cancel their procedures, preventing other surgeons from using their reserved operating rooms until permission was obtained.

Upon the completion of our new surgical suite in the early 1980s, some Schumpert surgeons began to schedule procedures at WK. They recited tales of how pervasive this practice of favoritism had become and its devastating impact on the morale of the younger surgical staff and on personal relationships with the favored surgeons, in some cases their senior practice partners. Jokes around town abounded, one being: "At Schumpert, a new surgeon is always assured an operating room any time after 10 p.m. on Christmas and New Year's Eve." This practice of favoritism forced many young surgeons to move their practices to other hospitals.

Don't Base Your Strategies on Flawed Information

At the time Schumpert was publicizing its decision to build the Sutton Children's Hospital, many community leaders who were approached for moral and financial support requested data regarding the need for another children's hospital. A consulting firm was engaged by Schumpert and a local foundation to conduct a feasibility study for a second regional children's hospital in Shreveport.

The consultant requested an interview with Willis-Knighton's administrative team. During the session the consultant asked us for statistical and demographical data regarding the continuum of pediatric services in our community. Our opinions of the financial health of the community and the probability of success of the proposed children's hospital were solicited. Our staff provided as much of the requested information as possible.

We were flabbergasted upon receipt of a rough draft of the consultant's report. Schumpert and Sutton leaders had gotten the go-ahead they wanted, despite what we felt were numerous errors, omissions and flawed assumptions:

1. The report's rosy financial projections were based on the higher Medicaid reimbursement rates of surrounding states, not Louisiana.

2. The report strongly suggested that the level of philanthropic giving in the Shreveport/Bossier City community would be adequate to offset the annual losses generally experienced by regional children's hospitals. Houston, Dallas and Little Rock hospitals were cited as examples of the magnitude of local giving for the proposed hospital.

3. No mention was included of the fact that over 85 percent of the region's practicing pediatricians had gone on record as opposed to the proposed children's hospital. Nor did it include the pediatricians' declarations in support of LSU Health Shreveport's children's hospital that if a new pediatric hospital was built, they would not admit or treat patients there.

4. There was no mention of the possible impact that the proposed hospital would have on the existing LSU Health Shreveport and Shriners hospital's patient volumes, teaching accreditation and their future abilities to recruit pediatric subspecialists.

5. Not included was the fact that the shortage of pediatric subspecialists in Shreveport/Bossier City would require the proposed hospital to rely on the willingness of LSU Health Shreveport's pediatric faculty to also provide patient coverage at the hospital.

6. LSU Health Shreveport's pediatric pharmacology unit, level one trauma center, burn center and its joint venture with St. Jude Children's Research Hospital were not included as relevant to the issue.

7. The conclusion of the study concerning the areas from which the proposed hospital would attract patients was puzzling since it extend-

ed far beyond Shreveport/Bossier City hospitals generally recognized patient catchment areas.

After studying the consultant's draft report, WK's team members were convinced that Schumpert's administration had gotten a report that would support their children's hospital initiative while ignoring negative factors. Our staff contacted the foundation to say that much of the data that we had provided to the consultant was not included in the draft report and to offer to meet again with the consultant to address omissions.

Prior to the release of the consultant's final report, Dr. John McDonald, chancellor of LSU Health Shreveport, and I were asked to resign from the board of the Hal Sutton Foundation. After hearing of the report's biased conclusions, we could understand why. Perhaps Schumpert's lay administrators, corporate officials and the Sutton board did not want either of us to sit on the governing board and be in a position to point out the obvious errors and weaknesses of the consultant's report. Incidentally, our staff was never provided a final copy of the consultant's report.

A media and public relations war of unparalleled proportions and emotions erupted in the region, causing a major rift in the relations between Schumpert and its small number of pediatricians on one side and LSU Health Shreveport, Shriners, Willis-Knighton and most of the area pediatricians on the other. The battle continues...pediatricians and philanthropists in the city continue to find themselves caught between two competing children's hospitals' quests for support. As a result, neither hospital is flourishing.

Short-Sighted Deals Come Back to Haunt You

In my opinion, Schumpert's corporate office and local lay administrators have appeared to be risk-averse, unwilling to try new concepts in the marketplace, choosing rather to do nothing or to replicate the services and marketing strategies of other providers. Their timing of projects and services has been consistently off and costly.

As a result of this lethargy and poor timing, it appears they made a number of short-sighted business deals in an effort to squeeze every dollar possible out of transactions without consideration of long-term consequences. The following examples illustrate some of these imperfect arrangements:

1. Schumpert's leaders, unwilling to face realities of the marketplace, continued to hype their once dominant hospital as it was formerly perceived. The reality was that their hospital was no longer the only significant player in the market and they no longer had a right to inherited markets. In my opinion, clinging to the past caused them to make a number of questionable strategic decisions:

    A. They took no action to ensure that their campus would be directly accessible from the new interstate highway (I-49) by way of on/off ramps to Olive Street and Margaret Place. Complacently, they believed that their patients would remain loyal to them despite the circumstances (access, security, new competitors and the exodus of physicians).

    B. They were slow in creating a safe and secure image for their Margaret Place campus with vehicular patrols, clearing of overgrown bushes, lighted and patrolled parking lots at night for visitors, employees and physicians.

    C. For years, the majority of southeast Shreveporters utilized Schumpert Hospital as their hospital of choice. Yet when Highland Hospital and Clinic moved into that area, Schumpert leaders did little to protect their turf. They were content to concede that area's less acutely ill patients to the new Highland Hospital as long as Schumpert remained their primary referral hospital. Their leaders did not consider the fact that another full service tertiary level hospital located in the area would take acutely ill referral patients away from them. They underestimated the desire of southeast Shreveporters to have access to emergency and specialty care health services closer to their homes.

    D. Their administrators were slow to move their operations into suburban locations with satellite hospitals, and their delays forced them to purchase three existing hospitals to counter WK's rapid expansion. Highland Hospital was purchased; however, the physicians of the multi-specialty Highland Clinic had little interest in inviting competitors and other non-clinic partner physicians to practice in their hospital, as this would impede the recruitment of new physicians to their clinic. The purchase of Bossier Medical Center was a move made several years too late to garner incremental market share in Bossier Parish. Physicians and Surgeons Hospital was a reasonable move for the building of a regional specialty (rehabilitation) hospital but for the fact that Schumpert's management closed the facility. The building then became ineligible for licensure and reopening as parts of it did not meet licensure requirements pertaining to fire, safety, handicap standards and asbestos abatement.

2. Several years after our health system announced that it was entering the Bossier market with the building of WK Bossier Health Center, Schumpert purchased Bossier Medical Center. This purchase took place after a substantial number of Bossier Medical Center's medical staff had either announced or relocated their practice to WK's new hospital. This slowness to react to changing market conditions eventually resulted in the closure of BMC in 2001, after an investment of millions of dollars and a continuing tie-up of Schumpert's capital.

3. Before bidding to purchase Bossier Medical Center, Schumpert officials were aware that several of the physician specialists at BMC had indicated an interest in relocating to WK Bossier Health Center. Their eventual relocation was facilitated by the failure of the BMC administration to contractually ensure the continued occupancy of the specialists' offices in a building being purchased by BMC on Doctors Drive. It appears that the BMC officials, at the urging of the Schumpert officials, were so anxious to purchase the building, in fear that WK might acquire it, that they negotiated a purchase contract that failed to include a requirement for the physician owners of the building and other lessees to continue to lease offices in the building. All of the leases expired at the time of purchase. Six of BMC's last remaining internal medicine specialists moved to WK Bossier shortly after the sale was completed. Schumpert's management was fully aware of these events, yet continued to pursue the purchase of BMC.

4. In late 1998, Schumpert Health System submitted a bid to acquire Bossier Medical Center. In my opinion, for several months thereafter, Schumpert had numerous opportunities to withdraw their bid due to additional demands being made by the seller (Bossier City). During this period, financial statements for fiscal year 1998 reflected that BMC had a loss of $2.8 million and that profits had fallen 76 percent since the opening of WK Bossier. In my opinion, Schumpert could have possibly backed out after learning of the loss, but apparently its leaders were determined to go through with the purchase. Two months before the hospital's operations were turned over to Schumpert, BMC recorded a loss of $783,661 in the month of April 1999.

5. In an apparent effort to squeeze every dollar possible out of the Bossier Medical Center debacle, Schumpert management sold a corner portion of its front parking lot for a chain drugstore building. This store devalued the remaining property by reducing parking and damaging the aesthetics of the front entrance of the hospital (the dumpsters were in full view of its front doors).

6. Another example of short-sighted thinking was Schumpert's sale of its orthopaedic and physical medicine clinic at the intersection of Line Avenue and Jordan Street to a large group of orthopaedists who were in active competition with them and other hospitals in Shreveport for outpatient surgery and rehabilitation therapy services. Shortly thereafter, the physician purchasers began remodeling the facility to provide not only outpatient services (surgery center and therapy services), but also a short-stay hospital that opened in direct competition with them for inpatients.

7. Upon the sale of the orthopaedic and rehabilitation facility to competing physicians, Schumpert's management directed three of its busiest employed primary care physicians to move their offices from a clinic adjacent to that facility to provide additional parking for the purchaser, their competitors. These physicians had ground floor offices and convenient parking but were directed to move to a multi-floor office building with less convenient parking. None of the three moved to the larger building. One moved and limited his practice to outpatients only, and the other two were so upset by the lack of consideration that they joined WK's physician network and relocated to other hospitals.

8. In 2011 the Physician's Square office building on Elizabeth Street was sold to the same orthopaedic group that purchased Schumpert's Line and Jordan orthopaedic and rehabilitation building. This sale to their orthopaedic competitors forced the eviction and relocation of several physicians to other hospital campuses while two others left town.

9. In the 1990s, two of the lay administrators had a *modus operandi* of purchasing the offices of physicians willing to relocate to their multi-level physician office building. Today, as I drive through this once vibrant area, I am struck by the air of pervasive desolation created by so many vacant office buildings.

10. Another tactic employed by Schumpert lay administrators for a number of years was to break up practice groups of their specialists by employing the younger physician associates, relocating them to their multi-floor office building on Fairfield Avenue. This practice left the older physicians having to assume the full costs of office ownership. Their practice expenses increased as a reduced number of physicians were left to share the overhead of these office buildings, many of which had been expanded to accommodate their former younger associates. This forced a number of physicians, who had hoped to further secure their retirement incomes by leasing or selling their buildings to their younger associates, to sell their properties to Schumpert, as they could not afford the increased costs of their overhead. Some physicians were so incensed they sold their properties to Schumpert and relocated their practices to other hospitals. The vacant office buildings made Schumpert look like a campus in decline.

11. In my opinion, Schumpert's leaders made a mistake when they merged their First Care (urgent care) and occupational medicine practice with the offices of family practice physicians at some distance from the previous locations. The entire cadre of terminated First Care physicians approached our health system and offered to staff a similar service, which became the WK Quick Care Clinics at WK Pierremont, WK Bossier and WK South. Several of the terminated occupational medicine physicians moved to WK WorkKare offices, which permitted the expansion of our one-campus program to all four of our hospital campuses.

12. Upon the announcement of WK Bossier's building of a health and fitness complex, Schumpert acquired land across I-220 to build a competing facility. This strategy was another "me too" project destined to disappoint when plans were announced to include children's memberships in their health and fitness programs. It has been my experience that adults do not want to socialize and exercise with children, especially without parental supervision.

Professional Ethics and Behavior are Always in Vogue

An old adage is "If you seek revenge, dig two graves." Everyone is hurt in vengeful actions. Some of the earlier lay administrators had pent-up feelings of bitterness toward Willis-Knighton and its management that began to extend all the way to corporate officials. After I sponsored a welcome luncheon to introduce the first Schumpert lay administrator to area hospital leaders, he informed me that he could not collaborate in any way with Willis-Knighton because he was sent to Shreveport "to derail our train."

The story of one administrator's vengeful action a few years ago shows that a person who seeks revenge can actually harm himself; his effort to thwart WK caused financial loss to Schumpert.

Schumpert engaged a realtor to sell a physician office complex on the west side of our city that had been only partially occupied for a number of years. The realtor approached us about purchasing the complex, which was across the street from two of our physician network offices. Expressing an interest, we entered into negotiations, only to be told a week or so later that he had been directed by Schumpert administration to discontinue any discussions with Willis-Knighton because the building could not be sold to us under any circumstance.

Two years later, after the departure of the lay administrator, WK bought this office complex at much less than Schumpert's original asking price. The vengeful administrator had his way at the time, but the institution learned the truth of the adage, "Revenge tastes like a delicious meal served cold."

Your Word Should Be Your Bond

The Schumpert lay administrators broke their words by violating conditions of oral and written commitments to WK and other entities on a number of occasions:

1. On one occasion, a Schumpert lay administrator approached me to request that we consider reducing marketing expenses at both institutions. This idea would include the reduction of a large number of billboards, newspaper ads and radio/television commercials. Our staff was agreeable to this proposal because it would reduce our marketing budget and free up funds for services and other functions. At that time WK enjoyed the benefits of leasing billboards at some of the most high-traffic count locations throughout the city. Based on the suggestion, WK cancelled contracts, giving adequate notice for several billboard locations and began reducing other marketing efforts. Shortly thereafter, I was notified by our billboard company that they had been contacted by a marketing firm representing our competitor, who wanted to lease a number of the billboards we were relinquishing. I confronted the administrator, who told me that he was following the direction of his corporate superiors. Fortunately, our cancellation notification carried with it a provision that it could be rescinded within a grace period. That was our last collaborative marketing effort.

2. Schumpert purchased Bossier Medical Center with an agreement to continue operating all services at the facility for a minimum of five years. Less than two years after the acquisition, without notice to WK Bossier, the city's only other hospital, nor the Bossier City council, Schumpert closed the obstetrics department and the emergency room, in violation of the agreement. Those most affected by the emergency room closing were the patients who were forced to wait hours for emergency care at other hospitals. The WK Bossier Health Center's emergency room, the remaining emergency facility in the city, was overwhelmed by the influx of patients from Bossier Medical Center. For months prior to the opening of an addition to the emergency department at WK Bossier, patients and families were

forced to wait for long periods of time for treatment, often in their automobiles, when our waiting rooms were overflowing. The number of EMS patients transported to WK Bossier almost doubled upon the closing of the BMC emergency room.

3. Another occasion when a Schumpert lay administrator violated an agreement (after the proverbial horse had left the barn) was when LSU Health Shreveport's entire staff of neurosurgeons resigned to take other positions. The six private practicing neurosurgeons in the area, four at Schumpert and two at WK, found themselves responsible for the care of all patients of LSU Health's trauma unit as well as their own practices. For almost two years the six worked themselves to exhaustion to provide neurosurgical expertise to Ark-La-Tex patients. Because LSU Health Shreveport could not offer competitive salaries, something had to be done. One of our WK physicians approached me with an idea: WK and Schumpert should pay competitive signing bonuses to attract two neurosurgeons to LSU Health. I approached the chief of surgery, Dr. John McDonald, with the idea that WK would fund the full signing bonus for the first neurosurgeon. He embraced this offer. Schumpert's lay administrator agreed to fund the bonus for the second candidate. Offers were extended to two of the top neurosurgical candidates in the nation and accepted by both. They began their moves to Shreveport. Upon the first recruit's arrival, WK paid his full signing bonus as agreed. Upon his arrival, the second neurosurgeon was informed that the lay administrator of Schumpert had decided not to participate in his guarantee as committed. WK paid the full signing bonuses of both recruited surgeons.[36]

4. In 1994, Schumpert's administrator violated a gentleman's agreement to partner with WK to purchase Physicians and Surgeons Hospital for a joint venture rehabilitation hospital. A stated goal was to provide as many of the P & S employees as possible continued employment with the proposed hospital. For several weeks, negotiations between the P & S owners, WK and Schumpert were ongoing. Both prospective purchasers believed that the price asked for the hospital was about a million dollars too high. Both parties agreed to wait for an acceptance of our lower offer, or both would have to agree on an increased offer before it could be submitted. While I was out of town, Schumpert leadership purchased the hospital for the earlier rejected price without letting us know of their acquisition. Upon learning of this action, I called the Schumpert administrator for an explanation. He was quite embarrassed as he told me that he had been instructed by his corporate superiors to abandon the joint purchase agreement with WK and quietly make the purchase before informing us of their withdrawal from the deal.

36 Dr. Anil Nanda and I always have a laugh at the circumstances of his initial arrival to Shreveport. Needless to say this region continues to greatly benefit from the services of this remarkable departmental chief and his team of seven talented and hard-working neurosurgeons.

5. Upon the purchase of P & S Hospital, in violation of our agreement for joint ownership, the managers of Schumpert shut down its operation, physically closing the hospital and relocating its inpatients to their facility down the street. Their initial plan was to close the acute care hospital only long enough for renovations and refurbishing, then to reopen it as a rehabilitation hospital after securing a new license to operate. Aware that older parts of the hospital were fraught with physical plant issues (asbestos, narrow corridors and HVAC), which might affect re-licensure, I had earlier cautioned the Schumpert administrator, presumably our future joint owner at the time, that it was imperative that we refrain from closing any parts of the hospital. A program to protect the hospital's existing license could be addressed during its continued operation through phased renovations of areas with correctable code issues and the razing of older portions of the building with difficult and expensive safety and environmental code issues. The unwise closure of the facility voided the P & S Hospital license to operate, eventually leading to the complete razing of the property after re-licensure was denied by the state.

Mistakes Can Change an Institution's Destiny

In my opinion, for a number of years after the last nun administrator departed, her successors made a number of critical mistakes that redirected Schumpert's destiny. The results of their actions not only impacted Schumpert's fortunes, but ultimately affected the daily lives of many in our community. Some of the lay administrators' missteps were buttressed perhaps by the absence of a sense of modesty on their parts: they presumed to have all the answers.

A number of the early lay administrators came to Shreveport with a profound lack of understanding, appreciation or respect for the quality of its people, life styles, customs and cultures. They failed to fully appreciate the history and heritage of our area's healthcare industry or the reality that their new home was a first-class regional medical center anchored by a recognized medical school, excellent hospitals, superb physicians and trained healthcare workers. However, they were not the first persons, or probably the last, to underestimate the intellectual prowess or misjudge the qualities and work ethic of the industrious citizens who call the piney woods of northwest Louisiana their home.

Some of their decisions not only cost Schumpert opportunities to continue to dominate the region's hospital scene, but also inflicted financial harm upon the institution. In my opinion, their major missteps were: 1) a failure to pursue a direct vehicular access onto and off the new interstate highway (I-49) to their campus, 2) rejecting their medical staff's recommendation to open the first heart transplant program in the region, at a time when they enjoyed the lion's share of the cardiology business and could have successfully preempted WK, 3) becoming complacent in attracting business, relying too heavily on marketing data that reflected the loyalty of a majority of Medicare (over 65) patients in the region, while neglecting to develop strategies to attract younger patients for the future, 4) unwisely relying on the inadequate reimbursements of Medicare and Medicaid to finance future hospital ventures, 5) deciding to compete with the children's hospital at LSU Health Shreveport while ignoring the negative impact this move would have on their future relations with the medical school and potential damage to its physician training programs, 6) bringing "West Coast" managed care concepts and strategies to this area, which also negatively impacted not only the finances of physicians and hospitals, but especially relationships between Schumpert and its physicians, 7) adopting a strategy of appeasement, taking no action to protect their business as the competitor entrepreneurial physicians were stripping the hospital of its most profitable outpatient surgery, radiation oncology and imaging income, to the great detriment of Schumpert's financial well-being, 8) outsourcing marketing programs and 9) their most egregious error: ignoring the voiced concerns and complaints of many of their physicians, who would never have relocated their practices to other hospitals if the lay administrators had only listened to them.

Conclusion

Since the departure of the last isolationist lay administrator at Schumpert, I am pleased to say that a number of ventures have been undertaken with our health system. The administrations of Joe Payne, M.D., Carolyn Moore and William Lunn, M.D., have been a different story. Warmer personal and professional relationships have emerged through their administrations, and they were willing to collaborate on initiatives that benefit our community.

As I engage in a little soul-searching and reflection on the past twenty years, I am certain that any number of the strategies and decisions I made were not always the right ones. Perhaps I could have made a greater effort to work with the isolationist lay administrators of Schumpert. In my quest to ensure my hospital's success in the marketplace, maybe some of my actions fell short of fostering a climate of friendship and professional camaraderie with these competitive colleagues.

While there is no way to determine whether additional efforts of cooperation would have made a difference in the past, I feel that increased collegiality between the last few administrators at Schumpert and me have put both organizations on a better path forward.

Schumpert and Willis-Knighton, two first-class institutions, could have shared a different destiny. Our complementary yet competitive strengths could have created collaborative patient care initiatives that further enhanced the image of Shreveport/ Bossier City as this region's medical center. I would have preferred that the rising tide of healthcare economics and reforms had lifted the boats of both Schumpert and Willis-Knighton, permitting us to better serve the healthcare needs of our community through our sacred ministries of healing.

CHAPTER 10

My Greatest Sources of Pride

A man has made at least a start on discovering the meaning of human life when he plants shade trees under which he knows full well he will never sit.

Elton Trueblood (1900-1994)

Lest the reader come to the impression that my sense of accomplishments are based primarily on Willis-Knighton's phenomenal financial performance, exponential growth or the impressive quality and continuum of patient services, allow me to declare the accomplishments of which I am most proud.

Tithing the Bottom Line

Willis-Knighton has tithed a portion of its net profit since 1979. This tithe helps to support those persons in our community less fortunate than ourselves, through no fault of their own. Not only does our system provide acute and emergency care for those unable to pay for services in our hospitals ($40 million in 2012), but WK also operates eight indigent clinics (six medical and two pediatric Medicaid clinics) in northwest Louisiana and southwest Arkansas and supports over 150 philanthropic causes of local and international scope. The clinics, staffed by physicians, dentists and nurse practitioners, are the centerpiece of our Project NeighborHealth, which provides services for over thirty-thousand of our region's medically indigent patients each year.

Since 1995 we have sent teams of physicians and nurses to train Ukrainian surgeons to perform laparoscopic surgical procedures in the interest of reducing the high death rate caused by post-surgical infections in that country. In addition to the surgical training program, under the leadership of William Norwood, M.D. and his wife, Jennifer Norwood, A.P.R.N., our health system provides financial support to orphanages with large numbers of physically deformed children, victims of the Chernobyl disaster.

In 2010 our annual financial tithe (cash contributions) in support of worthy causes was over five times the total distributions of the local United Way. I know of no other hospital in Louisiana or this region that has made this continuing budgeted commitment of resources to the impoverished, underserved and underprivileged of its community. This commitment of our health system is strongly embedded in the charitable fabric of our institution.

A number of years ago the financial needs of sponsored worthy causes became so great that our tithe of our net income was inadequate to sustain our growing charitable programs. A revised formula for calculating our tithe, now based on ten percent of our EBITDA (earnings before interest, taxes, depreciation and amortization) or cash flow, was implemented.

Integrating Our Facilities

Willis-Knighton was one of the first hospitals in our region to truly racially integrate its facilities and operations, while some hospitals were reluctant to follow the spirit and letter of the law. Our hospital's voluntary actions related to civil rights fairness and our willingness to step forth for right has played a major role in our acceptance by the African-American community. This acceptance was absolutely essential for the success of our tithe-funded Project NeighborHealth Program, which addresses health and well-being services to people of all races who have fallen through the cracks of healthcare coverage. It has been my experience that, until a person believes that you care for him as a human being, a precious child of God, he may not give you the privilege of helping, even at times of his need. Willis-Knighton has come to be viewed by the African-American community as one of the most color-blind hospitals in the state.

Paying Our Own Way

Willis-Knighton has never applied for or received any federal or state grants or other taxpayer funds in its history, choosing to pay for everything the old-fashioned way, by working for it. All projects undertaken by our health system have been paid for by funds generated from its operations: property acquisitions, physical plants, technology purchases, costs of our Duties of Conscience and all operational expenses. Of note is the fact that our health system's charges continue to be less than our only regional competitor (as determined by outside sources). Also, no public fund-raising drives, in any form, have ever been undertaken to encourage the solicitation of tax-exempt contributions. Nor does the hospital ever request contributions from patients or families or make applications to charitable organizations for financial support.

Perpetuating the Family Feel

The "family feel" of Willis-Knighton has become so strongly embedded in the fabric of our employees' spirit of loyalty, devotion, friendship and sense of self-esteem that it has become a driving force behind our health system's extraordinary growth. Our low rate of employee turnover and large number of long-tenured employees attest to our close personal relationships.

To transform an organization from a "place to work" into a "way of life" requires more than vision and material support; it requires spiritual leadership. While love may be absent from the dealings of most modern businesses, such cannot be said of our beloved Willis-Knighton. Our trustees, physicians and employees have worked to give their co-workers the gift of authorship, wherein every one of us can experience the satisfaction of a job well done. A sense of pride associated with contributing to the larger society has kept our hospital's routines from becoming empty and boring.

It has been said that "it is not the strongest of the species that survive, or the most intelligent, but the one most responsive to change." Many changes have been required as a result of the tremendous growth of our organization, and many of them required sacrifices on the part of nearly everyone. In my experience there is a greater willingness on the part of physicians and employees to make personal sacrifices if they have a strong sense of family.

The Code of Conduct chapter provides insight into some methods and activities that are practiced daily in our health system to nurture that special spirit. The most happy and motivated employees are those who have the opportunity to participate in charitable works that they believe are larger than themselves and will continue to serve their fellow men long after they are gone.

Developing Generosity among Competitors

An extraordinary thing happened to the Willis-Knighton Health System a few years ago: a competitor administrator offered his hospital to WK. For over eighty years, Doctors' Hospital of Shreveport (founded in 1917 as North Louisiana Sanitarium) competed with our health system. Charles Boyd, administrator, had operated this active acute care hospital for over thirty-five years, a formidable competitor to WK. We vigorously competed, yet our personal relationship was always one of warmth, mutual admiration and respect. When his wife was diagnosed with a terminal illness, he brought her to our cancer center for treatment.

This inner-city hospital situated on the edge of our major competitor's campus began to experience financial problems due primarily to the aging of its medical staff. Charles encouraged his board of trustees to donate Doctors' Hospital to Willis-Knighton, and they approved. Unfortunately, after seeking legal advice as to anti-trust issues, I informed him that our health system could not accept the offer as it would place us in a precarious position as related to restraint of trade. I thanked him for the offer, expressing my sincere regret that we could not accept his generous offer. Shortly thereafter, the hospital was sold to an out-of-town owner with long-term acute care and rehabilitation experience. I assumed that this was the end of any such considerations. Not so.

My dear friend and colleague was not to be deterred from ensuring that WK benefitted from his hospital's change of ownership. Much to my surprise, Charles invited me to accompany him to our state capitol to seek approval from the secretary of state to donate the proceeds from the sale of his hospital to our health system. Shortly thereafter, a multi-million-dollar gift was made to WK.[37] I am not aware of another instance where two long-time hospital competitors transcended their rivalry by virtue of their personal relationship, melding their institutional assets to become a stronger, single community health provider.

A few years later, this dear friend and colleague's last days were spent in one of our hospitals. I will always remember his extraordinarily generous gift of friendship as one of the most wonderful events of my life and cherish Charles's memory: a formidable competitor but even more, an unselfish friend.

A Proud Past

I revere the history of our health system and credit actions on the part of multitudes of physicians and employees, who laid their stones of devoted service in its foundation. Today, those stones are held sacred in our hearts and minds because their hands of labor and love touched Willis-Knighton.

37 To ensure that future generations are aware of this magnanimous gift, the health system's proton beam therapy facility will be dedicated in 2014 to Charles Boyd, this most special benefactor, colleague and dearest of friends. It was my honor to serve as a pallbearer for this wonderful man.

CHAPTER 11

Duties of Conscience: Tithing Our Financial Bounty

Give us such a vision of ministry that we can select for our philanthropy, for the expression of our love, those who cannot possibly recompense us at all.

Dr. Peter Marshall (1902-1949)

The following actions taken by our health system were not a strategy to grow Willis-Knighton, but a heart-felt commitment on our part to help those of our community who are less fortunate than ourselves. These "outside of our walls" charitable programs support and fulfill our mission to "continually improve the health and well-being of the community we serve." These programs are the fulfillment of our commitment to pledge a tithe of our financial bounty in the service of our fellow man.

Philosophy in Action

Everyone can have many perfect days if they are committed to acts of kindness that promote the health and well-being of the underserved of their communities. This holds true for all businesses as well, if their leaders choose to undertake acts that make this world a better place for every human being.

In a speech in New York City in 1927, Woodrow Wilson, the 28th President of the United States, said, "Business underlies everything in our national life, including our spiritual life. Witness the fact that in the Lord's Prayer, the first petition is for daily bread. No one can worship God or love his neighbor on an empty stomach." The basic daily needs of all of us must be met before we can muster the strength and energy to undertake good works in support of those less fortunate.

Business is therefore critical to the foundation and perpetuation of the nation we love. This nation offers so much opportunity for people, regardless of race, color, creed or national origin. As entrepreneurs are spawned through our nation's free enterprise system, the very foundation of our society, they become better positioned to be successful contributors to the American economy and culture.

However, being a productive player in the business world is not the way to the happiness and fulfillment of life that most caring, hard-working citizens, consciously or unconsciously, seek. It is found only when a person's entrepreneurial zeal is balanced with a hefty dose of empathy for his neighbors' plight and a passion for helping the less fortunate.

Why Willis-Knighton Has So Many Perfect Days

In 1979, blessed with growing community support and imbued with a heartfelt love for our fellow man, our health system's board of trustees voted to tithe the bottom line to support activities of worthy non-profit organizations promoting the well-being of residents of northwest Louisiana. This tithe is in addition to free services provided by the hospital for indigent patient care and the uncompensated care portions of the Medicare and Medicaid programs.

Our annual tithing far exceeds our obligations as a not-for-profit hospital to provide indigent care to the community we serve. At the time, we could find no other hospital in our country engaged in such budgeted, philanthropic giving to the community as this tithe.

Our trustees acknowledged that our health system has a responsibility not just to deliver healthcare services within our hospitals and clinics, but also to support a healthier, better community. However, we have not lost sight of the fact that as a community hospital system we must place our patients and their health first and our community

Duties of Conscience second. Our staff has embraced the fact that we can do both if the system is operated on a profitable basis through efficient and cost-effective management, which has been the case over the years. Our employees and physicians take great pride in the parts they play in the health system's ability to tithe the bottom line for the good of their families, friends and neighbors.

Beyond our IRS community benefit obligations as a tax-exempt organization, our Duties of Conscience permit us to extend our positive good will and influence beyond the brick and mortar walls of our hospitals. Our duties are now supported by a tithe of the hospital's cash flow (EBITDA).

In 2012 our health system's monetary gifts to charitable organizations were over five times the laudable distributions of our region's United Way. A Community Benefits Committee composed of system employees meets regularly to review funding requests from community not-for-profit organizations. Approximately 60 percent of our annual tithe goes to support our HealthWorks. The remainder supports humanitarian, civic and educational efforts in our region.

HealthWorks

HealthWorks projects provide a health resource for the underserved who have no other means to receive care. Project NeighborHealth, the cornerstone of our philanthropic giving programs, is comprised of eight indigent clinics financed and managed by the health system: WK Community Medical and Dental Clinic in north Shreveport, WK Pierre Avenue Clinic and Wellness Center in the downtown area, WK Children's Dental Clinic in mid-town Shreveport, WK Tots to Teens, in Shreveport, WK Care for Kids, also in Shreveport, WK Community Clinics in Plain Dealing and Oil City, La., and the WK Community Clinic in Bradley, Ark. These clinics are staffed by physicians, dentists and nurse practitioners who provide care for over thirty thousand patients a year, mostly indigent.

The Project NeighborHealth clinics were established upon confirmation of the following data: 1) large indigent populations, 2) lack of adequate numbers of health pro-

WK's six indigent clinics and two Medicaid pediatric clinics (not shown) provide medical and dental care for our community's most medically underserved.

viders in areas, 3) high death rates from cancer, diabetes and other diagnoses, 4) lack of availability or time constraints of public transportation and 5) excessive travel distances to LSU Health Shreveport or other providers.

Our first indigent clinic was the fulfillment of a mutual dream of Dr. C. O. Simpkins, his wife Elaine and myself. For years the three of us observed the deplorable health conditions prevalent in the Cooper Road area of Shreveport, home to some 25,000. This area's high death rate from cancer, heart attacks and strokes was primarily the result of the lack of access to healthcare. (There was one part-time 80-year-old physician with a poorly equipped clinic for the whole area.)

For years, the three of us had petitioned the state to build a medical/dental clinic in this underserved area. After numerous rejections, the Simpkins decided to donate a valuable corner lot adjacent to Southern University, while WK pledged to fund the $2 million complex. Thanks to these philanthropists, the clinic opened with a full staff (family practitioner, pediatrician and dentist).

Since inception, our mobile "Shots for Tots" initiative has been successful in raising the percentage of immunized pre-school children in northwest Louisiana from 47 to 94 percent.

Our international medical mission effort in Ukraine, training surgeons in the use of laparoscopic surgical techniques, has reduced post-surgical infection rates. Deaths were attributed to the lack of antibiotics and deteriorated conditions of Ukrainian immune systems resulting from the nuclear disaster at Chernobyl. Prior to the implementation of this training program in 1995, no Ukrainian patients benefitted from laparoscopic surgery. There has been a dramatic decrease in deaths from post-operative infections. Our project has had a profound impact on the health of Ukrainian citizens, reducing the death rate from post-operative infections from 40 percent to less than 1 percent in 2011.

This surgical training takes place in Ukrainian hospitals and the Willis-Knighton Laparoscopic and Robotic Surgical Institutes at our flagship hospital and WK Pierremont. Surgical equipment and supplies have been provided by our health system since the inception of the program. Today, thanks to our program, there have been over 500 surgeons trained in the use of laparoscopic surgery. In addition, a number of Ukrainian orphanages are financially supported through this international mission effort, as is the Shreveport Sees Russia pediatric retinal surgical program and a number of medical missions in Mexico and Central America.

Our health system provides free PET scans for Medicaid and indigent patients of LSU Health Shreveport hospital. (The State of Louisiana does not provide coverage for PET scans for Medicaid patients.) This continuing effort cost over $18 million between 2001 and 2012.

A major lifesaving initiative, Shreveport Fire Department's SPRINT (Single Paramedic Rapid Intervention Non-Transport) program was made possible by WK's commitment to fund its seven transport vehicles for $700,000. A similar offer has been made to the Bossier City Fire Department in addition to a gift of a $240,000 lot in mid-town Bossier City for a new central fire station.

As a not-for-profit, tax-exempt hospital WK must provide free patient care services and community benefits in an amount equal to the tax forgiveness the health system receives each year from governmental agencies. Our system never fails to exceed this requirement.

AngelWorks

Our AngelWorks programs are community humanitarian charities that address the issues of the homeless, hungry, mentally and physically challenged, physically abused, seniors and others with special needs. Examples of organizations of our recent focus are: the Food Bank of Northwest Louisiana,[38] Shreveport Bossier Rescue Mission,[39] St. Jude,[40] Salvation Army,[41] Volunteers of America, Providence House (homeless shelter for women and children), Evergreen Presbyterian Ministries (intellectual disabilities), Caddo Council on Aging (Meals on Wheels), The ARC (funded foundation for chil-

38 In 2012 WK employees contributed 3.6 tons of food and $1,038.34.

39 Contributions of over $1 million to the homeless shelter.

40 $540,000 in donations to St. Jude Hospital.

41 Over $1 million was contributed to the homeless shelter and the Boys & Girls Club.

dren with severe disabilities), Holy Angels[42] (children and adults with intellectual and developmental disabilities), Gingerbread House (child abuse victims) and Jambalaya Jubilee (camp for arthritic children). WK provided a large physician group's office for the Interfaith Pharmacy Service (free medications for the region's indigent population).

LearningWorks

The financial support of our LearningWorks programs for educational institutions also fulfills the "well-being" portion of our mission statement. This giving starts with contributions of money and in-kind support for pre-school through nursing and medical school education and allied health training programs. Contributions to the Alliance for Education are made to encourage schools to improve academically and provide a better educated future population. The schools must demonstrate improved academic performance. Examples of some organizations we annually support are LSU Health Shreveport Medical School, nursing and allied health programs at Northwestern State University, Southern University, Grambling State University, Bossier Parish Community College, and LSU Shreveport Health Administration and practical nurse programs.

ArtWorks

Cultural activities that provide opportunities for personal and community development are routinely included in our system's contributions as our ArtWorks programs. These quality of life activities are valuable assets that enhance our community and help us to attract new residents and new businesses to support community development, thereby assisting WK and other health providers in the recruiting of physicians, nurses and other workers. Some organizations we support are the Shreveport Symphony Orchestra,[43] Shreveport Opera Guild, Red River Revel,[44] Louisiana State Exhibit Museum,

42 WK made a $400,000 commitment in 2011 for expansion of the physical plant for residents with intellectual and developmental disability.

43 Annual major sponsor of Master Works musical presentations.

44 Major sponsor of the Junior League's Red River Revel (arts festival).

Robinson Film Center,[45] Sci-Port Discovery Center, Centenary College Choir, Shreveport Regional Arts Council, Red River (public) Radio and Louisiana State Fair.[46]

YouthWorks

YouthWorks are financial and in-kind contributions from our health system that sponsor and support activities for our youth. Included in this category are Boy Scouts, Girl Scouts, Salvation Army Boys and Girls Club, Biz Camp for inner-city youths, the Junior League Red River Revel, YMCA and YWCA programs, summer baseball leagues and school athletic trainers.[47] Caddo Sheriff's Safety Town[48] is a unique safety education program for regional elementary school students.

CivicWorks

Financial and in-kind contributions to not-for-profit organizations that provide social, economic and life-enhancing services to our community are funded by the system's tithe under our banner of CivicWorks. Examples are Chamber of Commerce commissioned studies, activities of the North Louisiana Economic Development Council, LSU-S Business Research Center[49] and Bio-Medical Research Institute.[50] A number of contributions have been made to the police[51] and fire departments of Shreveport and Bossier City and the fire and sheriff's departments of Caddo and Bossier parishes.[52]

45 Contributed the film center's major theater.

46 Largest financial supporter of the annual operating budget (annual employee day at the fair). Further, each year WK purchases several hundred Independence Bowl tickets for underprivileged youths distributed through the Project NeighborHealth clinics.

47 Sponsor ten athletic trainers for three professional teams, three colleges and five high schools, at a cost of $600,000 a year.

48 Funded the conference center at the Sheriff's Safety Town ($250,000).

49 Donated one-half of initial funding for the business research center.

50 Established $1 million chair in research at LSU Health Shreveport.

51 Provided new weapon systems and body armor for police SWAT team.

52 Donated patrol vehicles to the Bossier Parish sheriff's Posse (auxiliary deputy program) and surveillance equipment and weapons to Caddo deputies.

MilitaryWorks

MilitaryWorks refers to Willis-Knighton's commitment to serving those who risk their lives in defense of all Americans. Most recently, the health system's financial support provided the brave men and women of the 2nd Squadron, 108th Cavalry Regiment of the United States Army with their combat cavalryman's spurs upon their return from a combat tour in Iraq. This traditional adornment marks the uniforms of troopers who have returned from military action. The program also provides transportation for familial visits to the soldiers of the Louisiana National Guard deployed to aid communities during times of natural disasters (e.g., hurricanes and tornadoes), and WK sponsors their annual military ball.

The health system is a major sponsor of Barksdale Forward, a program to support the military personnel assigned to Barksdale Air Force Base. The program provides orientation to the community for new arrivals on the base, deployment assistance and support in job searches for family members. WK is also a major sponsor of the Eighth Air Force Museum (of vintage aircraft) on display at the base.

In addition, to preserve the memory of the men and women of our armed forces that make the ultimate sacrifice, WK provides college scholarships to fallen servicemen's children to defray some of the costs associated with obtaining a degree.

WK underwrote many programs in 2012 to support our mantra "You'll never have a perfect day until you do something for someone who cannot afford to repay you." Willis-Knighton has become not only the region's largest private employer, but also the major pillar of financial support for worthy causes as the programs touch the lives of so many of our less fortunate neighbors. On the following pages are ads in the local paper that both give the programs publicity and keep WK's name before the public.

THE SALVATION ARMY
Investing in Our Community
"By supporting The Salvation Army Boys and Girls Club, Willis-Knighton is investing in the future of Shreveport through the minds, hearts and souls of children and families."
Major Mark Smith
The Salvation Army
Willis-Knighton Health System is pleased to be a supporter of the Salvation Army and a leading contributor to the new Salvation Army Boys and Girls Club. Because we are a local health system, we are dedicated to making this a better community. . .for you and for us all.
WILLIS-KNIGHTON HEALTH SYSTEM
A Not-For-Profit Community Health Corporation

Investing in Our Community
"Oak Park MicroSociety Elementary, once deemed academically unacceptable, has flourished into a model of success with student performance scores increasing from 56.1 to an impressive 95.8. The Path to Excellence Award we've received from Willis-Knighton through the Alliance for Education for the past three years has helped us fund technology, which has been an integral part of our success."
Sabrina Brown
Principal, Oak Park MicroSociety
Willis-Knighton Health System is pleased to fund the Path to Excellence program administered by the Alliance for Education to reward academic performance in the public schools, with $100,000 a year distributed to local public schools since 2000. Because we are a local health system, we are dedicated to making this a better community . . . for you and for us all.
WILLIS-KNIGHTON HEALTH SYSTEM
A Not-For-Profit Community Health Corporation

Investing in Our Community
"Great music can elevate the spirit, enrich the mind and touch the heart. For many years now, the support of Willis-Knighton Health System has enabled the Shreveport Symphony to share the thrill of live orchestral music with our community through both our concert performances and our outreach in the schools.
We are grateful for their support and think we make a terrific team. Together, we are working to ensure the vitality of our community—body and soul."
Michael Butterman
Shreveport Symphony Music Director
Willis-Knighton is pleased to support organizations like the Shreveport Symphony that contribute to the quality of life in our community. Because we are a local health system, we are dedicated to making this a better community. . .for you and for us all.
WILLIS-KNIGHTON HEALTH SYSTEM
A Not-For-Profit Community Health Corporation

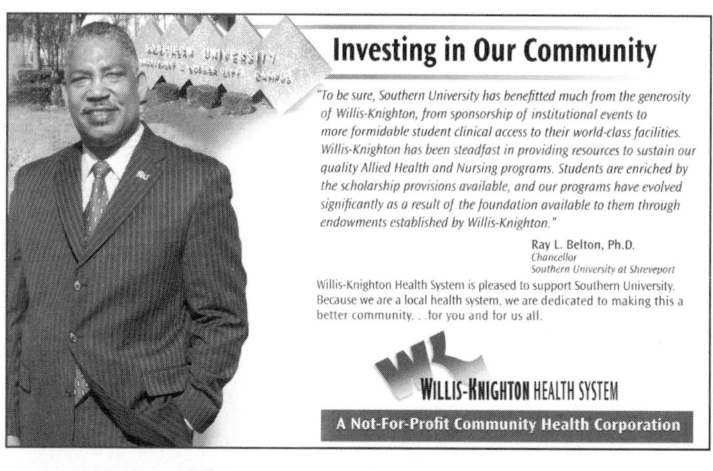

Investing in Our Community
"To be sure, Southern University has benefitted much from the generosity of Willis-Knighton, from sponsorship of institutional events to more formidable student clinical access to their world-class facilities. Willis-Knighton has been steadfast in providing resources to sustain our quality Allied Health and Nursing programs. Students are enriched by the scholarship provisions available, and our programs have evolved significantly as a result of the foundation available to them through endowments established by Willis-Knighton."
Ray L. Belton, Ph.D.
Chancellor
Southern University at Shreveport
Willis-Knighton Health System is pleased to support Southern University. Because we are a local health system, we are dedicated to making this a better community. . .for you and for us all.
WILLIS-KNIGHTON HEALTH SYSTEM
A Not-For-Profit Community Health Corporation

Investing in Our Community
"We are overjoyed with the results of the Willis-Knighton employee food drive. We received 8,436 pounds of food plus financial contributions. We appreciate the partnership with the entire Willis-Knighton staff in helping to feed food-insecure members of our community."
Martha Marak
Food Bank of Northwest Louisiana
Willis-Knighton is pleased to support the Food Bank of Northwest Louisiana through the annual food drive by employees of Willis-Knighton and The Oaks of Louisiana as well as generous financial support from our charitable giving committee. Because we are a local health system, we are dedicated to making this a better community. . .for you and for us all.
WILLIS-KNIGHTON HEALTH SYSTEM
A Not-For-Profit Community Health Corporation

Investing in Our Community
LSUS
"Willis-Knighton Health System has been a dedicated community partner to LSU Shreveport for many years. From the exchange of land to the financial support of student scholarships, faculty stipends, academic programs in Business, Health Administration, the Center for Business and Economic Research and Red River Public Radio, Willis-Knighton recognizes the importance of LSU Shreveport in our community. The impact of students who have received an education at LSU Shreveport through the support of Willis-Knighton Health System will be an integral part of the economic development in our community for generations to come. LSUS is proud to be among the many organizations that benefit from their generous policy of giving back to our community."
Dr. Vincent Marsala
Chancellor, LSUS
Willis-Knighton is pleased to support LSUS and the many educational opportunities it provides our employees and our community, including the area's only master's program in healthcare administration. Because we are a local health system, we are dedicated to making this a better community. . .for you and for us all.
WILLIS-KNIGHTON HEALTH SYSTEM
A Not-For-Profit Community Health Corporation

Investing in Our Community
"Willis-Knighton was the first community supporter to recognize how Sheriff's Safety Town could prevent injuries and save lives. When we approached Jim Elrod with our idea, he made a commitment to this project by donating not only funding, but other resources as well, like time and staff support, and continues to do so today. Because of our partnership with Willis-Knighton, more than 16,000 second-graders have received valuable safety information that could one day save their lives."
Sheriff Steve Prator
Caddo Parish Sheriff
Willis-Knighton Health System is pleased to support Sheriff's Safety Town because it teaches children the skills they need to protect themselves from harm. Because we are a local health system, we are dedicated to making this a better community. . .for you and for us all.
WILLIS-KNIGHTON HEALTH SYSTEM
A Not-For-Profit Community Health Corporation

ENGINE CO. 8
Investing in Our Community
"Because Willis-Knighton Health System shares the Fire Department's vision of providing EMS care to the citizens of Shreveport through a faster, safer, and more cost-effective medium, the Single Paramedic Rapid Intervention Non-Transport or SPRINT program was born. I thank Willis-Knighton Health System for providing $700,000 over two years to help firefighters save lives, and I thank them on behalf of the citizens of Shreveport - the true beneficiaries of this great new program."
Chief Brian Crawford
Shreveport Fire Department
Willis-Knighton Health System is pleased to support the Shreveport Fire Department's SPRINT project. Because we are a local health system, we are dedicated to making this a better community. . .for you and for us all.
WILLIS-KNIGHTON HEALTH SYSTEM
A Not-For-Profit Community Health Corporation

LOUISIANA NATIONAL GUARD
Louisiana Army National
2-108th Cava
Squadron
"Sound the Charge"
CDR - LTC WILLIAM T.
CSM - CSM ALB
Investing in Our Community
"I am honored to serve as the squadron surgeon for 2nd Battalion, 108th Cavalry Regiment, Louisiana Army National Guard and as an emergency physician at Willis-Knighton. I joined several WK employees and employee family members, who "saddled up" for a recent deployment to Iraq. Willis-Knighton was a huge supporter of our unit during this mission. They helped assure that we could present qualified members with the combat spurs, traditionally awarded to cavalry scouts after completion of their first combat mission. Recognizing WK's support, we named our squadron aid station "Willis-Knighton Middle East."
Lt. Col. Joseph A. Farquhar, MD
FARQUHAR
U.S. ARMY
Because we realize the debt of gratitude we owe those who protect this country, we offer support to our military organizations as they make this a better country and a better world for us all.
WILLIS-KNIGHTON HEALTH SYSTEM
A Not-For-Profit Community Health Corporation

Investing in Our Community
"Northwestern State University and Willis-Knighton Health System have been partners since NSU began its nursing program. That partnership has continued to flourish over the years and has been instrumental in helping Northwestern State's College of Nursing and Allied Health maintain its position as one of the best in the country. Willis-Knighton's assistance allows Northwestern to attract and retain top faculty and students."
Dr. Norann Planchock
Dean & Professor, Northwestern State University College of Nursing & Allied Health
Willis-Knighton Health System is pleased to support Northwestern State University's nursing program, one of the nation's largest and best programs, with financial and clinical support. Because we are a local health system, we are dedicated to making this a better community. . .for you and for us all.
Northwestern Stat
NURSING E
WILLIS-KNIGHTON HEALTH SYSTEM
A Not-For-Profit Community Health Corporation

Investing in Our Community
"Willis-Knighton Health System was among the first community partners to understand the benefits of our Jambalaya Jubilee camp. Through WK's generosity and continued support, Children and Arthritis and the Jambalaya Jubilee have empowered children and their families to better deal with the frustrations of arthritis and rheumatic disorders. Over the last 21 years, camps, free clinics (more than 12,500 clinic visits) and networking have comforted special families from ten states."
Thomas A. Pressly III, MD, APMC
Founder, Jambalaya Jubilee
Willis-Knighton is pleased to support Children and Arthritis and the Jambalaya Jubilee to help children and their families deal with chronic illnesses. Because we are a local health system, we are dedicated to making this a better community. . .for you and for us all.
WILLIS-KNIGHTON HEALTH SYSTEM
A Not-For-Profit Community Health Corporation

Investing in Our Community
"In 1992, Providence House, with the financial support of Willis-Knighton, developed a long-term solution to break the cycle of homelessness. Today, 85% of our graduated families live independently in the community. Two years ago Willis-Knighton again showed its support with a generous contribution to help us open the Safe House and formalize the Domestic Violence and Sexual Assault Advocacy programs. On behalf of Providence House and those we serve, thank you Willis-Knighton."
Simone Hennessee
Providence House
Willis-Knighton Health System is pleased to support Providence House. Because we are a local health system, we are dedicated to making this a better community. . .for you and for us all.
WILLIS-KNIGHTON HEALTH SYSTEM
A Not-For-Profit Community Health Corporation

CHAPTER 12

Take This Job and Love It

In the quiet hours when we are alone and there is nobody to tell us what fine fellows we are, we come sometimes upon a moment in which we wonder, not how much money we are earning, nor how famous we have become, but what good we are doing.

A. A. Milne (1882-1956)

Why Hospital Administration?

It is my hope that this book will serve to educate the public about the exciting and challenging, yet little known, profession of hospital administration. Over the years, I have often been asked three questions about my chosen profession:

1. The first question is: "How did you come to know about your profession?" My answer is that I was fortunate to have had a dear friend, an undergraduate classmate at Baylor University, whose father, the administrator of a large health system in Dallas, took time to share information about it with me. Hospital administration is a small career field because there are fewer than six thousand hospitals in the United States in which to practice the profession. Therefore, the career ladder is competitive and crowded, and advancement to top levels is slow. However, there are also numerous healthcare related professions that are available in the fields of insurance, consulting, teaching, pharmaceuticals and others. Educational requirements vary, but most administrators have earned either a master's of health administration (MHA) or a master's of business administration (MBA). Some of the programs awarding the degrees require a one-year residency for

practical experience in hospitals or health systems. In my opinion, a residency is the best way to gain valuable expertise and experience, an asset for an aspiring administrator.

2. The second question I am asked is: "How did you manage to survive more than forty-eight years as president of Willis-Knighton? Sometimes the inquirer adds, "Your job must be difficult and volatile." In support of the point that my profession is both complicated and volatile, I quote from a white paper prepared by the Lewin Group and presented to a trade group, the Voluntary Hospitals of America, in 2002: "Services are more complex to deliver in healthcare than in other industries. Because of the nature of the industry and its many regulatory oversight issues, the operations of a healthcare organization can be up to 200 times more complex than a similarly sized peer in the commercial sector." Healthcare is a complex industry, but I have found that the attributes and talents required are no different from those of other commercial enterprises. In my opinion, the most important qualities required for all effective executives are vision, a strong work ethic, humility in leadership and a deeply felt appreciation for the rights and dignity of patients and co-workers.

3. The third question regarding my profession is more personal: "What makes the job of a hospital administrator so special and rewarding?" The remainder of this section records why I love my job.

A Facilitator for Healers

There is no nobler profession than that of a healer.
Those who save lives achieve a form of immortality
of their own, in the generations they preserve, in the
descendants who would not otherwise be born.
To heal is to leave a stamp on the future.

Oliver Wendell Holmes Sr. (1809-1894)

Let me be clear from the outset. I am not a physician, nurse, technician or other direct giver of patient care. However, I consider myself a "facilitator for healers," as described by one of our health system's cardiologists, because as a hospital executive I am responsible for ensuring that all components of a hospital operation are available to the caregivers. The provision of a hospital physical plant of adequate size and design, furnishings and equipment, state-of-the-art technology, a team of qualified and, in some cases, licensed support staff and supplies is my responsibility. The components required for high-quality patient care necessitate that all financial operations of the hospital be strong.

Over the years, I have formed the analogy that a hospital is equivalent in scope and operation to an air force base, a military city with a critically sensitive mission. A base's strike force comprises skilled pilots and aircrews, analogous to our physicians, nurses and technicians. Both base commanders and hospital administrators are responsible for the provision of every service required to support the mission of their respective facilities.

A healthcare ministry offers one of the most exciting opportunities for service to our fellow men, for daily you're involved in the drama of life. While in one part of the hospital an elderly patient may be dying, on another floor a baby is being born and life is starting all over again. Your challenge each day is to deal with patients and families experiencing extreme emotions. It is during such times that you have an opportunity to impact in a positive way the lives of each of those parties.

A meaningful and comforting belief that I have come to accept in my many years of service is that death is not always our enemy. Health professionals come to accept death and dying in a more rational and understanding way as they participate daily in a hospital's drama of life. This does not mean that you should not be emotionally touched and inwardly share the pain of death, but professionals must remain composed to carry out their duties.

Challenges and Benefits of the Profession

The highest reward for a person's toil is not what
they get from it, but what they become by it.

Ralph Waldo Emerson (1803-1882)

Challenges and benefits of the profession of hospital administration are these:

1. Hospital administration demands passion for your work, for it is a 24/7/365 commitment; a hospital never closes. The professional rewards are worth the price you pay in a demanding schedule to play a role in a ministry of healing, and to transcend the mere living of life for your own blessings. I also believe that people rarely succeed at anything unless they enjoy doing it.

2. A hospital administrator seldom gets bored by his routine, since no two days are ever identical.

3. A hospital administrator has the opportunity to place his entrepreneurial skills in action on a daily basis. A friend quipped to me that hospital administrators get to play "real-life" Monopoly in the business world as they buy, build and add physical plants and services. There are times when this analogy is pretty accurate (generally without the chance to draw a "go to jail" card).

4. Opportunities for visioning, strategic thinking, implementation and marketing abound as hospital administrators team up with physicians and other health professionals to develop patient care initiatives and other good works.

5. A hospital administrator operates in a world of professional dress (no room for casual dress days), conduct and decorum.

6. Hospital administration is a profession of some "mystique" because few people know anything about it or what I do in my role. That's not all bad; and I kind of like it that way!

7. Unlike careers that may be suggested by college counselors or parents, hospital administration often becomes known only to students who have personal contact with someone in the field and learn about its responsibilities, challenges, demands and rewards.

8. It is a job that can truly make a difference. It is a chance to do so much for those in need because a hospital administrator has control over greater financial and labor assets than has merely one well-meaning individual.

9. The high community profile of a hospital administrator assures him or her of opportunities outside of the hospital's walls for service to other worthy causes. Invitations to serve other meaningful organizations abound.

A Chance to Mentor Others

He who teaches a boy teaches three:

a youth, a young man and an old man.

German Proverb

An administrator gets to serve as a role model for young people choosing this career path and to help them secure educational and employment opportunities in hospital administration or other health related careers.

Success is Never Final and Failure is Never Fatal

A sobering and humbling thought is, "There, but for the grace of God, go I." On twenty-three occasions I have been fortunate to find places in our health system for capable and experienced hospital administrators who have been the victims of job terminations, voluntary and involuntary, from health systems in our region.

Ray Hurst, long-serving president of the Texas Hospital Association, once jokingly said, "Longevity of a hospital administrator is shorter than the time a person spends going through a revolving door." While this is an obvious exaggeration, the truth is that tenures of some administrators have been quite short. In fact, *Modern Healthcare* reported in 2012 that "the median tenure of a hospital administrator is four years, with 58% of current CEOs at their posts for fewer than five years."

Most of these professionals were not blessed with the caliber of board of trustees that I have known. Our health system's trustees choose to serve their fellow man rather than themselves. Sometimes those unfortunate administrators took the fall for misguided decisions made by governing bodies who had less business acumen and more personal and financial conflicts of interests.

Every one of these unfortunate, yet experienced, capable and qualified administrators went on to serve this organization with credit and distinction, adding great value to our health system. Some served a long time with us, others attaining age 65 chose to retire, and others served faithfully and competently as they searched for challenging opportunities for executive positions in other hospitals. I am pleased and honored to call each of them my colleagues and friends. Great blessings were derived by our health system from the service of these remarkable men.

Business Realities of Healthcare

An economic fact is that hospitals do not have the luxury of handling downturns in an economic climate as most other businesses do. When the economy is in a funk, commercial industries can arbitrarily lay off workers and reduce operating expenses with little impact on their companies because an economic downturn is normally associated with reduced buying on the part of consumers.

In contrast, a hospital must continue to provide the same level of care in economic downturns because it cannot close units or reduce services without jeopardizing the quality and quantity of its services and thereby the lives of its patients. State-of-the-art technology must be continually purchased, installed and operated in all economic conditions if the institution is to provide the best healthcare. Regulatory and accrediting agencies mandate a hospital's course of action relative to staffing, documentation, compliance and instrumentation, which is not the case in most businesses.

The health of your patients is at risk in good times as well as bad, so a hospital must continue to enhance its ability to care for the community it serves. And, in fact, there is evidence that greater numbers of illnesses are treated during economically troubled times.

The Necessity for Sacrifice and Stamina

One of the major requisites that sets healthcare workers apart from most other professions is that they must be willing to sacrifice a great deal of their life's quantity of time for the well-being of others. Routine work schedules of health professionals often require overtime and additional days of service, due to the shortage of such workers.

Another indispensable need of health professionals is stamina, as hospitals and most healthcare services seldom close.

Napoleon once said: "The greatest characteristic that a soldier can have is not courage, it is stamina."

Some Spiritual Thoughts

It is not what a man does that determines whether
his work is sacred or secular; it is why he does it.

W. Tozer (1897-1963)

Hospital administration is a profession that a person can put his heart into as he:

1. **Exercises his faith** within an institution that is not merely a tool or edifice but one that becomes transformed into a "living heart" of the love of God, **through his acts and deeds of service to others.**

2. **Worships God** through acts of kindness to his neighbors and places his Judeo/Christian faith into practice for the benefit of the needy around him.

3. **Serves his "living God" by putting his heart into play** and focusing on doing good for his fellow man rather than on his own selfish desires.

4. **Gives generously** of his time and material assets as he helps those who cannot help themselves, through no fault of their own.

5. **Maintains a zeal for service**, not losing his determination to love others, and put the welfare of others ahead of his own.

6. **Surrenders his idols**–money, power, social standing–and thinks of others first.

7. **Treats everyone with dignity, respect and love**, as God expects of us.

Hospital administration is a wonderful and rewarding profession. My own experience in the field has helped fuel the passions of three family members who have also chosen careers in the healthcare industry. That said, before encouraging anyone to pur-

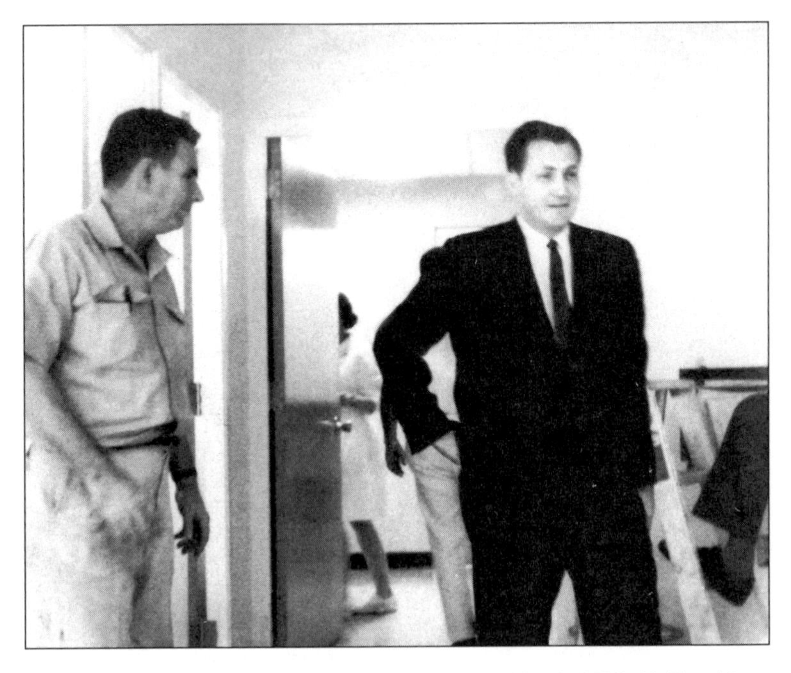

Practicing my "management by walking around" in 1965 with retired U.S. Air Force Master Sergeant William Bostick, my maintenance supervisor.

sue this profession or recommending anyone to a graduate program, I require him or her to serve an uncompensated, informal internship to observe and learn first-hand the demands of the job. During this period, I observe their behavior and interactions with others. Candidates must understand the demands before them and be willing to commit to the arduous work hours of a hospital administrator. An administrator is always on duty as far as responsibilities are concerned, even after normal work hours. An administrator may assign duties to others, but can never delegate accountability.

I am pleased to report that a majority of those interns who spent a reasonable amount of time in this endeavor chose to pursue some profession within the healthcare industry.

A Little Administrative Levity

A recently fired administrator was showing his replacement around the hospital when he said, "I want to give you these three sealed envelopes, which contain advice about how to handle difficult times around here. Keep them on your desk and open in their numbered order if you so choose."

A couple of months later, the new administrator began to have problems with his employees. Remembering the three letters, he opened letter number 1 and read, "Blame your predecessor." He did so and lo and behold! The issues went away.

Two months later, the new administrator was involved in a dispute with his medical staff. Remembering the letters, he opened letter number 2 and read, "Hire a consultant." He followed the advice and lo and behold! The problems were resolved.

A few months later, the new administrator discovered he was on the outs with his trustees. Remembering the last letter, he opened letter number 3 and read, "Write three letters."

CHAPTER 13

Codes of Conduct for Leaders

Behavior is a mirror in which everyone shows his image.

Johann Wolfgang von Goethe (1749-1832)

Some readers may consider the following advice and personal beliefs to be old school, or too military or just plain outdated. However, by continually trying to adhere to these principles of conduct, which are driven by my strong philosophical beliefs and empirical knowledge, I have been blessed to remain in my job as president and CEO of our health system for over forty-eight years. That tenure was made possible through institutional accomplishments and long-lasting positive relationships based on mutual respect. I would be remiss in not acknowledging the fact that I too, from time to time, have fallen short of my self-imposed expectations, but I face each new day with resolve to do better than the day before.

Wisdom

The following quotations regarding wisdom are some that I have come to cherish over my lifetime.

1. Years ago I read the Chinese maxim by Confucius, "A single conversation across the table with a wise man is worth a month's study of books." The truth is that all of us can benefit greatly from table talk with wise people from all walks of life. Do not confuse wisdom and formal education.

2. An old Jewish proverb says, "A most wise man is one who hears one word and understands two."

3. "Wisdom is fortified, not destroyed, by understanding its limitations," is a thought by Mortimer J. Adler.

Passion for Your Work

The following is an old story that I have told over the years that I believe best illustrates the vision, effort and dedication that all leaders hope to instill in their employees. Passion for one's work is key to happiness and success in our lives.

"What Are You Building?"

A reporter observing a building project wondered what was being built and decided to interview a few workers to find the answer. As he started around the first side of the project, he observed a brick mason, moving slowly and grousing to his helpers about work conditions, having laid only a few courses of bricks. The reporter asked him, "Sir, could you tell me what you are building?" to which the surly worker answered, "Can't you see? I'm laying bricks."

Turning the corner of the project, he saw another brick mason working somewhat faster than the first but grumbling to himself; he had laid a few more bricks than the first man. The reporter asked the same question, "Sir, could you tell me what you are building?" to which the mason replied, "Can't you see that I'm building a wall?"

As the reporter rounded the corner to the third side of the project, he observed that the mason on that side was moving rapidly, laying bricks, humming and standing back periodically to admire his work. This mason's wall was almost completed. The reporter repeated the question, "Sir, could you tell me what you are building?" to which the smiling and proud brick mason replied, "My friend, I am blessed to have a role in building this cathedral."

All of us should strive to build cathedrals through our best efforts and not be content merely to be laying bricks or building a wall without any sense of the ultimate goal of our efforts. A hospital, no matter the size or location, is a cathedral of healing, worthy and deserving of the best efforts of us all, trustees, physicians, management and staff.

Purpose

Purpose is what gives life meaning. Before choosing the profession you will undertake, consider the following advice: "Find a job you love, and you will never have to work a day in your life." Passion, purpose and excitement for one's work come from an inner sense of satisfaction and contentment derived from knowing that if you could have chosen any profession in life, you would have chosen yours and would do so over and over again.

Faith

Leaders must have confidence in their ability to lead others toward the accomplishment of worthy goals. Additionally, they must fervently believe in their plans for the future. One of my favorite definitions of faith is beautifully expressed by Barbara J. Winter:

> *When you come to the edge of all the light you know and are about to step off into the darkness of the unknown, faith is knowing one of two things will happen: There will be something solid to stand on or you will be taught how to fly.*

I believe this thought, which defines faith in a practical and secular sense, closely parallels the biblical definition of faith in Hebrews 11:1: "Faith is the assurance of things hoped for, the conviction of things not seen."

Belief in the Future is Essential

People who don't really believe in the future do not shape the future. Men and women of vitality have always been prepared to bet their futures, even their lives, on ventures of unknown outcome. If they had all looked before they leaped, we would still be crouched in caves sketching animal pictures on the wall.

John W. Gardner (1912—2002)

If you begin to doubt your institution's future and your ability to lead it to success, I believe it is in everyone's best interests to permit someone else to lead the organization. President Franklin Roosevelt warned about this dilemma when he said, "The only limit to our realization of tomorrow will be our doubts of today."

My prayer of support for those who venture forth with bold, visionary undertakings is: "May they feel the reassuring presence of a protective God during their undaunted, adventurous endeavors."

Patience for Understanding

Hospital patrons (patients and families) are purchasing a service they do not normally want. Therefore, be understanding of their lack of knowledge and familiarity with our routines and sensitive to their resultant fear of hospitals. You should promptly respond to their concerns, complaints or criticisms. Remember, we nurture those who come to us at some of the worst times in their lives.

Make a Difference in the Lives of Others

Hospital administration provides unique opportunities for service to your fellow man, a chance to help those around you who cannot help themselves, through no fault of their own. Because you have some control of community assets, those of your institution, you can do so much more for the needy and less fortunate than you could do individually.

1. Make a difference in the lives of others every day! The actions you routinely undertake to enhance the quality of care delivered by your health system and your acts of kindness are the essence of which our lives should be made.

2. Within our system lies a multitude of opportunities for personal and financial giving by our employees, activities beyond our walls that support the values of our Duties of Conscience. These duties define the obligations for sharing our God-given bounty with worthy community organizations to address the needs of those less fortunate than ourselves.

3. Making a difference in the lives of our fellow man is what happiness is all about. Our trustees, physicians and employees take pride in the fact that they are directly involved in helping their less fortunate neighbors through the support of our system's mantra of caring.

Dealing with Adversity

Failure is only the opportunity

to more intelligently begin again.

Henry Ford (1863-1947)

There are too many forms of adversity to give any useful advice on dealing with it, but I can suggest some attitudes that may help:

1. Shakespeare wrote, "Sweet are the uses of adversity." By accepting the truth of such a beautiful line, I make every effort to look at the bright side of difficult situations by considering problems to be merely opportunities. Besides, wouldn't life be much less interesting if there were never any challenging opportunities facing us?

2. Don't exacerbate situations by viewing them in terms of how difficult they might be, but rather approach them as just little bumps in your road. This positive view of issues, which was shared with me years ago and practiced religiously by one of my dearest physician friends, Dr. Albert Bicknell, will change your attitude and provide a positive approach to overcoming challenges. Problems and difficulties in life

will make you stronger. Consider the truth of the old saying, "adversity introduces man to himself."

3. Take the long view of your professional life and accomplishments by accepting the fact that not every decision you make or direction you take to improve your organization will be the right one. Early in my career I came to accept that failure is essential to success, a belief that was of great comfort to me as I attempted to move forward after making wrong decisions.

4. A baseball player batting .500 in the major leagues would be selected as an All-Star each season, and that is a hit only half of the times the player comes up to bat. This may not be the best analogy, but you get the idea: a leader cannot continue to ponder the mistaken directions he has taken in his career. Better to learn from your mistakes and move on, vowing never to repeat them. Make the mistakes of yesterday your lessons for today.

Humility Defines Relationships

Humility is the keystone of most positive and long-lasting relationships. This human quality fosters cooperation among coworkers in the interest of accomplishing shared goals.

Hospital administrators and managers in other fields can accomplish a great deal more with coworkers if they choose to view themselves in a humble light as competent jacks of all trades, but masters of none. Hospital administration is a complex field, but let's not delude ourselves, it is not rocket science. This advice is not intended, in any way, to disparage the job we do, but rather to help us accept our roles with a modicum of humility, one of the most important leadership prerequisites. I have found the most successful professionals in our field have humility and understanding, not necessarily advanced degrees.

1. Booker T. Washington penned a wonderful thought regarding the dignity of a person's work when he pointed out that there is never one person in any organization more important than any other person, no matter what kind of work they do, or talents or wealth they possess. He said, "There is as much dignity in tilling a field as in writing a poem."

2. I choose to view the job of a hospital administrator as like that of a minister or priest as it relates to material aspects of my life. I encourage our management team to be somewhat modest in their choice of autos and other high-exposure assets. Driving the most expensive model of automobile does not endear a manager to his employees or others who are paid less and unable to afford such luxuries. Maybe I find this advice easier to follow than some people because as a Texan, I was brought up to believe that a Mercedes-Benz is not a status symbol...an old pickup truck is!

3. A reflection on humility is, "If you forget where you came from, you're probably on your way back."

4. It is not a morale-enhancing move to place your name or the names of your officers on reserved signs for parking spots that are nearest the entrance, while employees are required to walk greater distances to their parking lots.

Why Am I in My Job?

1. Two soul-searching questions every hospital leader should routinely ponder are these: For what purpose was I placed in my position of leadership? What are the primary responsibilities of my position as related to the loyalties and duties owed to the physicians, patients and employees of the organization?

2. A leader who does not extend the courtesies of respect, support and warmth of relationship to his subordinates, co-workers and physicians should not expect the caregivers of the hospital to treat patients, families and co-workers with courtesy, thoughtfulness and attentiveness. A leader sets the caring and compassionate tone of an institution.

Your Acts of Today Purchase Your Future

What you plant now, you will harvest later.

Og Mandino (1923-1996)

1. The old saying, "divide and conquer" is relevant to the makeup of medical staffs of most hospitals. Why? Because, if your physicians begin to "bunch" into large groups, quite often these mega groups, through the elimination of competition, begin to exert negative influences on the conduct of the medical staff.

2. Medical staffs composed of a number of physicians from large group practices become inherently less democratic as they tend to dominate dialogue and actions. Quite often they shut out other physicians from equal participation in medical staff activities. Issues relating to disruptive behavior, quality oversight and conflicts of interest are more difficult to address when an offending physician is a member of a large practice group. The odds are that disciplinary committees will have physicians with business ties to the alleged offenders, which often means no disciplinary action will be taken.

Teamwork Through Respectful Actions

Executives expect respect and usually get it. A good leader shows respect to others in many ways.

1. Throughout your career you will meet and work with many people. All of them are significant. No one person in your organization is more consequential to its success than another. All play vital roles in the daily operation of your business. Therefore, they all deserve your attention and regard, which can be aptly manifested through merely a smile and a "hello" in passing. The ultimate affirmation of your respect and appreciation for a person's worth is accomplished when you take time to learn his or her name.

2. When you discipline a subordinate or question some action on his part, always give the offending party a graceful way out of the situation; don't embarrass him by verbally painting him into a corner unless you give him a door through which to retreat and save face. Never attack his character or integrity if you hope to have a continuing relationship with that person. You can apologize for misspoken words, but those words can never be retracted or completely erased from his mind.

3. If you desire to continue working with an organization for a long time, remember the old adage, "Never burn bridges that you may have to retreat across." You may need an individual's support at a later date.

4. A required leadership skill is to remember and practice common courtesies that show your respect for everyone with whom you interact. One important courtesy is the timely return of telephone calls, including complaints, compliments or requests for assistance. You may not always have a ready answer for the caller, but the fact that you returned his call is of utmost importance. Returned calls are unspoken recognitions of the esteem in which you hold the other person.

5. A list is always a useful and trustworthy device to remind a busy administrator of telephone calls, projects or actions that require at-

tention. The daily schedules of an administrator can be hectic and stressful, and having a continually updated list of incomplete projects may help to nudge your memory and save you from many embarrassing moments.

Familiarity and Its Abuse

"Familiarity breeds contempt!" was a lesson I learned in the Air Force and one I believe is all too often not taught in civilian life. Here's what I mean:

1. Always attempt to maintain a respectful relationship with your physicians. Address physicians as "doctor" around other physicians, patients and employees.
2. Address your elders with titles to show proper respect for their age and their achievements.
3. Address employees by their last name with a "Mr." or "Mrs." or "Ms." added, which eliminates gender and the potential for racial awkwardness.
4. My board chairman and I have worked together for forty-eight years, yet I have never addressed him in public or private by his given name, but always as "Mister" with his family name to show the proper respect for a gentleman of great achievement and stature in this community.
5. I believe physicians want the administrator to be their hospital leader and custodian of their patient workshop, not their buddy or golf partner.
6. A military rule requires a person to show the proper respect for a person's rank in the organization and the achievements that merited that rank. This respectful attitude should never be dependent on your personal feelings toward that person.

Advice for Managers

Here are some thoughts on leadership that apply to any field, but especially to hospital administration.

1. Manage by walking around your organization. This is the best way to know what's going on, get to know your co-workers and build the morale of your employees. The time you spend in developing *esprit de*

corps is never wasted. Thomas Jefferson expressed this concept when he said, "The best fertilizer is the owner's footprints."

2. Never allow too much complacency on the part of your administrative team. My experience is that without a sense of urgency, people may not give that extra effort or make sacrifices that are essential to the accomplishment of goals. An old saying is, "If something is worth doing, it should be started today."

3. Another thought on delay is the Donald Marquis line, "Procrastination is the art of keeping up with yesterday."

4. For over forty-eight years I have been of the mind that a job candidate's résumé of credentials (education and experience) is secondary to his cultural fit within the organization. A candidate's values must align with those of your company: work ethic, buy-in and excitement about mission, ability to team play and get along with fellow workers and a heartfelt concern for the welfare of others. Unfortunately, I know of no test that reliably measures these characteristics.

5. Approach every day with the belief that everything in your business could be improved or more customer-friendly by being more aesthetically pleasing, efficient or cost-effective. Concentrate on how the grounds and buildings of your campus and the work going on could be enhanced so the public's perception of your operations is one of high quality and caring behavior. Continually strive to improve your institution's appearance, operations, interactions with customers and overall image, which should be fine-tuned daily, so it will be a better institution tomorrow than it is today.

6. A mindset of complacency and inattention to details seems to grow stronger the longer you permit it to exist. Almost everything we do can be made better by constant scrutiny, noting of problems and solving them. Set an example of constant awareness of your surroundings and operations for your fellow employees and physicians.

7. Leaders should set an example during hospital rounds of noting and tidying areas that need attention. Dangerous or hazardous actions on the part of hospital workers should also be immediately corrected, but not in a publicly demeaning or demoralizing manner.

8. Your mission is to provide a first-class workshop for physicians, nurses and other caregivers to assist them in providing the highest quality of care to their patients. Without the legal authority to admit and treat patients, an administrator is the "facilitating partner" to all caregivers in the delivery of patient care services. Without our caregiver partners, there would be no requirement for our service-oriented administrative positions, and our hospitals would be worth less, in a financial sense, than the values reflected on our balance sheets. One

sobering thought and jolt of reality is that our hospitals were built and equipped for a special purpose and have very little resale value due to their singleness of purpose.

9. When disciplining or terminating an employee, always have a trustworthy witness of higher position than that of the person being confronted. It is also advisable to have a person of the same gender as the employee as a witness to the process.

Conservative and Realistic Financial Projections

One of the fastest ways to undermine the faith your board members, physicians and employees have in your ability to deliver on business operations is to present budgets or other projections that are unrealistic. To inflate your projections of profitability and volumes of service for the sake of getting through another period of operation is to fall into the trap of taking a short-term view of your career, for a day of reckoning will come. Continued failures to deliver on your projections and budgets may jeopardize your job.

Remember, it is always better to be reasonable and realistic with your financial and operational projections and budgets than to overstate your expectations, so they are a stretch to accomplish. To err on the side of conservative forecasts that you surpass at year's end will promote greater confidence in your abilities. To be totally unrealistic in your expectations is to find yourself dying of a thousand cuts throughout the year as you fail, month after month, to meet your budgets. Another advantage of this reliable conduct is to find yourself viewed as a responsible manager in whom others can place their confidence.

Acknowledge the Good Works of Your Coworkers

Willis-Knighton held a Ceremony of Tribute a few years ago to recognize and commemorate the service of a number of dedicated health system employees and physicians. Bronze plaques naming departments and sections of our four metropolitan hospitals in honor or memory of living and deceased persons who had made a difference in the life and service of the health system were officially placed in the areas of their service. I was proud to have the honor to deliver the following speech on this occasion:

> *Those persons who have come into contact with Willis-Knighton over the past eighty-seven years recognize that the heartbeat of this ministry of healing is the service of dedicated people, like our honorees, who have exemplified through their lives the best in Judeo-Christian love and stewardship. It is not our physical plants, bricks and mortar, but rather these dedicated workers who will long be remembered, not only for their untiring efforts and achievements, but more importantly, for the sharing of their talents through leadership.*
>
> *Our honorees have many special qualities that set them apart, but the one I choose to mention at this time is their collective, quiet, sweet spirits which they shared with all of us—that human quality that gives each of their lives passion and purpose and continues to inspire us to be our best, because I believe that only great passions can elevate our souls to great achievements. This is a most precious human gift.*
>
> *To transform an organization from a "place to work" into a "way of life" requires more than vision and material support; it requires spiritual leadership. Through such leadership by our honorees, Willis-Knighton has become a "way of life" to countless tens of thousands of patients, families, employees and physicians over the years.*
>
> *While it can be correctly stated that love is largely absent in the dealings of most modern businesses, such cannot be said of this institution, our beloved Willis-Knighton. Why? Because our honorees set the tone, by their example, of loving people by reaching out and opening their hearts to them through words and acts of kindness.*
>
> *Also, over the years, our honorees—board members, physicians and employees—helped give their co-workers the gift of authorship, wherein everyone could experience the satisfaction of a job well done as they enabled them to see*

their work as both meaningful and worthwhile. This sense of pride associated with contributing to the larger society has kept Willis-Knighton's routine from becoming empty and boring.

Through their lives these honorees have helped us come to fully appreciate the fact that the most perfect day you will ever have in your life is when you do something for someone who will never be able to repay you.

The book of Proverbs says that words spoken at the appropriate moment are as apples of gold in settings of silver. It is our hope that this tribute will be a treasure to you and the family of those deceased, all of whom will always be part of our Willis-Knighton family.

The Family Feel

1. Work to create a "family feel" among your employees. One of our employees described our "family feel" as meaning "when my co-workers bleed, I hurt." Listed in an earlier chapter, "Polishing Our Tarnished Halo, Strategy Five: Creating the Family Feel" are some activities we undertake on a routine basis at our health system to show the proper respect for our employees, physicians and their families at the time of death of loved ones. These services help to instill the "family feel," which I believe has generated the respect that our employees have for one another, no matter the job, position or station in life. These actions have become traditions over the years and amplify the respect and bonding that our co-workers share, producing our health system's very low turnover rate of personnel. Recognition of this achievement was recently given to our system by a major national professional magazine for nurses.

2. In WK's annual Nursing Report of 2010, the following thought by Thomas Campbell was included, which I believe conveys the strength of the "family feel" of our health system: "To live in hearts we leave behind is not to die." I believe the people honored at the ceremony of tribute continue to participate in every act, thought and decision we make.

Teamwork

It is easy to praise teamwork, but hard to instill it as a value in a workforce of hundreds. Here are some practices that nurture teamwork among hospital employees:

1. Connect every day with your physicians and co-workers. Acknowledge and compliment their efforts and work, when appropriate. By recognizing your employees in this way you show them that you care about them as persons more than merely physicians or employees.

2. Inspire loyalty in your staff. "It is better to have a thousand enemies outside your gates than one disloyal person within the castle." This saying was often quoted by one of our hospital's most loyal physicians, who added that the actions of disloyal coworkers were the root cause of the demise of many organizations.

3. Share the accolades of success you personally receive for your institution with your fellow workers by recognizing their efforts while downplaying your own involvement. President Harry S. Truman said, "You can accomplish anything in life provided you do not mind who gets the credit." The "halo effect" of a successful venture brought about by your unsung leadership should be more than enough recognition. Without comment, the public knows that the driving force behind an institution's undertakings and successes is its leadership.

4. Encourage your staff to work in a harmonious and productive manner toward achievement of your organization's goals while demonstrating by your actions that you respect them. General Colin Powell said, "A good officer leads by example." Be mindful that if you want respect from your trustees, medical staff, management and staff, you must earn it. If you want your co-workers to emulate your work ethic, your actions must be responsible at all times. At no time does a leader have any latitude for irresponsible behavior. Some examples of exemplary work ethic behavior are these:

   A. Never ask anyone to do something that you would not do yourself. To do so is to show disrespect for your co-worker.

   B. Set an example of adherence to dress codes. There is no place in our profession for casual days of dress if we are to inspire the life-saving services provided in our hospitals. In my opinion, a worker's performance is generally on par with his dress.

   C. Routinely arrive at work before posted work hours to set an example for your coworkers.

   D. Make rounds in the hospital at all hours of the day, evening and night shifts, to observe operations and enhance your staff's morale.

E. When making rounds to observe and inspire, select "hot spots of activity" or "crossroads of passage" for maximum exposure to physicians, patients, employees and visitors. Physicians and employees appreciate administrators who work after normal hours of operation. Quite often issues can be resolved on the evening and night shift visits.

F. Give credit for the accomplishment of goals to everyone involved in the project. Never take sole credit for successes even though you may have had the idea, developed the strategy and supervised the project. A one-man team is not the best way to ensure future wins.

Acceptance of Your Role

With an old Italian proverb in mind, "The best armor is to keep out of range," early in my career I decided never to take any action or make statements that reek of my practicing medicine. I often say, "Doctor, I'm not qualified to practice medicine, so I'm leaving all such decisions to you." The adoption of this rule led me to decline to comment or vote at medical staff committee meetings on issues involving medical expertise. Even though you may be a committee member with voting rights, refrain from voting on matters of specific medical care, which should be decided only by a physician. This decision has served me well over the years and is, in my opinion, one of the reasons our health system has experienced relatively little opposition to the formation of our employed physician network. A hospital administrator can avoid some problems by simply keeping his mouth shut, as you can see in these rules I follow:

1. You must never forget that a physician's practice is sacred in that his or her patient relationships and treatment protocols must remain within the discretionary dictates of that physician. This rule applies to employed physicians as well, as they should always be viewed as being in private practice.

2. Never make critical remarks to anyone regarding a physician's treatment of his patients. Such conduct is unethical and unbecoming of a professional; most hospital administrators do not hold medical degrees and therefore are not qualified to judge these professionals.

3. Never inject yourself into an argument between physicians or employees even if you feel you have something to contribute. You may

distort the issue, thereby becoming, an unintended target of anger, and possibly lose friendships as one or both antagonists turn against you for unsolicited interference.

4. Humble and self-deprecating demeanors go far in endearing you to your board members, physicians, employees and community members. We all want to be around someone who can laugh at himself. Remember a saying of Will Rogers: "If you get to thinking that you're a person of some influence, try ordering another person's dog around."

5. If you are approached by a person in need of some personal assistance, not only should you listen with your ears and mind, but also with your heart. You will never come to understand the needs of others and forge solutions to their problems if you do not attempt to empathize with their pain.

6. A leader can assign some of his duties to others under his supervision, but he can never delegate his responsibilities. President Truman's desk sign, "The Buck Stops Here" summed up his acceptance of his responsibility.

7. Though I have been a trustee of our health system for over thirty years, I have never voted at a board meeting. This is in deference to my fellow trustees because on some issues before the board I, a paid employee, may be viewed as having a conflict of interest. I often jokingly tell others, "My first recorded vote at a board meeting will be to prevent a vote to terminate my employment from being a unanimous one." On this subject a Yiddish adage comes to mind: "If you can't bite, don't show your teeth."

Honor and Revere Your Past

Never criticize your predecessors because they were probably doing the best they could under the prevailing circumstances. Never fail to give thanks for what we have today. Our predecessors laid the foundations upon which we build. The admonition, "Never criticize another person's actions unless you have walked in his shoes," applies here.

Never forget the history of your institution, always giving credit to your predecessors and the legions of workers who, over the years, helped establish its reputation and laid the groundwork for your successes. William Faulkner penned: "The past is never dead; it's not even past."

Changing Perceptions

The lines "You never get a second chance to make a first impression" and "perception is reality" are profoundly true. Therefore I encourage my staff to routinely tour our hospitals, attempting to visualize our physical plants, grounds and personnel behavior from the public's and patients' point of view. I have found that some people are more capable than others of seeing their facilities through the eyes of others. Caring and compassionate displays of conduct toward employees, patients and families go a long way to establish great first impressions.

Compliment Good Work Efforts

As you tour your health system facilities or visit patients, always compliment good work and attitudes. Never openly reprimand a worker unless his actions are endangering the immediate safety of patients, family members, visitors or himself. Even on these occasions, don't publicly humiliate the offending employee, but take him aside to help him understand the problem and how it can be solved.

If you choose to violate this rule, your movements through your facilities will become dreaded events; employees will fear your presence and view your well-intended rounds as inspections, and you may become "just another suit around here that doesn't care about us."

Handling Complaints

Make every effort to investigate complaints as soon as possible. Have the appropriate and responsible hospital representative make personal contact with the complainant to discuss the issue and chart a course of correction. Always consider complaints as a gift of opportunity, as they give your staff additional time with the complainant to show your sincere concern. A person whose issue you resolve is many times more apt to tell others of your caring spirit than a person who has no complaints.

Always let the complainants know that you appreciate their taking time to share concerns with you. Also, thank them for giving you and your staff the opportunity to correct their concerns.

Avoid Negative Public Relations

Don't overdo public relations exposure. The more you are featured in the media, the more you create subliminal thoughts in the minds of the public that you are a seeker of glory, not a servant of the public good. Too much exposure could give the impression that you are egotistical or even narcissistic, thereby diminishing your image and that of your institution. Remember the advice of a dear friend to "lie low, stay long."

Refrain from publicly involving yourself in politics. The day you take a political stand with any party or candidate is the day you are choosing to turn off one-half of your support from patients, physicians, employees and your community base.

When your competitors make public announcements of new services or projects and media reporters come to you for a comment, never respond negatively. Applaud their efforts in the interest of improving the healthcare of your community. Take the advice of an old friend of mine, Dr. Leonard Barnes, chancellor of Southern University in Shreveport, who promoted the idea that "you can never get too much of a good thing." Always remember that you represent your institution and that negative shots at competitors are cheap and unprofessional. They lower the public's respect for you and your institution. Even if you honestly disagree with the direction your competitor is taking, it is always better to refrain from negative comments; after all, it is their right to make such decisions.

Support Your Community

Each year, our health system is blessed by having the privilege of providing health services to thousands of people who are employed by or retired from hundreds of businesses throughout our region. Supported by a strong "conflicts of interest" policy adopted years ago by our board of trustees, our management team decided to transact as much business with as many local vendors, banks and other entities in our region as practical. The philosophy driving this strategy is to build our community by buying locally, financially touching the lives of as many employees of these local businesses as possible. We hope these employees will come to appreciate our spread-the-wealth business efforts and choose to become patients of our system when a health issue arises. Doing business only with your personal or business friends or those of your trustees is not the best way to grow your hospital's patient base or show support for the efforts of everyone in your business community.

Reflections on Change

No man was ever so completely skilled in the conduct of life,
as not to receive new information from age and experience.

Terence (190-158 B.C.)

1. Your word should always be your bond. When you promise actions to physicians, employees or the community at large, stick to your word. A promise made but not kept is seldom forgotten by the person to whom it was made. Nothing diminishes your image of credibility and integrity faster than promises not kept.

2. Take the advice of Will Rogers if you are unhappy with the town where you live and work: "Subscribe to the newspaper of the new town you are considering, and you will generally discover that your dream town has the same problems you have in your hometown." Don't be so quick to relocate! Relocations can be expensive and often deprive you of success in making differences in the quality of life in your community. In my experience, the administrators who have made the greatest contributions to the health and well-being of

their communities are those who have taken time to build long-term achievements, relationships and experiences.

3. Never go for a job interview unless you are quite certain you want to leave your present job, for such action can be a career-changing event. Even if you later choose to remain in your present position, the support you previously received from trustees, physicians and employees often becomes strained, thereby impacting the morale of your organization. Many of your constituents will harbor a belief that you may not have taken the last job offer for whatever reasons, but that you are dissatisfied with them and will continue to pursue other job opportunities. They may never completely get over that doubt. You can apologize, but you cannot retrieve a spoken word or take back an action.

4. For employees to believe in and be committed to an institution's mission, they must see that same loyalty and commitment in their leader. If their leader exhibits a lack of commitment, they will follow suit. "Short-timer" attitudes, expressed or implied, that convey the message that "I won't be here long because I'm climbing the corporate ladder" are extremely damaging to organizational efforts and do not endear you to your hospital team. Several administrators at a nearby hospital expressed such sentiments; none of their contracts were renewed.

Work Ethic

There are two kinds of people, those who do
the work and those who take the credit.
Belong to the first category.

Indira Gandhi (**1917-1984**)

A leader should always set the example for his institution's work ethic. Never expect a better work ethic from your staff than you, as the leader, show in your daily behavior. Our medical director once told his father that he could not do his chores because he didn't feel well. His father replied, "Son, seventy-five percent of things done in this world are done by people who don't feel well."

Over forty years ago an old retired sergeant who had attained only a high school education said to me, "There are a lot of people around here with more education, but I am not going to let any of them outwork me." And no one outworked him as he rose to a prominent position in our organization.

Stick with it! Perseverance is required for all jobs. And remember that the difference between a "big shot" and a "little shot" is that a big shot keeps on shooting, never giving up until he has mastered the job.

The High Costs of Battles and Conflicts

Pick your battles. Far too often, leaders have taken on battles that are just not worth the fight. When considering your response to issues facing your organization, always let your rational thinking take precedence over your emotional response. Conflicts take a great deal of energy that could be directed toward more worthy goals. Refrain from being drawn into internal or external struggles that siphon the well of cooperation, coordination and accomplishment from an enterprise. If the rewards of the battle will have a lasting impact on your organization, then and only then should you permit yourself to be drawn into impassioned confrontations. Also, if you recall the history of wars in Europe, you are aware of the gross mistakes made by Napoleon and Hitler in choosing to take their countries to war on more than one front of battle at the same time. Too many simultaneous battlefronts could inflict permanent damage on your organization.

Acts of Retribution and Retaliation are Unhealthy

Remember that success is the best form of revenge. Put aside thoughts of merely getting even with someone and concentrate on more productive and worthwhile accomplishments. Time has a way of curing hurtful memories and dulls our desire for acts of retaliation.

Personal Relationships Can Impede Effectiveness

Decisions involving close friendships sometimes have to be made and may require a hard stance against a close friend. Relationships tend to be damaged when such actions are taken. Being everybody's buddy is an unrealistic approach in business and often a barrier to actions required by your job. My rule is, in your organization, "friendly" to all, "friendship" with caution.

Refrain from personal and financial conflicts of interest in your business life. Managing to do so will assist you in objectively carrying out your fiduciary duties as a steward of your organization's assets.

Proper Preparation for Meetings Shows Respect

While developing agendas and preparing for meetings, remember that some of your attendees will not know about your operations or possess a business background. Keep the following rules in mind:

1. Do not get too complicated or technical in your presentations.
2. Refrain from using acronyms and other abbreviations.
3. Use graphic and digital projections as often as possible.
4. When presenting a lot of data, always allow enough time to let the data sink into the minds of your audience.
5. Never waste the time of attendees by lack of preparation or inadequate subject matter.
6. Never miss opportunities to sell your organization or bolster the morale of your staff.
7. When giving credit for successes, include all of those deserving credit other than yourself.
8. Attempt at every meeting to stress the important role that each person in attendance has played in the overall accomplishment of objectives. Inspiration for further efforts will arise from morale-enhancing sessions.

9. Try to anticipate questions from your audience, including as many answers as possible in your presentation.

10. Never miss the chance to stop talking when your points have been made.

11. The most important point is never to schedule a meeting just for the sake of having a meeting.

Vision

A hospital administrator must always keep in mind the future of his organization.

1. When interviewing an applicant for a position, always be mindful of plans of your organization and the positions for which that person may be most qualified. If there are no openings at the time for him, you may choose to employ him with an understanding that his assignments may change, or you could tell him that you will keep him in mind and his contact information at hand. A number of our most valuable employees have entered employment this way.

2. Never stop dreaming! If you can't dream it, you can't achieve it.

3. Merely addressing the needs of today is short-sighted. A large portion of a leader's time each day should be devoted to contemplating the future direction of his health system. Proverbs 29:18 reads, "Where there is no vision, the people perish."

4. A goal is simply a dream with a deadline. Pursue your dreams with a passion! Put as much energy into achieving them as you can without adversely impacting your personal life. The future never just happens, it is always created.

5. Not having a goal is more to be feared than not reaching one.

Body Language and Seating Arrangements

At a round table, every seat is the head place.

German Proverb

Pay attention to your body language and your choice of seating when you hold meetings with physicians, patients, families, community and other non-hospital leaders.

One tip I give young administrators is never to hold a meeting in which they remain seated behind a desk with physicians or guests in front of them. Such positioning tends to convey the subconscious feelings to your visitors that you consider yourself their superior. I always receive physicians and guests around a table setting, which promotes a sense of equality and greater openness of communication. Consciousness of such details of respect helps to prevent the perception that I consider myself superior to my guests.

Sometimes it is appropriate for you to be seated behind your desk when meeting with subordinates for purposes of instruction, directions, discipline or reprimands. This formal seating plan establishes authority.

A leader's goal in a group discussion should be to promote a consensus, mutual acceptance of ideas and courses of action. To accomplish such outcomes it is important to remember that a leader should always attempt to persuade, not to command.

Courage of Your Convictions

Lead courageously! But always remember, when leaders step out, other people may try to pull them down. Ignore your detractors and move on with your efforts. If you choose to lead an orchestra, you must be willing to turn your back on the crowd.

Continuity of Service

Build a team of trustees, physicians, managers, employees and outside consultants with long tenures of service. Experience and continuity are invaluable to organizations. Experience, in my opinion, often trumps many other managerial qualities. This strength is like the ability of a person who can cross a river without a bridge or boat because he knows the location of every rock just beneath the surface of the water. Health executives must come prepared to make an immediate contribution to their organizations because most hospitals do not have the luxury of time for on-the-job training. (Note: At a recent WK trustee meeting, it was noted that our chairman, president and CEO, hospital attorney and certified public accountant had been serving the health system for a total of over 188 years–further proof that we practice what we preach.)

Enjoy Your Journeys of Life

There is often more enjoyment in the pursuit of a goal than in its accomplishment. This revelation came to me after a dear friend, a physician, rightfully chided me for not taking time to enjoy my journey as I relentlessly pursued my goals. He reminded me that it is not the destination but the journey that is the most exciting and enjoyable part of any project. Greg Anderson wrote, "Joy is not found in finishing an activity but in doing it."

Another wonderful friend remarked to me, "Jim, take more time to smell the flowers as you walk through your garden of life." She would say, "Friends are the flowers in your garden of life. Take time to enjoy them as well." Even though it has been years since her death, I remember Rosalind Foster as one of the most beautiful flowers in my garden of life.

A Life of Service

I slept, and dreamt that life was all joy.
I awoke, and saw that life was service.
I served, and understood that service was joy.

Rabindranath Tagore (1861-1941)

The patient asked the hospital employee, "What is your job around here?" to which the response was "To provide any service that patients or their families require." The employee assisted the patient from her automobile at the lobby entrance and pushed her wheelchair to her physician's ninth-floor office. As the employee was leaving the physician's office, the patient turned to the receptionist and asked, "What is his job around here?" to which she answered, "he is our hospital administrator."

CHAPTER 14

The Antics of Dr. B, Or What is Political Correctness?

The magnificent and the ridiculous
are so close that they touch.

Bernard le Bovier de Fontenelle (1657-1757)

The following recollections are of events in the life of one of the most interesting and lovable characters that I have ever had the good fortune to know and love. Dr. B was a skilled surgeon with a generous heart the size of a barrel and an unbridled wit. Yet in spite of these qualities, Dr. B, who was in his mid-seventies when I joined WK, was actually a shy person who was somewhat standoffish with most people. He chose to interact only with those people to whom he felt personally close, and I was fortunate to be included in that circle.

When I reported for duty in April of 1965, I was told by several physicians that because of my youth–I was 27–I might not be readily accepted by four older physicians and one board member of the hospital. One of the physicians, Dr. B, became one of my dearest friends. As it turned out, I was also honored to be asked upon their deaths to serve as a pallbearer for all five of them and helped arrange the funerals of two. We bonded through our shared love and devotion to our beloved Willis-Knighton.

What an Introduction!

Upon my introduction to Dr. B by my predecessor, he looked at me and said, "Boy, you should be on thyroid medication," pulled out a prescription pad and wrote an order for a thyroid medication for me. Without another word, he walked away, leaving me with an awkward first impression. I kept the prescription for over 30 years as a memento of the occasion. I guess I should not have become such a good friend to Dr. B. Maybe I would have continued to be called "boy" by him rather than his endearing nickname for me, "Numbnuts."

So Much for Professionalism...

From the outset of my tenure at WK one of my strategic goals was the recruitment of a registered pharmacist with hospital experience. After almost a year I managed to employ a highly qualified pharmacist to join our hospital team. A few weeks after the pharmacist's arrival I received an irate phone call from him. He told me that Dr. B had sent a prescription for hemorrhoid suppositories that was most unprofessional and upsetting to him. The pharmacist told me the instructions Dr. B wanted typed on the prescription label read "Stick one up your a-- twice a day." I suggested to the pharmacist that he telephone Dr. B and ask if he could change the order to "Insert one in your rectum twice a day." He replied, "I've already tried that." I asked, "What was Dr. B's reply?" to which the pharmacist said, "Dr. B said to type it exactly like he wrote the prescription because he didn't want to confuse the patient as to where he was to insert it." The pharmacist resigned after a few encounters with Dr. B. The last straw was when the physician added a second instruction to his prescriptions for suppositories: "Don't forget to take them out of the foil wrapper." To birth control pills he added, "Next time, don't take all of these pills at one time."

The radiologist at WK at the time of my employment told me of one of his most embarrassing moments, caused by Dr. B. The radiologist had received a call from him with a question regarding breast cancer. Then Dr. B asked the radiologist to come to his office to examine a patient. In the exam room, the radiologist was introduced to the patient and the surgeon's nurse and found the patient draped for an examination. The radiologist proceeded to perform a breast exam on the draped patient. Finding no lumps or other abnormal breast pathology, he repeated his examination before informing Dr. B of his negative findings. Dr. B said, "I'm not surprised because I called you to examine this spot on her leg." The embarrassed radiologist turned to the patient to apologize only to find the patient and the nurse both laughing heartily. But Dr. B was laughing the hardest.

On a Saturday morning, shortly after the opening of the hospital's new addition, I encountered Dr. B in Bermuda shorts, entering the new lobby entrance with a poodle in his arms. I commented on how cute his dog was and asked where he was going. He replied that he and his poodle, Fifi, were going to make rounds on his patients. I asked him not to take the dog with him on his rounds, quoting state health and licensure laws prohibiting such behavior. Since he had been warming up in friendship with me, he agreed to leave the dog in the lobby. Handing the poodle to me, he said, "I'm just following the rules, and I can't leave her without a babysitter." For over thirty minutes, I held his poodle in my outstretched arms because she continued to growl and snap at me. "I hope you two got along together," he said upon retrieving the dog. Dr. B never brought his poodle to make rounds with him after that, but if he had done so, I had made up my mind that I would look the other way—even if he brought an alligator.

I Can Get You a Real Deal!

As purchasing agent for the adjacent WK Clinic, Dr. B handled the ordering of all supplies. On one occasion he purchased a large quantity of paper towels that had not undergone the factory wet strength application process, which minimized disintegration of the towels as a person dried his hands. I heard of this purchase and of complaints from clinic physicians and employees about the poor quality of the paper towels. I ribbed him about his "great deal," and he replied, "The joke's on you because those complainers are now going over to your building to wash their hands, and this is saving the clinic a lot of money."

A refrigerated truck belonging to a national meat brand broke down on the interstate near the hospital. Repairs would take so long that the company authorized the driver to dispose of the cargo, and Dr. B came along and offered a low-ball price. It was accepted, and he took the meat to WK's dietitian, who called me to authorize the purchase. (The dietitian was upset by his reference to his prize as "chicken boobies.")

A shipment of wine was delivered to the clinic for storage and pick-up by physicians, and one physician shared a number of bottles with his domestic helper. This helper tried one and returned the remaining unopened bottles to him, commenting, "Doctor, are you sure you want to take a chance drinking that awful stuff?" After sampling a bottle, the physician put the entire stock of wine in the trash. Just another of Dr. B's "Boy, do I have a deal for you" events.

One day Dr. B asked me if I liked grapefruit. I answered yes, and within ten minutes he had filled the entire rear seat and luggage compartment of my station wagon with baskets of grapefruit. He told me that he had encountered a broken-down fruit truck near the hospital and had negotiated a "real deal" on the grapefruit.

On another occasion Dr. B called our dietary supervisor asking if she would prepare and cook the ducks a hunting friend had given him. He delivered the ducks in a burlap sack to the kitchen for the cooks to roast them. After he left the kitchen, the cooks discovered that the ducks were not dead; they began jumping around in the sack, frightening everyone.

You've Got the Wrong Realtor...

For almost eight years after my arrival at the hospital WK made numerous offers to the owner of the largest retail building near our campus. Its presence precluded any significant expansion of the hospital's physical plant. One morning I was approached by Dr. B, who asked me why I had not purchased the building in question. I answered that the chairman of the board's property committee and I had made offers, after appraisals, but were firmly rejected without interest on the part of the owner. He said, "Your problem is that you have not had the right person dealing with the owner." I asked, "Who is the right person to deal with her?" He answered, "Me." Thinking he was just joking, I asked, "Why you?" He replied, "When I was a young man, she and I were romantically involved, and we have maintained a friendship over the years. I know that if I let her know that the hospital desperately needed her property to expand, she would sell it to you." I told him that every offer we extended was at the appraisal value. He replied, "That sounds fair to me. I will let her know that I think she should sell to you. I'll have her call you this afternoon to sign the legal papers." He then walked away as I thought to myself, "Boy, is he in for a surprise." Much to my surprise and excitement, the owner called me that afternoon to say that Dr. B had spoken to her and that, if the hospital still wanted the property at the last offered price, that her attorney would have the paperwork ready for my signature the next day. She added that Dr. B was one of the finest people she had ever known and that she couldn't let him down by not selling. I thanked God for their friendship, which had lasted over fifty years and opened the door for our hospital's future.

A Real "Friendly" Sort of Guy

One afternoon I received a call from the manager of the national brand grocery store on our campus, which Dr. B often frequented on his lunch hour. His method was to haggle with the manager over meat prices, generally winning out in the bargain. The manager said that Dr. B was looking at aged beef when he spotted a woman from the rear dressed in a nurse's uniform, bending over the frozen food unit. He said to the manager, "That is my old buddy, Mrs. Cox, head nurse on third floor at the hospital." He walked up to the woman and patted her on her derrière. The woman straightened up, turned around and looked at Dr. B with surprise. But Dr. B was much more surprised when he realized that the woman he patted was not Mrs. Cox. According to the manager, Dr. B made a quick exit from the store, putting his feet on the floor no more than four times. Needless to say, Dr. B never mentioned the incident to me. (He probably knew I would enjoy it too much.)

The Town Crier Goes Confidential

Forty years before the implementation of the federal Health Information Portability and Privacy Act, Dr. B's conduct regarding the confidential nature of his patients' hospital medical charts followed the precepts of this recently passed law. During the Joint Commission surveys, Dr. B would go ahead of the surveyors to retrieve his patients' charts to keep them from seeing them. Our nurses would comment that orders on Dr. B's charts were always properly completed and signed, never incomplete. I asked, "Then, why does he do that?" Their reply: "Dr. B is sensitive to the confidentiality of his patients and doesn't think that the surveyors have a right to see this information."

Solemn Occasions and Dr. B

About six months after my acceptance into his inner circle of friends, Dr. B came into my office on the day of the funeral of the wife of one of his clinic partners and offered me a ride to the funeral. Dr. B stated that he was member of the church where the funeral was being held and could give me a guided tour. We parked outside the cathedral and entered by a rear door. This route took us through the chapel, which was in full view of the crowded sanctuary. In earshot of the congregation, Dr. B in a loud voice pointed out that the floors were slate from Wales and the huge pipe organ was given by a wealthy lady in the church.

Since I was facing the congregation, which was clearly overhearing us, I whispered to Dr. B that the service was under way and the processional party and casket halfway up the aisle to the altar. He said, "What's the rush? She's not going anywhere." In spite of my protest, he directed me into a front row pew reserved for the pallbearers, saying, "Why shouldn't we sit here? I knew her as well as any of those guys." Imagine my astonishment and that of the pallbearers, who were forced to sit very close to one another after finding us in their reserved seats.

My wife and I now attend this church, and every time I enter the chapel I think of this embarrassing moment of my life, but always with fond memories of Dr. B. A few years later I was honored to be asked to serve as a pallbearer at his funeral in that same church. During the service I found myself thinking about how much more room on the pews we pallbearers had that day.

While working with the family of Dr. B on funeral arrangements, I learned that he had left a list of pallbearers he wanted to serve. It was only at their gathering prior to his service that I was introduced to each one and realized that six of them were over eighty years of age. And all of these older pallbearers were recovering from either recent heart attacks or major surgical procedures, which negated any possibility that they could assist in carrying the casket. The other pallbearer was Dr. B's partner, who was less than a month post op from major back surgery. I went into the congregation and recruited seven younger persons to assist me with pallbearer duties.

As we proceeded to the cemetery in the limousine, Dr. B's partner smiled and said, "I guess you could say Dr. B got the last laugh as he caused us to have to shanghai seven surprised but able-bodied pallbearers from the congregation."

You could say Dr. B. was a man larger than life; certainly his antics were legendary. But I would be remiss if I failed to mention that he was also an exceptional surgeon and was never sued for malpractice. To this day, his former patients whom I encounter never fail to credit him with literally saving their lives. The privilege of observing Dr. B, who had the courage to provide superb medical care while never forgetting how to laugh, has taught me volumes.

Life is a jest, and
All things show it;
I thought so once,
But now I know it.

John Gay (1685-1732)

Epilogue

Breathing New Life Into an Abandoned Hospital

All men dream but not equally. Those who dream by night in the dusty recesses of their minds awake to find that it was vanity; but the dreamers of day are dangerous men, that they may act their dreams with open eyes to make it possible.

T. E. Lawrence (1888-1936)

Hold the Presses

On the day *Breadcrumbs to Cheesecake* was initially submitted for copyright, a major event in the history of the Willis-Knighton Health System occurred: the unforeseen acquisition of the formerly city-owned hospital, Bossier Medical Center (BMC). After only a brief period of ownership and operation in competition with WK Bossier Health Center, the facility was effectively shuttered by its later owner. Bossier Medical Center lay vacant and crumbling for years in the heart of this vibrant city: an eyesore in midtown Bossier City on the city's busiest traffic corridor.

Often, I would drive by the abandoned facility; its over-grown grounds, rotting fencing and bent light standards were a metaphor for the pain I knew so many people felt at the functional loss of this cornerstone of their community. There are few residents of Bossier City—or the parish—that do not feel some emotional connection to this landmark building. For decades, BMC was the only acute care hospital on the east bank of the Red River. So many had been born, healed or died within its walls. Such memories are not often forgotten. At a minimum, all city residents had given their hard-earned taxpayer money to ensure the future and success of this facility. Most had a personal story of affection for their hospital.

In my opinion, the Bossier City council's politics of the day (during the 1990s) played a major role in the eventual demise of BMC. Its physicians were not fully appreciated or permitted critical roles of leadership or decision-making in BMC's operation. Rather, their recommendations were often discounted or disregarded by some council members. Nor did the council require the new owner of BMC to honor its five year commitment prior to eliminating services, thus the exodus of BMC physicians to our WK Bossier Health Center, the only acute care hospital remaining in the parish.

A few hours after our purchase was completed, I toured the facility by flashlight (the power plant had been idled for months) with members of our administrative and engineering staff. Stepping over fallen ceiling tiles, discarded equipment and bumping into empty desks I marveled at the possibilities that lay before us. I was frequently reminded of T. E. Lawrence's thought on dreaming, visioning and staying awake and alert to opportunities when you are tasked to lead.

While some believe that a vacant hospital is a single-purpose use facility not suited for other-use retrofitting, this cannot be said of the prospects for the former Bossier Medical Center as a little creativity/ingenuity is being applied. At WK we call it innovation at its best.

The low purchase price of $3.8 million for the thirteen acres and 300,000 square feet of building permits Willis-Knighton great latitude of affordable uses for the facility. (note: WK's offer to purchase BMC in 1994 was $37 million cash plus BMC would retain its cash and receivables totaling approximately $15 million, a windfall to the city of $52 million).

A Phoenix Rises from the Ashes

Following targeted demolition and renovations, the WK Innovation and Career Center plans call for: 1) the establishment of a public assembly center with four large auditoriums within a conference center (all health system employees will attend orientation programs in these facilities), 2) a large board room for meetings of not-for-profit organizations, 3) virtual hospital and simulation center including two twelve-bed intensive care units, a number of surgical suites with scrub and recovery units and a fully equipped LDR (obstetrical labor, delivery and recovery unit), 4) two virtual physician offices for training WK Physician Network employees, 5) classrooms for computer education and training in electronic medical records, financial computer systems and other technical skills, 6) the health system's Talbot Medical Museum will be located immediately adjacent to the assembly auditoriums to permit all employees undergoing orientation to the system and community seminar participants to learn about the history of WK which spans almost ninety years, 7) a secure archival area of approximately 100,000 square feet will provide system-wide records storage with fire walls and sprinkler protection, 8) the system's document printing, processing and distribution facility and 9) a food/beverage court for the convenience of attendees.

To date, eight nursing schools, LSU Health Shreveport Medical School and other allied health programs have expressed an interest in utilizing the virtual hospital for the training of medical and allied health students. Its clinical simulation labs will be one of the first such facilities to be operated by a community, non-teaching hospital in the south.

The facility will house the WK home health, hospice and Shots for Tots programs. This location will permit their staffs to provide more expeditious care to the thirty-five percent of their patients that reside on the eastern side of the Red River.

So begins another chapter in Willis-Knighton's history. Our Bossier mission has come full circle as WK breathes new life back into what was sadly becoming a high profile, deteriorating visual blight.

The WK Innovation Center's newly constructed entryway has a high-tech look with lots of glass, aluminum trim, wood paneling and heavy sky-lighting (top). A water wall greets guests in the main lobby (middle). The pristine and modern ICU serves as a realistic setting for WK's virtual hospital (bottom).

Author's Note

Please continue to free our WK family from a need for the world's applause as we carry out our duties of servanthood.

What a ride the past forty-eight years have been! As I reflect upon this time at the helm of what was once a small neighborhood hospital, I marvel at the loyalty and dedication of the legions of physicians and employees of the health system. They have been my inspiration for my entire career, and their footprints and prayers are on every project that I have ever undertaken. But our place in history is not yet finished!

Hopefully, this book will explain to my children and grandchildren why I chose to spend nearly a half century in the service of this wonderful institution. Often, much to my sorrow, my dedication to WK required my absence from family activities and gatherings. I hope they will forgive me for not always having been present at important events of their lives; my heart and mind were always with them on those occasions.

I also pray that my grandchildren will someday come to accept some of these convictions and apply the codes of conduct in their personal lives. These beliefs have been my guide for personal and professional behavior as I have striven to conduct my business affairs and personal relationships as a ministry, not merely a job.

One thing I know: constant change and motion are the elixirs of my being. I cannot just be still or satisfied with the status quo. I believe that everything on this earth can be made better with just a little effort. Sometimes, just being good can also be the nemesis of being great. How is it possible that, after all these years, I still have so much to learn?